NHBC STANDARDS

C000088384

National House-Building Council, Buildmark House, Chiltern Avenue, Amersham, Bucks HP6 5AP

Part 6 SUPERSTRUCTURE (excl. Roofs)

informing the industry

CI/SfB	81	(21)	F	
CAWS	F10	F20	F30	

Operative from January 1992

Chapter **6.1**

NHBC STANDARDS

External masonry walls

This Chapter gives the Technical Requirements and
recommendations for external masonry walls.

LIST OF CHAPTERS

THE STANDARDS

The NHBC Standards give:
● Technical Requirements in red
● Performance Standards in dark blue
● Guidance in light blue
for the design and construction of dwellings acceptable to NHBC.

Diagrams may contain text in red. This is to highlight points but has no mandatory significance.

The Standards come into effect for every NHBC registered home whose foundations are concreted on or after the publication date shown on the cover of each Chapter and apply throughout the UK, unless otherwise stated.

COMPOSITION OF THE STANDARDS
The Standards are divided into 10 Parts, each containing one or more Chapters covering a particular aspect. The Parts follow the usual construction process.

In general, each Chapter is made up of sections dealing with Design, Materials and Sitework. In some cases one or more of these aspects may not be included.

TECHNICAL REQUIREMENTS
Each Chapter (except former Practice Notes) contains the five mandatory Technical Requirements which MUST be met by the Builder.

The Technical Requirements are printed in red. Chapter 1.1 'Introduction to the Standards and Technical Requirements' contains full details.

PERFORMANCE STANDARDS
Most Chapters consist of detailed Performance Standards printed in dark blue, normally in the left-hand column of each Design, Materials or Sitework page, subdivided into Clauses designated D, M or S, respectively.

Alternative standards of performance will be acceptable ONLY if, in the opinion of NHBC, the Technical Requirements are met and the standard achieved is not lower than the stated Performance Standard.

GUIDANCE
Guidance on how the Performance Standard may be met is normally shown, printed in light blue, in the right-hand column opposite the relevant Performance Standard. Some Chapters contain pages which are all Guidance.

Guidance is based on normal procedures and recommended practices shown by experience to be satisfactory and acceptable. NHBC will consider alternative methods to meet specific requirements, subject to prior consultation and evaluation.

SCOPE

This Chapter gives the Technical Requirements and recommendations for external masonry walls.

NHBC Standards do not cover aspects of health and safety relating to building operations and to the handling and use of certain building materials. Such matters are covered by statutory requirements.

FINDING INFORMATION

To find information on a particular subject, the following procedure is recommended:

1 Identify the **Part** most appropriate for the subject.

2 Identify the **Chapter** which deals with the particular element of construction.

3 Decide whether the information required relates to the Design, Materials or Sitework **Section** of the Chapter.

4 Decide from the Contents list the **heading** under which the required information is most likely to be found.

5 Review the **clauses** listed against the heading to see which has the relevant Performance Standard.

6 Review the **items** under the Performance Standards and decide which is relevant.

7 Review the guidance in the right-hand column opposite the item most relevant to the subject. If a clause number is known, use the above procedure to find the clause.

For example: **6.1 - S2(b)** means:

6	Part 6	Superstructure (excluding roofs)
1	Chapter 1	External masonry walls
S	Section	SITEWORK
2	Clause 2	CONSTRUCTION
(b)	Item (b)	setting out.

CONTENTS   Clause

TECHNICAL REQUIREMENTS

Technical Requirements	Performance Standards

R1 **Statutory requirements**
Work shall comply with all relevant Building Regulations and other statutory requirements

Chapter 1.1 gives the detailed Performance Standards which relate to these Technical Requirements.

R2 **Design requirement**
Design and specification shall provide satisfactory performance

R3 **Materials requirement**
All materials, products and building systems shall be suitable for their intended purpose

R4 **Workmanship requirement**
All work shall be carried out in a proper, neat and workmanlike manner

R5 **Structural design requirement**
Structural design shall be carried out by suitably qualified persons in accordance with British Standards and Codes of Practice

Performance Standards	Guidance

DESIGN STANDARD

6.1 - D1 Design shall meet the Technical Requirements

Design that follows the guidance below will be acceptable for external masonry walls.

STATUTORY REQUIREMENTS

6.1 - D2 Design shall comply with all relevant statutory requirements

A list of statutory references applicable to this Chapter is given in Appendix 6.1-A.

STRUCTURAL DESIGN

6.1 - D3 External cavity and solid walls shall be designed to support and transfer loads to foundations safely and without undue movement

Items to be taken into account include:

(a) standards

Structural design should be in accordance with BS 5628.

Intermediate floors and roofs should be designed to provide lateral restraint to external walls, in accordance with BS 8103 and BS 5628.

Walls of dwellings or buildings containing dwellings over three storeys high should be designed in accordance with Technical Requirement R5.

(b) lateral restraint provided by concrete floors

Concrete floors, with a minimum 90mm bearing onto the wall, provide adequate restraint.

Concrete floors running parallel to and not built into walls require restraint straps to provide restraint to the wall (reference should also be made to Chapter 6.4 'Timber and concrete upper floors' (each section).

(c) lateral restraint provided by timber floors

Timber joisted floors can provide adequate restraint when joists are carried by ordinary hangers to BS 6178 and connected to the wall with restraint straps.

In buildings of not more than 2 storeys, timber joisted floors can provide adequate restraint without strapping when:
- the minimum bearing onto masonry is 90mm (or 75mm onto a timber wall plate), *or*
- joists are carried by restraint type hangers, as described in BS 5628 : Part 1, at not more than 2m centres.

Performance Standards

Guidance

STRUCTURAL DESIGN (continued)

6.1 - D3   **(d) point loads**

Padstones and spreaders may be necessary and, where required, should be located beneath areas of concentrated loads.

(e) chases

The position and depth of chases for services should be considered. Horizontal chases should be limited to one-sixth the thickness of a single leaf, and vertical chases to one-third the thickness of a single leaf.

Particular care is needed where hollow blocks are specified. There should be a minimum 15mm thickness between the void and the back of the chase, unless the manufacturer recommends otherwise.

Chases should not be formed in external walls within 650mm of a sound-resisting wall.

(f) bonding

When partition walls abut the external wall and are of similar materials, they may be either fully bonded or tied together. Where materials have dissimilar shrinkage or expansion characteristics, eg dense concrete and aerated concrete, a tied joint is preferable as this will reduce the risk of random cracking.

In the case of a connection between a loadbearing wall on foundations and a non-loadbearing wall supported on a ground bearing slab, it is preferable to tie, not bond, the walls. This will reduce the risk of cracking due to differential vertical movement.

Tied joints should be formed using expanded metal, wire wall ties or a proprietary equivalent, at maximum 300mm intervals.

(g) chimneys

The overall height of an unrestrained chimney should not be greater than 4.5 times the minimum width at its highest point of restraint, unless designed by an Engineer in accordance with Technical Requirement R5.

(h) movement joints

Movement joints should be provided, where necessary, and in such a way that stability is maintained. If no provision is made for both initial and long term movements, masonry walls may crack.

Performance Standards

Guidance

Vertical movement joints should be provided in the outer leaf to minimise the risk of major cracking, as shown in the following table:

Material	Joint width [mm]	Normal spacing
Clay brick	16	12m (15m maximum)
Calcium silicate brick	10	7.5 to 9m
Concrete block and brick	10	6m
Any masonry in a parapet wall	10	half the above spacings and 1.5m from corners (double the frequency)

The spacing of the first movement joint from a return should not be more than half of the above dimension.

When different materials are used together, consideration should be given to potential differential movement. Wall ties are needed on either side of movement joints (reference should be made to Clause D6 and Sitework clause 6.1 - S5).

Movement joints should run the full height of the masonry wall. Any movement joints provided in the substructure must be carried up into the superstructure. Movement joints may be needed in the superstructure where none are required in the substructure - however suitable allowance should be made for relative movement.

Where masonry walls form panels in a framed structure, movement joints should be provided in accordance with BS 5628 : Part 3.

Expansion joints in clay brick walls should be filled with an easily compressible resilient material and be sealed to prevent water penetration. Acceptable materials are:

● flexible cellular polyethylene

● cellular polyurethane

● foam rubber.

The following materials should not be used for expansion joints in fired clay brickwork:

● hemp

● fibreboard

● cork.

Where movement joints are provided to control shrinkage in concrete blockwork, they may be simple vertical joints filled with mortar and sealed.

DESIGN

Performance Standards

Guidance

STRUCTURAL DESIGN (continued)

6.1 - D3(h) (continued)

To ensure the sealant is effective, there should be a good bond with the masonry. The sealant should be at least 10mm deep or in accordance with manufacturers' instructions.

Movement joints are not normally necessary to the inner leaf of cavity walls but consideration should be given to providing:
- movement joints in rooms with straight unbroken lengths of wall over 6m. This is unnecessary for fired clay bricks
- bed joint reinforcement as an alternative to movement joints in areas of risk, eg under window openings.

To reduce cracking and to maintain the level of thermal resistance:
- bricks and blocks, or blocks of different densities, in a wall should not be mixed
- a joint should be formed where dissimilar materials abut
- the joint should be tied (eg with expanded metal in the bed joint) unless the joint is to act as a movement joint.

Where cracking is likely, walls should be dry lined or clad (reference should also be made to Sitework clause 6.1 - S2(g)).

(i) cladding to framed structures

Allowance should be made for differential movement between cladding and frame.

The following precautions should be taken to prevent buckling and fracturing of masonry panels:
- flexible movement joints should be provided at the underside of each horizontal support member
- the masonry outer leaf should have at least two-thirds of its width supported securely by the concrete frame or a metal angle
- the inner leaf should be adequately tied to the structural frame. Forked plate ties held in dovetail slots, cast into the column or an equivalent are acceptable
- vertical movement joints should be provided at corners.

For timber framed construction, reference should be made to Chapter 6.2 'External timber framed walls and wall panels' (Design).

(j) corbelling

The size of corbels should not exceed the dimensions given in Sitework clause 6.1 - S2(j).

Performance Standards	Guidance

EXPOSURE

6.1 - D4 **External walls shall be suitable for their exposure and resist the passage of moisture to the inside of the dwelling**

In this Chapter, reference is made to exposure to:
● wind driven rain
● frost attack.

Details of how these are defined are contained in Appendices 6.1-B and 6.1-C.

Items to be taken into account include:

(a) general aspects affecting durability

Masonry in the following locations is particularly likely to become saturated and may remain so for long periods. Precautions as necessary should be taken to resist frost damage and sulphate attack in:
● chimney stacks
● parapet walls and copings
● sills and projections
● masonry below dpc at ground level
● freestanding walls.

The selection of bricks and mortar should follow the recommendations given in BS 5628 : Part 3 : 1985 and manufacturers' recommendations.

In addition to the mortar designations given in BS 5628, the following mortar mixes can be used:
● 1 : 1 : 5½, cement : lime : sand, with plasticiser, or
● 1 : 1 : 5½, cement : lime : sand, with plasticiser using sulphate-resisting cement.

Sulphate-resisting cement should be used where clay bricks have no upper limit on their soluble salt content and are used as follows:
● below dpc where there are sulphates present in the ground
● below dpc where there is a high risk of saturation
● retaining walls
● parapets
● freestanding walls
● rendered walls
● areas of *Severe* or *Very severe* exposure to driving rain.

Reclaimed bricks should be used only in accordance with Technical Requirement R3.

DESIGN

Performance Standards | **Guidance**

EXPOSURE (continued)

6.1 - D4 **(b) rain penetration**

Rainwater will penetrate the outer leaf of a masonry wall in prolonged periods of driving rain. Total resistance to rain penetration can only be achieved by cladding the wall (eg tile hanging, timber boarding or an impervious cladding).

The following should be taken into account to minimise the risk of rain penetration:

● determination of the exposure to wind driven rain

● a suitable wall construction and insulation method

● design detailing for the local exposure, taking into account the likely quality of workmanship on site.

Advice on selecting a suitable construction is given in the BRE Report 'Thermal insulation: avoiding risks', part of which is reproduced in Appendix 6.1-B.

A very high standard of workmanship is required to ensure that cavities are not bridged. Manufacturers' recommendations should be followed strictly.

The most exposed part of the building should be given particular attention when selecting a suitable construction method as this may affect the choice for the whole building.

The following aspects of design can reduce the risk of rain penetration:

● *providing cladding (other than render) to the wall.* Even if cladding is only added to gable walls and upper floors, it reduces rain penetration

● *increasing the clear cavity width or the width of full cavity insulation.* Increasing the cavity width from 50mm to 100mm greatly reduces the risk of rain passing through the cavity. A nominal cavity of 50mm is always required on the outside of partial cavity insulation

● *rendering the wall* (reference should also be made to Clause D15). Specify backing material carefully to avoid cracking which can reduce the effectiveness of render against rain penetration

● *designing protective features to keep the wall dry,* eg projecting sills and deep overhanging eaves and verges

● *mortar joints.* All joints should be fully filled. In areas of *Severe* or *Very severe* exposure to driving rain, recessed joints should not be used.

Performance Standards

Guidance

In Scotland, Northern Ireland, the Isle of Man and in other places where the exposure to driving rain is *Severe* or *Very severe*, masonry should form a rebate at the reveals of openings to avoid a straight through joint where the frame abuts the masonry.

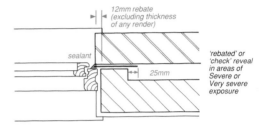

Proprietary cavity closers may be an acceptable alternative provided they have been assessed in accordance with Technical Requirement R3. For information on doors and windows, reference should be made to Chapter 6.7 'Doors, windows and glazing' (each section).

In Scotland and areas of *Severe* or *Very severe* exposure to driving rain, cavities should be continuous around chimney stacks, enclosed porches and habitable areas.

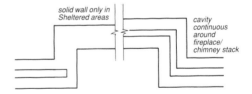

Cavity trays should be used at junctions with roof (reference should also be made to Clause D6).

Sills, copings and the like should be weathered and throated unless adequate alternative provision is made to protect the brickwork from saturation, frost damage and staining. For areas of *Severe* or *Very severe* exposure to driving rain, wall ties should be stainless steel or non-ferrous. Recessed joints should not be used.

DESItG

Performance Standards

Guidance

EXPOSURE (continued)

6.1 - D4 (c) frost attack

The main factors affecting frost attack are:
- degree of exposure (incidence of frost)
- saturation of the masonry
- frost resistance of the masonry
- localised protection of the masonry by roof overhangs, trees and other buildings.

Areas of *severe* frost exposure are shown on the map in Appendix 6.1-C.

In areas of *exceptionally severe* frost exposure, which is defined as a location which is in a *severe* frost exposure area and, in addition, faces long stretches of open countryside, only frost-resistant bricks (FL or FN to BS 3921) are acceptable for the superstructure.

In areas of *severe* frost exposure, the following are acceptable:
- clay facing bricks which are frost-resistant (FL or FN to BS 3921). Reference should be made to Appendix 6.1-F for the frost resistance classification of bricks to BS 3921
- clay bricks which are classified in manufacturers' published recommendations as satisfactory for the exposure
- calcium silicate bricks (in accordance with Classes 3 to 7 of BS 187)
- concrete bricks with a strength not less than 20N/mm^2
- concrete blocks with a density not less than 1500kg/m^2 or of strength not less than 7N/mm^2
- most types of aerated concrete blocks with render.

In Scotland, all clay bricks used as facings should be frost-resistant (FL or FN to BS 3921).

If there are doubts about the suitability of a facing brick for sites in areas of *exceptionally severe* frost exposure classification, written confirmation should be obtained from the brick manufacturer that the brick is suitable for:
- its geographical location, and
- its location in the structure.

This applies particularly to bricks such as fletton facings which are moderately frost-resistant (ML or MN). In addition, follow manufacturers' recommendations on suitability, including the choice and use of mortar and the type of pointing.

Recessed joints should only be used in compliance with Clause D5(c).

Bricks that are not frost-resistant (OL or ON to BS 3921) may not be acceptable for use externally, unless completely protected by a cladding which can adequately resist the passage of water.

Performance Standards

Guidance

Good brickwork detailing can limit persistent wetting of brickwork and reduce the risk of frost attack. For example:

● paths should drain away from walls to avoid saturating bricks near the ground

● sills, copings and the like should have a weathered upper surface

● a coping should be provided for all parapet walls, chimneys and freestanding walls unless clay bricks of FN or FL classification to BS 3921 have been used. Copings should have a generous overhang, throatings at least 40mm clear of the wall and a continuous, supported dpc underneath which projects beyond the line of the wall. Single leaf parapet walls should not be rendered on both sides.

Where there is a risk that brickwork may be persistently wet, bricks should be specified that are low in soluble salts (if clay, FL or ML to BS 3921).

Note

Only clay bricks designated L by BS 3921 have a limit on their soluble salt content. In persistently wet conditions, clay bricks of N designation may create sulphate attack on the mortar.

Painted or decorated finishes can trap moisture in external brickwork and increase the risk of frost damage, sulphate attack or other detrimental effects. They should not be applied to N designation bricks without the brick manufacturer's written agreement.

MORTAR

6.1 - D5 **Mortar shall be of the mix proportions necessary to achieve adequate strength and durability and be suitable for the type of masonry**

Items to be taken into account include:

(a) geographical location and position within the structure

Recommended mortar mixes for different locations are given in Appendix 6.1-D.

(b) sources of sulphate

Ordinary Portland cement mortar can expand, crumble and deteriorate badly if attacked by sulphates. Sufficient soluble sulphate to cause this problem may be contained in clay bricks. Clay bricks with an N designation have no limit on their sulphate content. The problem is most acute when brickwork is saturated for long periods; mortar is vulnerable to attack by any soluble sulphates present.

DESIGN

Performance Standards	Guidance

MORTAR (continued)

6.1 - D5(b) continued

To reduce the risk, sulphate-resisting cement to BS 4027 should be used:

- below dpc level when sulphates are present in the ground
- when clay bricks with no limit on their salt content (FN and MN to BS 3921) are used, and there is a high saturation risk, for example in the following situations:
  - parapets
  - chimney stacks
  - retaining walls
  - freestanding walls
  - rendered walls
  - areas of *Severe* exposure to driving rain.

(c) joints

Struck (or weathered) and bucket handle joints are preferable.

Recessed joints should not be used where:

- bricks are perforated nearer than 15mm to the face
- bricks are not frost resistant (if clay MN or ML to BS 3921), unless the brick manufacturer has agreed in writing for their use in a particular location
- there is no reasonable shelter from driving rain (reasonable shelter could be from buildings or groups of trees if these are within 50m and of similar height to the dwelling)
- the dwelling is built on steep sloping ground, facing open countryside or within 8km of a coast or large estuary
- the dwelling is in Northern Ireland or the Isle of Man and where the cavity is to be fully filled with cavity insulation.

Jointing is preferable to pointing because it leaves the mortar undisturbed.

(d) admixtures

Calcium chloride should not be used as an admixture to mortar. The contents of admixtures should be checked to ensure that they do not contain calcium chloride.

Admixtures should only be used in accordance with manufacturers' recommendations/instructions.

Mortars containing a plasticiser are more resistant to frost damage and are therefore recommended for use in winter.

White cement and pigments to BS 1014 may be used, but pigments should not exceed 10% of the cement weight or 3% if carbon black is used.

Further advice concerning admixtures is given in Appendix 6.1-D.

Performance Standards	Guidance

DAMP-PROOF COURSES AND CAVITY TRAYS

6.1 - D6 **Damp-proof courses and related components shall be provided to prevent moisture rising or entering the building**

Items to be taken into account include:

(a) dpcs

Damp-proof courses should be provided in accordance with the Table in Appendix 6.1-E.

At complicated junctions, clear drawings should be provided and preformed profiles specified. Isometric drawings can sometimes be clearer than the combination of plan and section/elevation drawings.

(b) cavity trays

Cavity trays should be provided at all interruptions to the cavity, eg window and door openings, air bricks, etc, unless otherwise protected, eg by overhanging eaves.

A cavity tray should:

- provide an impervious barrier and ensure that water drains outwards
- project at least 150mm beyond the inner face of the cavity closure or, where a combined cavity tray and lintel is acceptable, give complete protection to the top of the reveal and vertical dpc where provided
- provide drip protection to door and window heads
- have an overall minimum upstand from the inside face of the outer leaf to the outside of the inner leaf of 140mm
- be shaped to provide at least a 100mm vertical protection above a point where mortar droppings could collect.

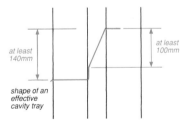

at least 140mm

at least 100mm

shape of an effective cavity tray

In Scotland, Northern Ireland, the Isle of Man and areas of *Very severe* exposure to driving rain, the upstand part of the damp-proof protection should be returned into the inner leaf of masonry. In all other areas, the upstand should be returned into the inner leaf unless it is stiff enough to stand against the inner leaf without support.

Performance Standards   **Guidance**

DAMP-PROOF COURSES AND CAVITY TRAYS (continued)

6.1 - D6(b) (continued)

Where fair faced masonry is supported by lintels, weep holes are recommended at maximum 450mm centres with a minimum of two weep holes per opening.

Where full fill insulation is placed in the cavity:
- cavity trays should be fitted with stop ends
- a cavity tray should be used above the highest insulation level, unless the insulation is taken to the top of the wall. (Manufacturers' recommendations should be followed.)

(c) abutment details

Cavity trays should be provided at abutments of roofs and cavity walls. This will ensure that any water penetrating into the cavity does not enter the enclosed area. This only applies where the roof is over an enclosed area, including an attached garage, but does not apply to open car ports and open porches.

Where the roof abuts at an angle with the wall, preformed stepped cavity trays should be provided.

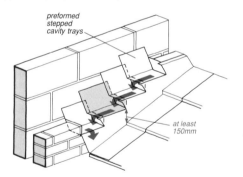

preformed stepped cavity trays

at least 150mm

(d) parapet details

Dpcs below the coping should be supported over the cavity to prevent sagging. A dpc should be specified that can achieve a good key with the mortar.

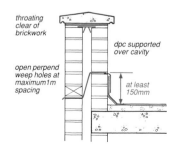

throating clear of brickwork

dpc supported over cavity

open perpend weep holes at maximum 1m spacing

at least 150mm

Guidance

(e) chimneys

The chimney dpcs should link with the flashings, particularly in areas of *Severe* exposure to driving rain.

Two dpcs should be provided when the roof is steeply pitched. The lower dpc should be 150mm to 300mm above the lower intersection of the roof.

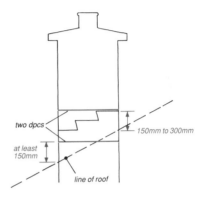

(f) materials

Materials that are suitable for use as dpcs are given in Materials clause 6.1 - M6.

WALL TIES

6.1 - D7   Wall ties shall be provided, where required, to tie together the leaves of cavity walls

The spacing of wall ties in masonry walls should be in accordance with Sitework clause 6.1 - S5.

Wall ties should comply with BS 1243 or have been assessed in accordance with Technical Requirement R3. When partial fill cavity insulation is used, wall ties (with retaining devices) which have been assessed in accordance with Technical Requirement R3 should be specified.

For cavities over 75mm wide, vertical twist type ties should be specified or others approved for use in wider cavities.

In areas of *Severe* or *Very severe* exposure to driving rain, only stainless steel or non-ferrous wall ties are acceptable.

Ties should be specified which are long enough to allow a minimum of 50mm to be bedded into each leaf, taking into account the thickness of any insulation in the cavity and the width of the cavity.

DESIGN

Performance Standards	Guidance

STONE MASONRY

6.1 - D8 **Elements constructed of stone masonry shall comply with the performance standards for brick and block masonry, where applicable**

Stone masonry should be designed to meet the requirements of BS 5390 'Code of Practice for stone masonry'.

LINTELS

6.1 - D9 **Lintels shall support safely the applied loads**

Items to be taken into account include:

(a) structural support

Concrete, steel and reinforced brickwork are acceptable materials for use as lintels.

Timber lintels should not be used, unless:
- they are protected from the weather, and
- they do not support masonry or other rigid or brittle materials.

Lintels should be designed in accordance either with Technical Requirement R5 or manufacturers' published data. A lintel should be provided where frames are not designed to support superimposed loads.

Lintels should be wide enough to provide adequate support to walling above. Masonry should not overhang the lintel support by more than 25mm. A lintel should extend beyond the opening at each end by at least the following lengths:

| Span [m] | Minimum bearing length [mm] | |
	Simple lintel	Lintel combined with cavity tray
Up to 1.2	100	150
Over 1.2	150	150

To avoid overstressing, composite lintels should have the required depth of fully bedded brickwork stipulated by the manufacturer above the lintel, before point loads are applied. Where necessary, padstones should be provided under the bearings of lintels. Reference should be made to Chapter 6.5 'Steelwork support to upper floors and partitions' (Design) for details of padstones.

Performance Standards	Guidance
(b) adequate durability against corrosion and resistance to water entering the dwelling	Cavity tray/damp-proof protection should be provided over all openings, either as a combined part of the lintel or separately. Separate cavity tray protection should be provided: ● when the corrosion protection to the lintel is less than that given in Table 2 to BS 5977 : Part 2, or ● when the profile of the lintel is not as shown in Clause D6(b). In Scotland, Northern Ireland, the Isle of Man and areas of *Severe* or *Very severe* exposure to driving rain, separate damp-proof protection should be provided over *all* lintels in accordance with the guidance for cavity trays given in Clause D6. Lintels should be of such a size and be located so that the external edge of the lintel projects beyond, and therefore offers protection to, the window head.
(c) cold bridging and condensation	The risk of condensation at reveals and soffits becomes more likely as the wall insulation increases. Cold bridge paths should be avoided. Where they occur, they should have a U value of $1.2W/m^2K$, or lower, in order to avoid condensation. To avoid a cold bridge, the wall insulation should ideally abut the head of the window frame. Clause D4(b) details methods of preventing rain penetration which may also be required.

DESIGN

Performance Standards	Guidance

LINTELS (continued)

6.1 - D9(c) (continued)

These are the points where cold bridging can lead to condensation:

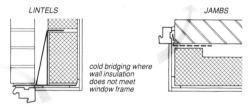

These are suggested ways of avoiding cold bridging:

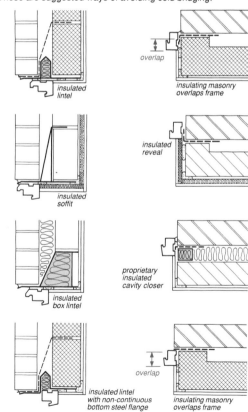

(d) adequate fire resistance

Where steel lintels are used, manufacturers' recommendations for providing adequate fire resistance, particularly to the lower steel flange, should be followed.

Performance Standards

Guidance

THERMAL INSULATION

6.1 - D10 External walls shall be designed to provide the required standard of thermal insulation

The insulation value of the wall must meet the requirements of the relevant Building Regulations. A list of statutory references is given in Appendix 6.1-A.

Design should avoid cold bridging at openings and at junctions of external walls with roofs, floors and internal walls. The maximum U value of any cold bridge path should be 1.2/Wm²K, or lower.

6.1 - D11 External walls shall be designed to ensure the correct use of insulation materials

Items to be taken into account include:

(a) acceptable insulation materials

Insulation, or super lightweight blocks, or blocks with face bonded insulation, or voided blocks with insulation infill should be used in accordance with:

● an assessment which complies with Technical Requirement R3, or

● a British Standard and used in accordance with a relevant Code of Practice.

(b) full cavity insulation

In Northern Ireland and the Isle of Man, it is not permissible to fill cavities with *pumped* thermal insulants at the time of construction.

In Scotland, it is not permissible to fill the full width of the cavity with *any* thermal insulants at the time of construction.

The local exposure of the site (reference should be made to Clause D3) should not exceed the exposure limit given in the relevant certificate of assessment or in BS 5618 for UF foam.

Materials clause 6.1 - M9 sets out the range of acceptable insulation materials and the relevant British Standards.

Wall cavities should not be fully filled with insulation where *all* of the following conditions exist:

● where the site is classed as having *Moderate/Severe* or greater exposure to driving rain, *and*

● the external leaf is constructed of clay bricks which have no upper limit on their soluble salt content (as defined in BS 3921), *and*

● the wall is to be rendered.

Full cavity insulation should only be used where the wall design and standard of workmanship are in accordance with Table 3 in Appendix 6.1-B.

DESIGN

Performance Standards	Guidance

THERMAL INSULATION (contir

6.1 - D11(b) (continued)

The following design points should be noted:
- stop ends should be provided to cavity trays
- mortar joints should not be recessed
- painted finishes on bricks or render are not acceptable if they are likely to cause frost damage or sulphate attack or other damage.

(c) partial cavity insulation

Partial cavity insulation should be fixed only against the cavity face of the inner leaf. The clear cavity width between partial cavity insulation and the outer leaf should be at least 50mm nominal.

Partial cavity insulation should be used only where the wall design and standard of workmanship are in accordance with Table 3 in Appendix 6.1-B.

Wall ties should be long enough to allow a 50mm embedment in each masonry leaf.

(d) inner leaf of insulated blockwork

Types of blockwork include:
- lightweight aerated concrete
- voided blocks with insulation infill
- blocks faced with insulation material.

Manufacturers' recommendations should be followed and particular note taken of the following:
- a clear 50mm wide cavity should always be maintained
- the blocks should be capable of supporting concentrated loads
- the correct type of joist hanger for the type and size of block and size of joist should be used
- long unbroken lengths of blockwork should be avoided
- precautions should be taken to reduce risk of shrinkage cracking
- dry lining should be used where shrinkage cracking might be unsightly and to avoid long term pattern staining at mortar joints
- restrictions on chasing for services when using voided blocks should be noted (reference should be made to Clause D3(e)).

Performance Standards	Guidance

(e) dual insulation

Where partial cavity insulation is used in addition to an insulated block inner leaf (reference should be made Clause D11(c)), the whole composite construction should have been assessed in accordance with Technical Requirement R3.

(f) insulated dry linings

Where an insulated dry lining contains a combustible insulant, the plasterboard should be at least 12.5mm thick and mechanically fixed to the masonry inner leaf. This is to prevent early collapse of the lining in a fire.

FIRE SAFETY

6.1 - D12 Cavity walls shall resist adequately the passage of fire

Cavities should be closed with cavity closers in accordance with statutory requirements. A list of statutory references is given in Appendix 6.1-A.

SOUND INSULATION

6.1 - D13 External walls adjacent to sound-resisting walls shall be designed to resist adequately flanking sound transmission

Acceptable levels of sound reduction between dwellings may be achieved by:
- the inner leaf of an external cavity wall having sufficient weight, and
- sealing of air paths
- allowing appropriate spacings between openings in external walls.

The density of external walls and the position of openings adjacent to sound-resisting walls should be in accordance with statutory requirements and, where relevant, an assessment which complies with Technical Requirement R3. A list of statutory references is given in Appendix 6.1-A.

When the same type of block is used for both the sound-resisting wall and the inner leaf of the cavity wall, the blockwork may be bonded. Where dissimilar blocks are used, the blockwork should be butted and mechanically tied at centres not exceeding 300mm vertically.

DESIGN

Performance Standards	Guidance

CLADDINGS

6.1 - D14 Cladding shall resist satisfactorily the passage of moisture

Items to be taken into account include:

(a) battens

Where battens are required, they must be pre-treated with preservative, as described in Chapter 2.3 'Timber preservation (natural solid timber)' (each section).

(b) joints

Joints between claddings and adjacent materials should be detailed to be watertight under the particular exposure conditions of the site. Where necessary, provision should be made for differential movement.

(c) moisture barriers

Moisture barriers should be provided between masonry and boarding, slates, tiling and other similar claddings, unless specifically not required for a proprietary cladding. The moisture barrier may be roofing underfelt or equivalent.

Vapour barriers such as polyethylene sheet are not an acceptable moisture barrier as they can trap moisture in the structure.

For timber framed walls clad with masonry, reference should be made to Chapter 6.2 'External timber framed walls and wall panels' for details.

(d) vertical tile or slate cladding

Every tile or slate should be nailed with two nails. Nails should be aluminium, copper or silicon bronze.

Bottom edges should be finished with an under-course and tilting batten.

(e) timber cladding

Timber claddings should be pre-treated with preservative in accordance with Chapter 2.3 'Timber preservation (natural solid timber)' (each section).

Performance Standards	Guidance

RENDERING

6.1 - D15 Rendering, in conjunction with the surface to which it is applied, shall resist satisfactorily the passage of moisture

Items to be taken into account include:

(a) rain penetration

External rendered finishes should comply with BS 5262 and the guidance given below.

It is important to prevent rainwater penetrating behind the rendering. Design features around openings and at the head of the rendering should provide shelter, where possible, and help to shed water away from the surface below.

(b) exposed elements

It is not advisable to render exposed parts of a building, such as parapets and chimneys constructed of clay bricks of N designation, without the use of sulphate-resisting cement.

(c) movement

Movements can occur at a change in material. In such cases, the render should be either stopped at specially formed movement joints or, if the expected movement is small, be reinforced by metal lathing carried across the joint. If metal lathing is used, three rendering coats should be applied.

(d) background

To achieve a good bond, the masonry backing should be moderately strong and porous to give some suction and a mechanical key. Dense masonry with a smooth surface should not be rendered.

Aerated or lightweight aggregate concrete blocks can be used, as a background, but more care is needed when selecting a rendering mix and surface treatment. Strong render mixes should not be used. Roughcast and dry dash finishes that require a strong mix are not recommended for use on aerated or lightweight aggregate blocks. Block manufacturers' recommendations should be followed.

In Scotland, render should be applied only to bricks:
● which are keyed, or
● where a spatterdash coat has been applied before the first render undercoat.

In other areas, render should be applied only where either:
● keyed bricks are used, or
● the joints are raked out at least 15mm deep.

DESIGN

Performance Standards	Guidance

RENDERING (continued)

6.1 - D15(d) continued

Render may be applied to bricks which have no upper limit on their soluble salt content (if clay, FN and MN to BS 3921) only if the following conditions are met:

● cement for brickwork mortar is sulphate-resisting to BS 4027

● the brick manufacturer has confirmed, in writing, that the brick is suitable, taking account of the brickwork detailing and the particular exposure of each rendered element. (If sulphate-resisting cement is used in the mortar, it should be used also in the first render undercoat.)

Care should be taken when specifying render to walls with full cavity fill. The lack of a ventilated cavity can slow down the rate at which the wall dries out.

Rendered finishes should not be used over fully filled cavity walls if:

● the outer leaf is built in bricks with no upper limit on their soluble salt content (FN and MN to BS 3921), and

● the site is in an area classed as *Moderate/Severe*, *Severe* or *Very severe* exposure to driving rain (see Appendix 6.1-B).

In Scotland, it is not permissible to fill the full width of the cavity with any thermal insulants at the time of construction

Rendering may be used on brickwork with partial cavity insulation provided a clear cavity width between insulation and outer leaf of at least 50mm nominal is maintained.

(e) mixes

The rendering mix should be appropriate to the strength of the background. No render coat should be stronger than the background or richer than the preceding coat. The render should be of adequate strength to achieve durability.

Mixes should comply with the recommendations of BS 5262. When rendering on bricks that are MN or ML to BS 3921, the Table to Sitework clause 6.1 - S8(b) should be followed. The manufacturer of the background masonry should be consulted regarding particular requirements for the mix or its application.

Pigments complying with the requirements of BS 1014 may be added to the finishing coat up to a limit of 10% of the cement weight or 3% in the case of carbon black. White Portland cement may be used.

Performance Standards	Guidance

(f) number and thickness of coats

The number of coats should be chosen with regard to the background and the exposure conditions of the site.

In *Moderate* exposure to driving rain, one undercoat and one finishing coat is acceptable. In *Severe* or *Very severe* exposure to driving rain, a minimum of two undercoats and a finishing coat should be used.

Initial undercoats should not be less than 10mm and not more than 15mm thick. Any further undercoat should be thinner than the preceding coat. Finishing coats should be generally between 6mm and 10mm thick.

Undercoats should be allowed to shrink and dry out before applying following coats. When rendering onto dense concrete blocks, adhesion can be improved by use of proprietary bonding agents or a spatterdash coat.

(g) detailing of timber/brick/render

Dwellings which incorporate rendered panels between timber boards should have at least one coat of render applied over the whole wall face before the boards are fixed. The second coat may be applied between the boards.

Rendering and timber can shrink causing gaps. Precautions should be taken to prevent rain from penetrating the junction as this might cause the render to fail as a result of frost damage.

All exposed timber, except naturally durable species, must be treated in accordance with Chapter 2.3 'Timber preservation (natural solid timber)' (each section).

Where timber is used on brick or render, it is essential that all cut ends, mortices, etc made after treatment are flood coated with preservative.

Large section timbers must be fitted with suitable weather bars, flashings, etc to prevent moisture penetration through joints with adjacent materials.

Non-ferrous fixings should be used. Aluminium is not suitable when the preservative is Copper/Chromium/Arsenic.

(h) proprietary and local rendering systems

Proprietary rendering finishes should be applied in accordance with manufacturers' recommendations.

Traditional local rendering should comply with the above guidance, as appropriate, and with established local practice.

DESIGN

Performance Standards	Guidance

PROVISION OF INFORMATION

6.1 - D16 **Designs and specifications shall be produced in a clearly understandable format and include all relevant information**

For external masonry walls, the drawings should show:

- wall layout with all dimensions shown
- position and size of openings
- coursing of the bricks and blocks in relation to storey heights and opening positions
- details at all junctions, indicating position of dpcs and cavity trays. Isometric sketches are recommended for complicated junctions
- position and type of lintels
- position of restraint straps
- details of cavity closers
- details at reveals
- details of how support is given to other elements, eg padstones and wall plates
- position and detail of movement joints
- acceptable methods of pointing or mortar joint finish
- type of insulant to be used
- type and location of wall ties.

6.1 - D17 **All relevant information shall be distributed to appropriate personnel**

Ensure that design and specification information is issued to site supervisors and relevant specialist subcontractors and/or suppliers.

Where proprietary products are to be used, manufacturers usually have specific requirements for fixing and/or assembly of their products. This information should also be made available for reference on site so that work can be carried out satisfactorily in accordance with the design and specification.

Performance Standards	Guidance

MATERIALS STANDARDS

6.1 - M1   All materials shall:

(a) meet the Technical Requirements

(b) take account of the design

Materials that comply with the design and the guidance below will be acceptable for external masonry walls.

Materials for external masonry walls shall comply with all relevant standards, including those listed below. Where no standard exists, Technical Requirement R3 applies (see Chapter 1.1 'Introduction to the Standards and Technical Requirements').

References to British Standards and Codes of Practice include those made under the Construction Products Directive (89/106/EEC) and, in particular, appropriate European Technical Specifications approved by a European Committee for Standardisation (CEN).

BRICKS

6.1 - M2   Bricks shall:

(a) be capable of supporting intended loads

Requirements for the design strength of bricks are given in BS 5628 : Part 1. The brick specified in the design should be used. Clay bricks to BS 3921 with a minimum compressive strength of $5N/mm^2$ should be adequate for 1 and 2 storey dwellings and $7N/mm^2$ for 3 storey dwellings.

(b) have appropriate resistance to the adverse effects of frost and sulphate attack

CLAY BRICKS

BS 3921 classifies clay bricks according to their frost-resistance and soluble salt content (see Appendix 6.1-F).

Only bricks that are frost-resistant (FL or FN to BS 3921) should be used where there is a high risk of prolonged wetting and freezing. Such areas include:

● all external facing work in Scotland

● exposed parts including copings, sills and parapets and chimneys which have no overhang to provide protection. Reference should be made to Design clause 6.1 - D4(c)

● areas of the country subject to *exceptionally severe* frost exposure (see map in Appendix 6.1-C).

In areas of *severe* frost exposure outside Scotland, bricks that are moderately frost-resistant (MN and ML to BS 3921) may be used for general wall areas, provided they are classified in manufacturers' published recommendations as satisfactory for the exposure.

Bricks that are not frost-resistant (OL or ON to BS 3921) are not acceptable for use externally, unless completely protected by a cladding which can resist satisfactorily the passage of water.

Performance Standards | **Guidance**

BRICKS (continued)

6.1 - M2(b) (continued)

Where brickwork may become saturated, *moderately* frost-resistant bricks (MN or ML to BS 3921) are not appropriate if there is a risk of vulnerability to frost. In saturated conditions, sulphate-resisting cement mortar is required for N designation bricks.

CALCIUM SILICATE BRICKS

Bricks of strength Class 3 (to BS 187) possess good frost resistance for most applications. Strength Class 4 is recommended in areas of *severe* frost exposure (see map in Appendix 6.1-C) or for use where bricks may be persistently wet (eg parapets, chimneys, sills and below dpc).

Calcium silicate bricks do not contain significant amounts of soluble sulphates and may be suitable where sulphate bearing soil and ground water conditions exist. Manufacturers' recommendations should be followed.

CONCRETE BRICKS

In concrete bricks there is a direct relationship between strength and durability, including frost resistance. Most concrete bricks in production have a strength of $20N/mm^2$ and are durable in most situations. For copings and sills, bricks with a compressive strength of $30N/mm^2$ should be used.

RECLAIMED BRICKS

Reclaimed bricks could be unsuitable for external work because of a high salt content or a lack of frost resistance. Their use is permitted only in accordance with Technical Requirement R3. It is advisable to know where they come from, both geographically and within the previous building. Bricks used internally or fully protected may be unsuitable in external situations.

Reclaimed bricks should be considered as MN or ML to BS 3921 and used accordingly. Independent certification of suitability may be required.

BLOCKS

6.1 - M3 **Concrete blocks shall:**
(a) be capable of supporting intended loads

Blocks should comply with BS 6073 : Part 1, be specified in accordance with BS 6073 : Part 2 and be used in accordance with BS 5628 : Part 3.

Statutory references on blockwork selection are listed in Appendix 6.1-A.

In general, $2.8N/mm^2$ blocks are suitable for 1 and 2 storey dwellings.

Performance Standards	Guidance

For 3 storey dwellings or dwellings with storey heights over 2.7m, 7N/mm^2 blocks are required for certain parts of the structure.

Structural design may show that lower strengths than 7N/mm^2 are adequate.

Other factors may dictate the strength of blocks required in certain circumstances, eg sulphate-resistance, may require blocks of greater strength.

The maximum loadbearing capacity of the wall should not exceed manufacturers' recommendations.

(b) have appropriate resistance to adverse effects of frost and sulphate attack

Concrete blocks used in the outer leaf without protective cladding or render, should:
- have a compressive strength exceeding 7N/mm^2, or
- have a density exceeding 1500kg/m^3, or
- be made with dense aggregate to BS 882 or BS 1047, or
- be aerated concrete blocks having had their suitability confirmed by the manufacturer.

Concrete blocks should not be used below dpc where there are sulphates in the ground, unless suitability is confirmed by the block manufacturer. Sulphates may attack the cement used in the block. Sulphate-resisting cement will be required in the mortar. The proportions will depend on the level of sulphates in the ground.

(c) have an adequate thermal resistance, where required

The designer may have specified a particular type and thickness of concrete block because of its thermal insulation performance in addition to its strength. Alternative concrete blocks should not be used without the designer's acceptance.

STONE MASONRY

6.1 - M4 Stone masonry shall be capable of supporting the intended loads and have appropriate resistance to the adverse effects of frost

Stone for masonry should comply with the requirements of BS 5390.

Reconstructed stone masonry units should comply with BS 6457.

MATERIALS

Performance Standards	Guidance

MORTAR AND RENDERING

6.1 - M5 **Mortar and rendering materials shall be of the mix proportions to achieve adequate strength and durability to comply with the design**

Items to be taken into account include:

(a) cement type

Ordinary Portland cement should be to BS 12.

White Portland cement can be used.

Sulphate-resisting cement should be to BS 4027.

(b) defects caused by sulphates

To reduce deleterious effects of sulphate attack, sulphate-resisting cement should be used in the following situations:
- below dpc level when sulphates are present in the ground
- when clay bricks with no limit on their salt content (FN or MN to BS 3921) are used and there is a high saturation risk, as in:
  - parapets
  - chimney stacks
  - retaining walls
  - freestanding walls
  - rendered walls
  - areas of *Severe* exposure to driving rain.

(c) sand type

Sand and aggregate should be to BS 1199 and BS 1200.

(d) mortar type

Ready-mixed mortars should comply with BS 4821.
For recommended mortar mixes, see Appendix 6.1-D.

(e) additives

Calcium chloride should not be used as an admixture to mortar. The contents of admixtures should be checked to ensure they do not contain chloride.

Proprietary plasticisers, if specified, should be used strictly in accordance with manufacturers' recommendations.

Air entraining and set retarding admixtures should comply with BS 4887.

Pigments complying with the requirements of BS 1014 may be added up to a limit of 10% of the cement weight or 3% if carbon black is used.

MATERIALS

Performance Standards

Guidance

(f) render

Where sulphate-resisting cement is used for masonry mortar, it should also be used in spatterdash coats and base coats of the render.

Sand for render should be sharp sand to BS 1199, preferably from the coarse end of the grading scale. Sand with excessive fine material will shrink and crack.

Metal reinforcement to rendering should be galvanized or stainless steel, in accordance with one of the specifications in BS 5262.

Decorative finishes that contain asbestos are not acceptable.

DPC MATERIALS

6.1 - M6 Materials for damp-proofing shall resist adequately the passage of moisture

Items to be taken into account include:

(a) dpcs

The following materials are acceptable for use as dpcs:
- bitumen to BS 6398
- polyethylene to BS 6515 (except below copings and in parapets)
- proprietary materials assessed in accordance with Technical Requirement R3.

Dpcs and flexible cavity trays should be of the correct dimensions to suit the detailed design.

Brick dpcs should consist of two courses of clay dpc bricks or clay engineering bricks to BS 3921, laid breaking joint and bedded and jointed in a 1 : 0-¼ : 3, cement : lime : sand, mortar. Brick dpcs are only suitable to resist the upward movement of moisture, they are not suitable to resist the downward or lateral movement of water.

For complicated junctions, preformed cavity trays are recommended. Care should be taken to order the correct type and shape.

MATERIALS

Performance Standards	Guidance

DPC MATERIALS

6.1 - M6   (b) flashings

The following are acceptable as flashings:
- milled lead sheet (at least Code 4) complying with BS 1178
- aluminium and aluminium alloys complying with BS 1470 (0.6mm to 0.9mm thick)
- zinc alloy complying with BS 6561 and 0.6mm thick.

(c) tanking

Materials acceptable for use as tanking are detailed in Chapter 5.1 'Substructure and ground bearing floors' (Materials).

WALL TIES

6.1 - M7   Wall ties shall be appropriate for their location and intended use

Wall ties shall be in accordance with either:
- BS 1243, or
- an assessment in accordance with Technical Requirement R3.

BS 1243 deals with three types of wall tie:
- butterfly
- double triangle
- vertical twist.

Butterfly and double triangle wall ties are suitable only for cavities up to 75mm wide. Vertical twist ties can be used in cavities up to 150mm wide.

Ties should be long enough to be embedded at least 50mm into each leaf.

In areas of *Severe* or *Very severe* exposure to driving rain, wall ties should be of stainless steel or suitable non-ferrous metal.

Where partial cavity insulation is used, it should be held in place by retaining devices which may be clipped to the wall ties. These devices should be assessed in accordance with Technical Requirement R3 and used only with compatible wall ties.

Performance Standards

Guidance

LINTELS

6.1 - M8 Lintels shall be of the type and dimensions appropriate to their position within the structure

Steel and concrete lintels should comply with BS 5977.

Lintels up to 1.2m length which do not need a separate dpc tray should have a minimum 100mm end bearing. Normally, other lintels should be long enough to have a minimum 150mm end bearing each side of the opening.

Cavity trays may be required over the lintels. This should be specified in the design.

Stop ends are required to cavity trays where full cavity fill insulation is used.

THERMAL INSULATION

6.1 - M9 Insulation materials shall provide the degree of insulation to comply with the design

Insulants specified and installed in accordance with the following British Standards will be acceptable:

BS 6232 Thermal insulation of cavity walls by filling with blown man-made mineral fibre

BS 6676 Thermal insulation of cavity walls using man-made mineral fibre batts (slabs).

UF foam to BS 5617 and installed by a specialist company registered by BSI in accordance with BS 5618 will be acceptable.

The following should be noted:

● the introduction of pumped thermal insulants to cavities at the time of construction is not permitted in Northern Ireland and the Isle of Man

● the introduction of thermal insulants which fully fill the width of the cavity at the time of construction is not permitted in Scotland.

Other insulation materials, whether for full cavity insulation, partial cavity insulation, insulated blockwork or internal insulation, may be used only if they have been assessed in accordance with Technical Requirement R3.

The thickness of materials required by the design should be used.

Some materials, such as those blown or pumped into the cavity, should be installed by a company approved by the manufacturer and/or the assessment authority. The assessment certificate, where relevant, should be checked.

MATERIALS

Performance Standards	Guidance

CLADDING MATERIALS

6.1 - M10 Cladding materials shall be of the quality, type and dimensions required by the design

Items to be taken into account include:

(a) tiles and slates

Clay tiles for tile hanging should be to BS 402.

Concrete tiles for tile hanging should be to BS 473.

Slates for vertical slating should be to BS 680.

(b) timber boarding

Timber should comply with BS 1186 and be Class 3 or better.

Timber should be a naturally durable species or pre-treated with preservative. Reference should be made to Chapter 2.3 'Timber preservation (natural solid timber)' (each section) for guidance on preservative treatments.

Boarding to be painted or stained should be primed or sealed before fixing. For further details, reference should be made to Chapter 8.5 'Painting and decorating' (each section).

(c) underfelt behind cladding

Type 1F felt to BS 747 is acceptable as an underfelt behind cladding.

(d) battens

Battens should be of the size specified in the design and pre-treated with preservative treatments. Reference should be made to Chapter 2.3 'Timber preservation (natural solid timber)' (each section) for guidance on preservative treatments.

(e) proprietary cladding systems

Proprietary systems should be assessed in accordance with Technical Requirement R3.

Performance Standards	Guidance

MOVEMENT JOINTS

6.1 - M11 Materials for movement joints shall be suitable for their intended purpose

When choosing materials, account should be taken of the following:
- joint width
- joint depth
- anticipated movement
- movement capability of material
- surface preparation
- backing materials
- projected life span of joint.

Acceptable materials for movement joints in clay brick walls are:
- flexible cellular polyethylene
- cellular polyurethane
- foam rubber.

Materials which are acceptable for use in contraction joints with concrete bricks or blocks, but *not* acceptable for use as expansion joints in fired clay bricks, are:
- hemp
- fibreboard
- cork.

Performance Standards | Guidance

SITEWORK STANDARDS

6.1 - S1 **All sitework shall:**
   (a) meet the Technical Requirements
   (b) take account of the design
   (c) follow established good practice and workmanship

Sitework that complies with the design and the guidance below will be acceptable for external masonry walls.

CONSTRUCTION

6.1 - S2 **Construction shall ensure a satisfactory standard of brickwork and blockwork**

Items to be taken into account include:

(a) appearance

The appearance of a masonry wall depends upon the materials used, the setting out and the workmanship. Further details are given throughout Clauses S2 to S10.

(b) setting out

When setting out masonry, avoid cutting bricks or blocks except when it is essential and avoid irregular or broken bonds, particularly at openings.

Where a number of openings of similar width are being formed, use a rod cut to the required size to check the width of openings as the work rises.

To keep courses to the correct height, use a gauge rod. The rod should be marked with the height of windows, doors and floors.

All work should be reasonably level and true. The bond detailed in the design should be used. Perpendicular joints should be kept in line and plumb. Courses should be kept level by using lines and spirit levels.

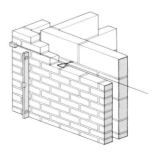

Performance Standards	Guidance

CONSTRUCTION (continued)

6.1 - S2   (c) mortar

Different types of bricks and blocks need different strength mortar mixes. Some parts of the building, such as below dpc, chimneys and copings, may need a different mix to the main walling. Make sure the mix is right for the job.

Recommended mortar mixes are given in Appendix 6.1-D.

Plant and banker boards should be kept clean. Mixers should be kept clean to operate efficiently. The mortar colour should be consistent.

Mortar which has started to set should not be re-tempered.

All bricks and blocks should be laid on a full bed of mortar and all perpends should be solidly filled.

Joints should be filled to reduce the risk of rain penetration and dampness in the wall. Solid mortar bedding and fully filled perpends are particularly important in exposed areas and where the cavity is to be fully filled with insulation.

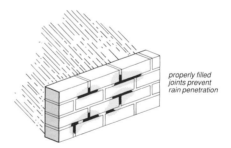

properly filled joints prevent rain penetration

Unless the design states otherwise, flush or bucket handle pointing should be used. In Northen Ireland and the Isle of Man, recessed joints should not be used in full fill insulated cavity walls.

Where pigments (to BS 1014) are used they should not exceed 10% of the cement weight or 3% if carbon black is used.

For precautions to take in cold weather, reference should be made to Chapter 1.4 'Cold weather working'.

Performance Standards	Guidance

(d) cavity walls

Cavities should be uniform and of the width specfied in the design. All cavities should be at least 50mm nominal clear width. Partial cavity insulation should be fixed against the inner leaf of the cavity. Check that the correct wall tie is being used (reference should be made to Clause S5).

To keep the wall plumb, do not over-reach at changes of lift. It is better to wait for the next scaffolding lift.

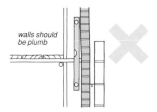

walls should be plumb

The difference in heights between the two leaves of a cavity wall under construction should be:

Type of tie	Difference in height
Vertical twist	approximately equal to vertical spacing of consecutive rows of ties
Double triangle and butterfly	not greater than 6 block courses

Cavities should be constructed so that:
- mortar is struck off from all joints as work proceeds
- wall ties are kept free of droppings and debris
- cavity trays are clear of droppings and debris.

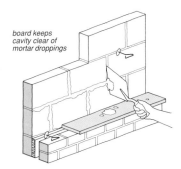

board keeps cavity clear of mortar droppings

Clean cavities with mortar droppings removed are particularly important in exposed areas and where partial cavity fill is used.

SITEWORK

Performance Standards   **Guidance**

CONSTRUCTION (continued)

6.1 - S2(d) (continued)

Where cavity insulation is used, mortar droppings should be cleaned off from the top edge. Mortar left on the top edge may transmit dampness to the inner leaf. The use of a cavity batten will prevent this. Cavity battens should be wrapped with flexible material to allow easy withdrawal.

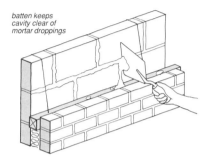

batten keeps
cavity clear of
mortar droppings

(e) movement

Brickwork/blockwork should not be subjected to vibration until the mortar has set.

(f) openings

Masonry may be built around either:
● the frame in-situ, or
● a profile or template to enable the frame to be fitted later.

Openings should be the correct size and square. The brickwork should butt closely against the frame. The frame should not be distorted by forcing bricks against the jamb.

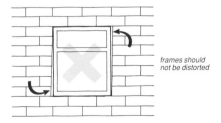

frames should
not be distorted

Window and door frames, when built-in, should be fixed with:
● frame cramps, or
● proprietary cavity closers, or
● plugs and fixings.

Timber plugs should not be used in vulnerable positions, such as the outer leaves of walls.

Performance Standards

Guidance

(g) bonding

A regular bonding pattern should be maintained. External walls should be bonded to partitions and party walls, as required by the design. Either:

- tooth every alternate course, or
- tie with wall ties, expanded metal or equivalent at centres not exceeding 300mm vertically.

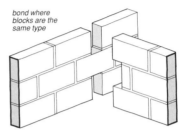

bond where blocks are the same type

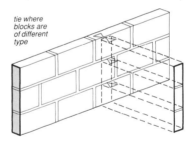

tie where blocks are of different type

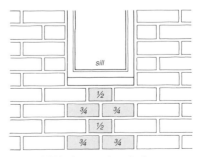

brick bond set out at base of wall so that cut bricks occur below openings

SITEWORK

Performance Standards

Guidance

CONSTRUCTION (continued)

6.1 - S2(g) (continued)

Where joist hangers are not used, joist filling should be brick or blockwork, without excessive mortar joints. Clay bricks and concrete blocks should not be mixed. Joist filling should be kept 12mm below the top of flat roof joists to allow for timber shrinkage, but check also that cold roof ventilation is not blocked (reference should be made to Chapter 7.1 'Flat roofs and balconies' (Design and Sitework)).

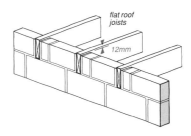

Where a different size of masonry unit is needed to ensure correct coursing, small units of the same material should be used to reduce cracking and problems due to different thermal insulation properties.

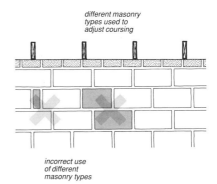

Where the inner leaf of a cavity wall is being used for thermal insulation and where a different size of masonry unit is used to ensure correct coursing, the unit should have similar thermal insulation properties to the masonry used for the rest of the wall. For example aerated concrete blocks should not be mixed with clay bricks.

Performance Standards

Guidance

(h) chasing for services

Chases should be cut with care. Impact power tools can damage the wall and should not be used.

The depth for horizontal chases should be limited to one-sixth of the thickness of the single leaf. The depth for vertical chases should be limited to one-third of the thickness of the single leaf. Hollow blocks should not be chased unless specifically permitted by the manufacturer.

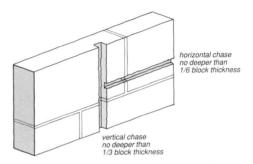

horizontal chase
no deeper than
1/6 block thickness

vertical chase
no deeper than
1/3 block thickness

Chases should not be formed in external walls within 650mm of a sound-resisting wall. Chases in this area could affect sound resistance.

(i) movement joints

Movement joints should be formed where required by the design. Movement joints are necessary in long lengths of walling to reduce unsightly cracking. Joints are often hidden in corners, or behind rainwater pipes. Normally, movement joints are not needed in internal walls and partitions.

The correct materials should be used to form movement joints. Clay bricks expand and require an easily compressible material.

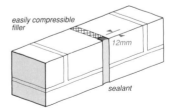

easily compressible
filler

12mm

sealant

Suitable materials are:
- flexible cellular polyethylene
- cellular polyurethane
- foam rubber.

Performance Standards

Guidance

CONSTRUCTION (continued)

6.1 - S2(i) (continued)

The sealant should be at least 10mm deep to ensure a good bond. If the joint is in a freestanding wall, the filler will require sealant to both exposed edges and the top (where the joint is carried through the coping).

(j) corbelling

Where courses are corbelled out in ordinary masonry, one above another, the extent of corbelling should not exceed that shown below:

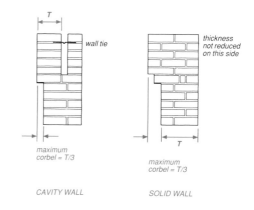

maximum corbel = T/3

CAVITY WALL

SOLID WALL

Where reinforcing is used, corbels should be designed by an Engineer in accordance with Technical Requirement R5.

STONE MASONRY

6.1 - S3 **Stone masonry shall be constructed to an acceptable standard**

Stone masonry will be acceptable if it:

- complies with brickwork/blockwork clauses (where appropriate)
- gives an adequate weather-resisting structure (in conjunction with any brick or block backing and/or vertical damp-proof membranes)
- is laid on its natural bed (unless local practice is otherwise)
- follows good local recognised practice.

Performance Standards   Guidance

DAMP-PROOF COURSES AND CAVITY TRAYS

6.1 - S4   Dpcs and cavity trays shall be installed to prevent moisture entering the building

Items to be taken into account include:

(a) horizontal dpcs

Dpcs and cavity trays should be in one continuous piece, whenever possible. Joints in horizontal wall dpcs positioned to prevent rising damp should be lapped 100mm or sealed or welded. The manufacturer's recommendations should be checked. Elsewhere, joints in dpcs and cavity trays should be sealed to prevent water seeping through the joints.

At ground level, all parts of the dpc should be at least 150mm above finished ground or paving level.

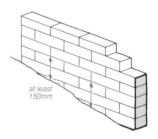

at least 150mm

Special dpc detailing may be required at doorways where the dwelling is to be designed to allow access for the disabled.

Dpcs should:
- be of correct width
- be fully bedded on fresh mortar
- not project into the cavity
- not be set back from the edge of the masonry
- lap the dpm.

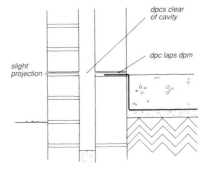

slight projection

dpcs clear of cavity

dpc laps dpm

Performance Standards   **Guidance**

DAMP-PROOF COURSES AND CAVITY TRAYS (continued)

6.1 - S4(a) (continued)

The concrete fill in a cavity wall should stop at least 225mm below the base dpc. This may be reduced to 150mm where special foundations, such as rafts, are used.

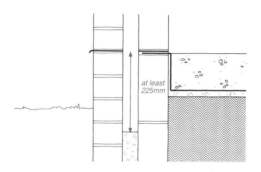

(b) dpcs in chimneys

In chimneys, a dpc should be provided:
- 150mm to 300mm above the highest point where the chimney meets the roof.

In order to avoid the use of a large flashing upstand, it may be preferred to use two dpcs and a stepped flashing. Reference should be made to Clause S4(d) for guidance on sealing dpcs.

A dpc tray should be used in conditions of *Severe* exposure to driving rain.

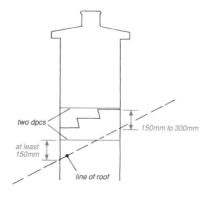

Performance Standards	Guidance

(c) dpcs in parapet walls

Parapet walls should have:
- a dpc under the coping, and
- a dpc tray starting 150mm minimum above the roof.

The coping throating should be clear of the brickwork. Reference should be made to Clause S4(d) for guidance on sealing dpcs.

All dpcs should be fully bedded in mortar.

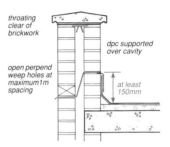

throating clear of brickwork

dpc supported over cavity

open perpend weep holes at maximum 1m spacing

at least 150mm

(d) dpcs to prevent downward flow of water

Where dpcs are intended to prevent the downward movement of water, joints should be sealed or welded. Lapped joints, unsealed, are unacceptable.

Where flashings link with dpcs, rake out 25mm of mortar *below* the dpc to allow for the flashing to be tucked in. It is easiest to rake out the joints as the work proceeds.

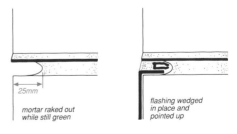

25mm

mortar raked out while still green

flashing wedged in place and pointed up

STAGE 1   STAGE 2

SITEWORK

Performance Standards   Guidance

DAMP-PROOF COURSES AND CAVITY TRAYS (continued)

6.1 - S4   (e) dpcs around openings

A dpc should be provided at jambs of openings and at heads and sills as required by the design.

Where a jointed or permeable sill is used (all sills in Northern Ireland and the Isle of Man), a dpc should be placed between the sill and the outer leaf, turned up at the back and ends of the sill.

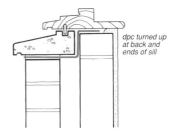

dpc turned up at back and ends of sill

150mm wide vertical dpcs should be nailed to the full height of the frame. The dpc should protrude into the cavity by about 25mm and extend up to the underside of the lintel where it should be turned back towards the inner leaf.

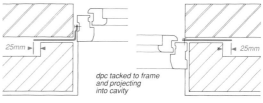

25mm

dpc tacked to frame and projecting into cavity

25mm

NORMAL EXPOSURE   SEVERE EXPOSURE

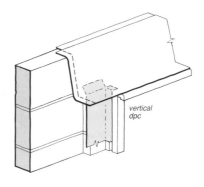

vertical dpc

Performance Standards	Guidance

Where there is a sill dpc, it should be lapped with the reveal dpc.

If there is no sill dpc, the vertical dpc should be continued 150mm below the sill level.

A fillet joint of sealant should not be considered as a substitute for good workmanship or dpcs. However, in *severely* exposed areas, a bead of mastic should be used as an additional protection around openings.

(f) cavity trays

The single brick thick external leaf of a cavity wall can allow moisture into the cavity. Cavity trays should be used so that water drains outwards above openings.

Cavity trays over lintels should extend 150mm beyond the inner face of the cavity closer and cover the ends of the lintel. Where the lintel does not require a dpc, the lintel itself should have a suitable profile and durability and should extend 150mm beyond the inner face of the cavity closer.

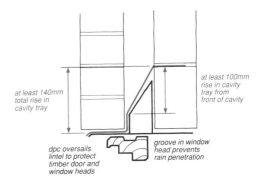

at least 140mm total rise in cavity tray

at least 100mm rise in cavity tray from front of cavity

dpc oversails lintel to protect timber door and window heads

groove in window head prevents rain penetration

The upstand part of the cavity tray should be returned into the inner leaf masonry unless stiff enough to stand against the inner leaf without support.

In Scotland, all lintels should have a dpc built into the inner leaf.

SITEWORK

Performance Standards

Guidance

DAMP-PROOF COURSES AND CAVITY TRAYS (continued)

6.1 - S4(f) (continued)

In Scotland, Northern Ireland, the Isle of Man and areas of similarly *Severe* exposure to driving rain, the upstand part of the damp-proof protection must be returned into the inner leaf of masonry.

It is recommended that where fair faced masonry is supported by lintels, weep holes should be provided spaced at maximum 450mm intervals. Each opening should have at least two weep holes.

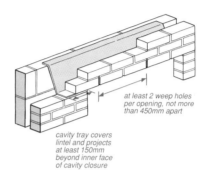

at least 2 weep holes per opening, not more than 450mm apart

cavity tray covers lintel and projects at least 150mm beyond inner face of cavity closure

In areas of *Severe* exposure to driving rain or where cavity insulation is used, stop ends may be specified. The details should be checked. Where stop ends are required, they should be bonded to the cavity tray to coincide with a perpend joint.

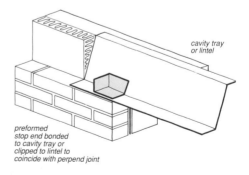

cavity tray or lintel

preformed stop end bonded to cavity tray or clipped to lintel to coincide with perpend joint

Performance Standards

Guidance

A cavity tray should be provided where the cavity is bridged by air bricks, etc. The dpc should extend 150mm beyond each side of the bridge.

Where not otherwise protected (eg by a roof at an appropriate level), a dpc tray should be provided over meter boxes.

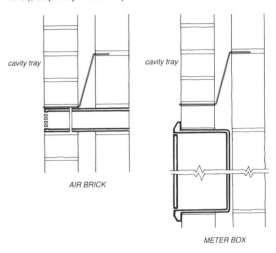

AIR BRICK

METER BOX

(g) stepped cavity trays

At the abutment of pitched roofs to cavity walls, stepped cavity trays should be provided 150mm above the roof surface. The lowest cavity tray should have two stop ends and a weep hole to allow water to drain from the cavity.

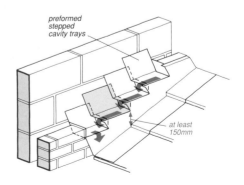

SITEWORK

6.1 | External masonry walls

Performance Standards   Guidance

WALL TIES

6.1 - S5 **Wall ties shall be installed correctly**

Items to be taken into account include:

(a) type

The type of wall tie specified by the designer should be used.

(b) position

If ties slope down to the inner leaf, if drips are off-centre or if ties have mortar droppings on them, water can cross the cavity.

The two leaves should be coursed so that the wall tie is level or slopes outwards.

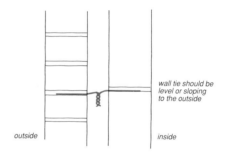

wall tie should be
level or sloping
to the outside

outside   inside

Ties should be bedded a minimum of 50mm into each leaf of the wall as work proceeds. The drip should face downwards. Ties should be built-in, not pushed into joints.

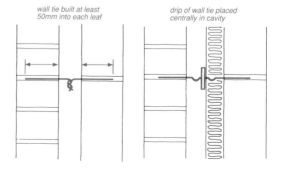

wall tie built at least
50mm into each leaf

drip of wall tie placed
centrally in cavity

Performance Standards

Guidance

Where one leaf is built in advance of the other, the wall ties should project enough from the built leaf to bed at least 50mm into the unbuilt leaf.

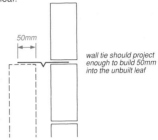

50mm

wall tie should project enough to build 50mm into the unbuilt leaf

(c) spacing

Wall ties should be spaced above and below dpc as follows:

Cavity width between masonry faces [mm]	Maximum spacing [mm]	
	Horizontally	Vertically
50 to 75	900	450
76 to 100	750	450
50 to 100 (At jamb openings, movement joints, etc)	within 150 of opening	300 or each block course

At openings and movement joints, wall ties should be spaced at maximum 300mm centres vertically even if this means cutting cavity insulation to insert the tie. Doubling the number of wall ties at 450mm or 600mm centres vertically is *not* an acceptable alternative.

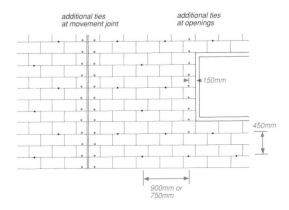

additional ties at movement joint

additional ties at openings

150mm

450mm

900mm or 750mm

Performance Standards	Guidance

WALL TIES (continued)

6.1 - S5   (d) use of partial fill insulation

Where partial cavity fill insulation is being used, it should be retained against the inner leaf by retaining devices.
The retaining devices should be compatible with the wall ties and used in accordance with an assessment which complies with Technical Requirement R3.

Unless the independent assessment states otherwise, where partial cavity fill is being used the wall ties should be spaced more closely to provide adequate support and restraint for the 1200mm long boards. Ties should be spaced at 600mm centres horizontally and in vertical as well as horizontal rows, ie not staggered.

LINTELS

6.1 - S6   Lintels and beams shall be installed correctly

Items to be taken into account include:

(a) span and placing

Lintels should be the correct size for the opening and have the correct bearing at each end:

	Minimum bearing length [mm]	
Span [m]	Simple lintel	Lintel combined with cavity tray
Up to 1.2	100	150
Over 1.2	150	150

Longer span lintels may require padstones (the design should be checked).

Setting out should ensure that lintels bear on a full block, where possible, or on a whole brick, and be installed level on a solid bed of a mortar. Soft or non-durable packing should not be used. Small pieces of cut brick or block should not be used around lintel bearings.

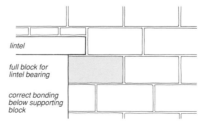

lintel

full block for lintel bearing

correct bonding below supporting block

Performance Standards

Guidance

Lintels and masonry should form openings of the correct size for the frame of the window or door.

A check should be made to ensure that concrete lintels are the right way up.

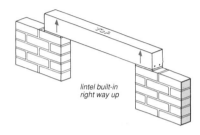

*lintel built-in
right way up*

Concrete floor units or other heavy components which bear on lintels should be positioned carefully to avoid damage or shock load.

Composite lintels should have:
● sufficient compression brickwork above with fully filled perpends
● no direct point loads applied
● temporary support to ensure the span of the lintel is not greater than one metre during construction.

Temporary support should not be removed until the mortar has gained sufficient strength.

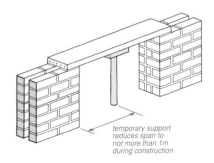

*temporary support
reduces span to
not more than 1m
during construction*

SITEWORK

Performance Standards   **Guidance**

LINTELS (continued)

6.1 - S6(a) (continued)

The lintel toe should:
- project past the window head
- have a flexible sealing compound between toe and window.

Brickwork or masonry should not overhang the lintel by more than 25mm.

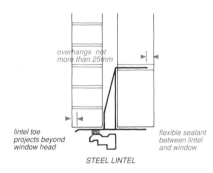

STEEL LINTEL

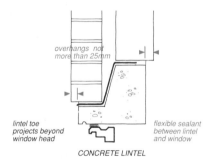

CONCRETE LINTEL

(b) thermal insulation

Insulation may help to prevent cold bridges at the heads of openings in external walls. The design should be checked for this requirement.

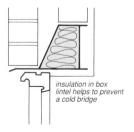

Performance Standards	Guidance

(c) use of dpc cavity trays

A separate cavity tray should be provided over some lintels if:
- the corrosion protection to the lintel is inadequate, and
- the shape of the lintel is unsuitable.

This should be checked with the designer or buyer.

In Scotland, Northern Ireland, the Isle of Man and areas of *Severe* exposure to driving rain, a cavity tray is required over all lintels. Reference should be made to Clause S4(f) for details of cavity trays.

(d) use of steel lintels

Where steel lintels are being used, the inner and outer leaf should be built up together to avoid twisting the lintel flange. The difference in height between the leaves should not exceed 225mm.

THERMAL INSULATION

6.1 - S7   Thermal insulation shall be installed correctly

A high standard of workmanship should be maintained to minimise the risk of damp penetration to the inside of the dwelling where cavity insulation is used.

In particular:
- mortar joints, including perpends, should be solidly filled with mortar
- mortar droppings should be removed from wall ties and the edges of insulation materials
- excess mortar should be struck smooth from the inside of the outer leaf.

Where insulation is built-in, manufacturers' instructions should be followed. These are normally printed on the insulation packaging and include a recommended sequence of construction.

In Northern Ireland and the Isle of Man, recessed joists should not be used where the cavity is to be fully filled with insulation. It is not permissible to fill the cavity with *pumped* thermal insulants at the time of construction.

In Scotland, it is not permissible to fill the full width of the cavity with *any* thermal insulants at the time of construction.

Performance Standards   **Guidance**

THERMAL INSULATION (continued)

6.1 - S7 (continued)

The first row of insulation boards or batts should be supported on wall ties, two ties to each board or batt.

Wall ties should coincide with horizontal joints in the insulation.

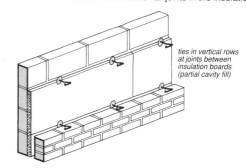

ties in vertical rows at joints between insulation boards (partial cavity fill)

Where wall ties need to be closely spaced, for example at reveals, it is acceptable to make a clean cut neatly in the insulation to accept the extra ties. The insulation manufacturer's instructions should be followed.

Insulation should be close butted with no gaps. Gaps provide routes for dampness, and condensation can form on the cold spots where insulation is missing.

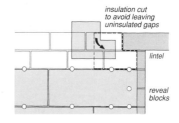

insulation cut to avoid leaving uninsulated gaps

lintel

reveal blocks

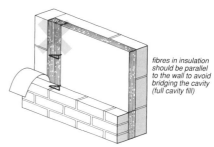

fibres in insulation should be parallel to the wall to avoid bridging the cavity (full cavity fill)

Insulation boards for partial fill should be stored flat without bearers otherwise they may warp making it difficult to fix them against the wall. Warped boards should be rejected.

Performance Standards

Guidance

RENDERING

6.1 - S8   Rendering shall be to the correct mix, have a good bond and be free from significant cracking and crazing

Items to be taken into account include:

(a) preparation of backing surface

The surface to be rendered should be free from dust, loose particles, efflorescence and organic growth.

Where necessary, surfaces should be treated to provide an adequate key by:

● raking out joints
● hacking the surface
● applying a bonding agent
● applying metal lathing
● applying a spatterdash coat, or
● other appropriate means.

The surface suction should be checked by splashing water onto the wall. The result should be observed and appropriate action taken as follows:

● if too much suction, spraying with water may be needed - do not use too much water
● if too little suction, a spatterdash coat or bonding agent may be needed
● if the background is too wet, delay rendering until conditions improve.

The design requirements should be checked where rendering is continuous over different materials. Corrosion-resistant metal lathing should be fixed across the joints or, alternatively, provision made to accommodate movement.

Expanded metal should be fixed with the correct side towards the wall (see manufacturers' literature). If metal lathing is used to bridge changes in background material, a separating strip, eg breather paper, should be fixed behind the lathing so that the render does not bond at the background joints. Lathing should be set away from the wall so that rendering can be forced through the mesh to achieve a good bond.

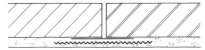

*separating strip used
behind expanded metal when
plastering across dissimilar
backgrounds*

Performance Standards	Guidance

RENDERING (continued)

6.1 - S8 (b) mix

The mix proportions should be checked against the specification, especially whether sulphate-resisting cement should be used.

Mixes for rendering on brickwork using clay bricks with no limit on their soluble salt content (FN or MN to BS 3921) should be as follows:

Exposure conditions	Undercoat mix proportions (by volume)	Finishing coat mix proportions (by volume)
Parapets, freestanding walls, pillars, retaining walls and chimneys	rendering not recommended	
All walls other than those above	1 : 5, sulphate-resisting Portland cement : sand, plus integral waterproofer	1 : 5, ordinary Portland cement : sand, dry dashing strongly advised

For backing brickwork, it should be ensured that sulphate-resisting cement which complies with Appendix 6.1-D is used in the mortar.

If water-resisting properties are required, Portland cement can be obtained with a waterproofing agent already incorporated. Otherwise, a waterproofing agent should be used and added to the rendering mix in strict accordance with manufacturers' instructions.

(c) application

The number and thickness of coats should be in accordance with the design.

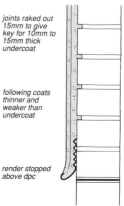

joints raked out
15mm to give
key for 10mm to
15mm thick
undercoat

following coats
thinner and
weaker than
undercoat

render stopped
above dpc

Performance Standards

Guidance

In Scotland, a spatterdash coat should be applied before the first render coat if the background is of Scottish common bricks and bricks to BS 3921.

Undercoats should be applied at least 3 days before applying the following coat.

If coloured pigments are specified, batching should be undertaken with care to ensure colour consistency.

(d) cracking and crazing

Rendering should be free from significant cracking and crazing.

To avoid surface crazing:
- use properly graded sand (fine sand increases the risk of crazing)
- strong mixes should not be used as the finishing coat
- overworking, which causes laitance to be drawn to the surface, should be avoided
- the finishing coat should be kept damp for at least 3 days. In warm dry weather, spraying or protection by polyethylene sheet may be needed. Rendering should not be carried out during hot weather or in bright sunshine.

COLD WEATHER WORKING

6.1 - S9   Precautions shall be taken to protect walls and rendering from damage by frost during construction

Freshly laid mortar and render may fail if it freezes because the frozen water expands and forces apart the particles of mortar.

Admixtures which contain calcium chloride should not be used.

The use of air entraining agents in cold weather gives better frost resistance. The use of accelerating admixtures, proprietary plasticisers and other admixtures should not be relied on as an anti-freeze precaution.

Check what effect additives have on setting times.
Cold weather slows setting, as do plasticisers and retarders.
If the set is retarded too much, the next lift might squeeze out the mortar below.

SITEWORK

Performance Standards   **Guidance**

COLD WEATHER WORKING (continued)

6.1 - S9 (continued)

Brick and blockwork should not be built nor rendering carried out when the air temperature is 2°C and falling.

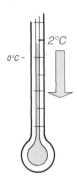

Walls should be protected from frost until the mortar has set sufficiently to resist frost damage. Covers should be provided to form a still air space to insulate the wall. Walling damaged by frost will not regain strength and should be taken down and re-built when conditions improve.

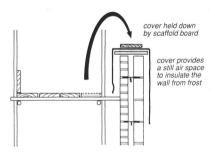

cover held down
by scaffold board

cover provides
a still air space
to insulate the
wall from frost

Reference should be made to Chapter 1.4 'Cold weather working' for more detailed advice.

Performance Standards

Guidance

HANDLING AND PROTECTION

6.1 - S10 Materials shall be handled, stored, used and protected in such a way as to ensure that the construction shall be neat, clean and undamaged upon completion

Items to be taken into account include:

(a) avoidance of damage

It is cost effective to protect and store materials properly and maintain good quality control during construction. For detailed information on protection and storage, reference should be made to Chapter 3.2 'Setting up the site'.

(b) handling

The unloading of all bricks and blocks, especially facing bricks, preferably should be by mechanical means, directly onto a firm level surface. Bricks that are tipped on delivery or moved about the site in dumper trucks often have a high degree of wastage. Chipped or fractured bricks are not acceptable for facework.

(c) storage

Stacks of bricks and blocks should be protected from rain, mud splashes, etc by covering with waterproof covers. Bricks and blocks that become excessively wet can suffer from:

● staining and efflorescence
● increased drying shrinkage with a greater risk of cracking
● lack of mortar adhesion to mud stained surfaces.

SITEWORK

Performance Standards | **Guidance**

HANDLING AND SITE PROTECTION (continued)

6.1 - S10(c) (continued)

Cement should be stored off the ground and protected from weather. Sand should be prevented from spreading and be protected so that it remains clean.

The work place should be kept clean to reduce mortar splashes to a minimum. Any accidental mortar smears should be lightly brushed off the face after the mortar has taken its first set.

(d) workmanship

Materials should be handled with care during construction to avoid damage and staining. Badly chipped bricks should not be used for facework.

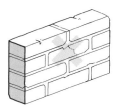

At night, the scaffold board closest to the brickwork should be removed to prevent rain splashing off boards onto facework. The inner board should be turned back onto other boards or placed on top of the day's work to protect cavities and voids from rain.

Performance Standards

Guidance

Unless bricks have been blended by the manufacturer, bricks from different batches should be mixed to avoid colour patching.

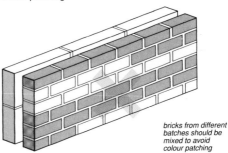

bricks from different batches should be mixed to avoid colour patching

To reduce the risk of efflorescence, newly erected masonry should be covered. This also prevents the mortar being washed out of the joints by rain and stops masonry becoming saturated.

Guidance

Statutory references

The following table lists references to building legislation and associated documents applicable at August 1990.

Clause	Subject	Statute			
		Building [1] Regulations	Building [2] Standards (Scotland)	Building [3] Regulations (N Ireland)	Isle of Man [4] Bye-laws
D3(a)	Structural design	A1/2	Part C	Part D	Part D
D3(a)	Lateral restraint	A1/2	Part C	Part D	Part D
D10	Thermal insulation	L1	Part J	Part F	Part F
D12	Fire safety	B2/3/4	Part D	Part E	Part E
D13	Sound insulation	E1/2/3	Part H	Part G	Part G
M3(a)	Blockwork selection	A1/2	Part B	Part B	Part B
		Associated documents			

[1] Approved Documents to the Building Regulations 1985 for England and Wales (and 1990 edition).
[2] Building Standards (Scotland) Regulations 1981 and all published amendments.
[3] Building Regulations (Northern Ireland) 1990.
[4] Isle of Man Bye-laws 1976, amended 1980 and 1987.

APPENDIX 6.1-B

Guidance

Exposure to rain penetration

The four pages in Appendix 6.1-B are taken from those parts of pages 12 to 15 of the BRE Report 'Thermal insulation: avoiding risks' which deal with the risk of rain penetration.

2 WALLS

There is a wide range of constructions that can meet U values below 0.6 W/m²K. The main risks are rain penetration, durability, condensation at cold bridges and within the construction and spread of fire gases in cavities.

The technical risks outlined in Table 1 need to be considered whatever level of insulation is adopted.

Rain penetration

Rainwater will penetrate the outer leaves of masonry walls under certain conditions of driving rain.

Total resistance to rain penetration can only be achieved by cladding the wall (eg with tile hanging, timber boarding, uPVC siding or an impervious cladding).

Clear cavities, if properly constructed, can prevent rainwater passing from outer to inner leaves. Filled cavities provide adequate resistance to rain penetration, provided the walls are built and the insulation installed as indicated in the following pages.

Reproduced from 'Thermal insulation: avoiding risks' by permission of BRE.

Guidance

201 To minimise the risk, follow the procedure below to determine the local exposure to wind driven rain, and select a suitable wall construction, carefully considering the design, detailing, workmanship and materials to be used.

Determine the degree of exposure

202 The map shows the variation in exposure across the country, based on data in BSI Draft for Development DD93 and related to the exposure categories defined in BS 5628:Part 3.

The contour lines dividing categories have been determined from an analysis of the worst likely spell of wind driven rain, occurring on average every 3 years, plotted on a 10km grid. The analysis is based on the "worst case" for each geographical area, ie the wall has a clear line of sight to open country and is facing the prevailing wind. Examples are a gable wall on the edge of a suburban site facing the prevailing wind and with a clear view of open countryside, one which is set back from the edge but also has a clear view of open country between other houses, or walls of a tall building projecting above other buildings within an urban area.

203 Buildings that have no clear line of sight of open country (ie they are sheltered by surrounding buildings and trees) can be considered to be located in an exposure category ranging from one lower in nominally *Sheltered* parts of the country to two lower in *Very severe* zones.

204 Because the exposure categories overlap in BS 5628:Part 3, the contour lines represent only an approximate division between zones. However, the map does provide a simple starting point for selecting a suitable form of construction. **[28]** For a more detailed analysis using larger scale maps, refer to DD93.

28   Map showing categories of exposure to wind driven rain

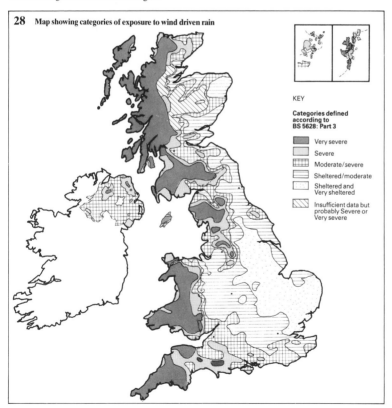

KEY

Categories defined according to BS 5628: Part 3

- Very severe
- Severe
- Moderate/severe
- Sheltered/moderate
- Sheltered and Very sheltered
- Insufficient data but probably Severe or Very severe

Reproduced from 'Thermal insulation: avoiding risks' by permission of BRE.

APPENDIX 6.1-B

External masonry walls

Guidance

Select a suitable form of construction

205 A range of common wall constructions and the highest exposure category for which they are suitable is given in Table 2. To be suitable for the exposure levels shown, the walls must comply with good practice recommendations given in British Standards and BBA Certificates. For masonry walls, the table assumes that walls comply with the items listed in Table 3.

206 If the designer departs from the detailing items listed in Table 3, or the standard of workmanship cannot be relied upon, the exposure rating of the wall should be downgraded. Table 4 provides some advice on the factors that affect the exposure rating — other factors are discussed below.

Other factors affecting the exposure rating

207 Rendering can enhance the rain resistance of a wall, but it is *essential* to ensure *correct specification* and *application* to an appropriate backing material to minimise cracking, which may otherwise reduce the effectiveness of render against rain penetration.

208 Render over external insulation when correctly applied can provide very high resistance to rain penetration. However, rendering on insulation is subject to greater fluctuations in temperature and impact damage than when applied directly to masonry. The following have been found to minimise cracking:

- Reinforcing the render with a mesh.
- Providing movement joints at maximum 6m intervals.
- Using a white or light coloured finish.
- Using a render either incorporating a polymer emulsion or with a flexible topcoat.

209 Protective design features can greatly reduce the amount of rainwater running down the outer face of the wall. Deep overhanging eaves and verges are features that reduce the amount of rain that falls on a wall and so help to keep it dry. Projecting sills and overhanging string courses throw water clear of the wall.

210 Absorbent masonry can limit the amount of rain that penetrates the wall by absorbing it. The periods of wind driven rain are usually short enough to prevent the outer leaf becoming completely saturated, and intervening dry periods allow moisture to evaporate. In contrast, low absorbency bricks with a smooth impervious finish can be more susceptible to rain penetration. During heavy rain, water runs down the surface and can rapidly penetrate the outer leaf through small cracks and unfilled perpends.

Maximum exposure category	Suitable wall constructions	Notes
Very severe	Any wall with cladding of metal, plastics, slate, tile hanging, timber boarding or similar	Assumes flashings are correctly detailed and insulation directly behind the cladding is faced with a breather membrane
	50mm clear cavity wall with a rendered finish, including timber frame	
Severe	Fairfaced cavity wall with an unfilled clear cavity at least 50mm wide	Applies to masonry or timber framed inner leaf. May also be used in certain *Very severe* locations as defined by map (see BS 5628)
	Fairfaced cavity masonry wall with partial fill and a residual clear cavity at least 50mm wide	With a 50mm residual clear cavity and correct installation, partial fill can be expected to perform as well as an unfilled cavity
	Fairfaced cavity masonry wall with full fill (except UF foam)	Check BBA certificate for any restriction to use. Minor imperfections in workmanship may assume greater significance than with a clear cavity and will reduce the exposure rating
Moderate/severe	Fairfaced cavity masonry wall with any cavity insulation	Assumes installation in accorance with relevant BS or BBA certificate
Sheltered	Unrendered solid masonry wall	Minimum 330mm thick With rendered solid walls, the resistance to driving rain depends on the type and thickness of masonry (see Table 11 in BS 5628: Part 3). Highest exposure category for rendered solid walls is *Severe*

Note: assumes all masonry walling complies with BS 5628: Part 3 and cavity insulation is installed in accordance with the relevant BBA Certificate, or BS 5618 for UF foam (see Table 3).

Table 2 Maximum exposure categories for locally exposed wall constructions (see 202)

Reproduced from 'Thermal insulation: avoiding risks' by permission of BRE.

Guidance

Design requirements (BS 5628: Part 3)

- The following types of cavity should be at least 50mm wide:
  - an unfilled cavity
  - a residual clear cavity with partial fill
  - a structural cavity with full fill construction

  Wider cavities reduce the likelihood of rain penetration.

- Provide cavity trays and dpc's at all interruptions to the cavity so they direct to the outside any water that enters the cavity.

- Cavity trays should rise 150mm within the cavity, be self supporting or fully supported and have joints lapped and sealed.

- Provide cavity trays with stop ends.

- Provide weepholes at no more than 1m centres.

- Provide continuous cavity trays over short piers between closely spaced openings.

- For complicated openings, provide clear drawings and use of pre-formed profiles.

- Projections at sills, copings and below cladding to be at least 50mm and incorporate a throating.

- Mortar joints should be tooled, either bucket handle, or weathered.

- Use a mortar mix and strength compatible with the strength and type of masonry units.

Workmanship requirements (BS 5628: Part 3)

- Well fill all mortar joints, particularly perpends.

- Build the outer leaf ahead of the inner leaf (except for partial cavity fill fixed against the inner leaf).

- Strike off projecting mortar from the inside of the outer leaf.

- Keep the cavity free of mortar droppings and other debris.

- Position wall ties centrally in the cavity and slope them downwards towards the outer leaf.

- Project vertical dpc's 25mm beyond cavity closers at openings.

Additional points for built-in cavity insulation

- Closely butt boards and batts to avoid gaps at the joints.

- Remove mortar droppings from the exposed edges of the insulation.

- Take the insulation to the top of the wall, or protect with a cavity tray.

- Follow the installation procedure given in the BBA Certificate and the manufacturer's literature.

- For partial fill, use the special ties or clips recommended by the manufacturer.

- For full fill, build the cavity width within the specified tolerances — to avoid compression or sagging of the insulation.

Additional points for installers of cavity fill systems.

- The builder and installer should liaise on design, particularly in *Severe* and *Very severe* exposure categories.

- Check that the necessary design and constructional standards have been achieved particularly in respect of the information given in BS 8208: Part 1.

- Ensure the cavity is completely filled.

Table 3 Design and workmanship requirements

Possible changes to wall built to BS 5628: Part 3		Effect of changes on exposure rating of the wall
Add cladding to wall	↑	Can improve the exposure rating of the clad area to *Very severe*
Ground floor fairfaced walls with cladding added to upper floors	↑	Improves the exposure rating of the fairfaced wall by up to two categories
Increase clear cavity width, or width of full cavity fill from 50 to 100mm	↑	Increase of up to two categories in the exposure rating of the wall
Detailing and workmanship to BS 5628: Part 3	=	No change (see Table 3)
Installation of cavity insulation in accordance with BBA Certificate or British Standard	=	No change (see Table 3)
Workmanship less than BS 5628: Part 3, or installation not to BBA Certificate requirements	↓	Reduces exposure rating of the wall. More critical when insulation is placed in the cavity
Strong mortar for the wall generally, flush detailing at sills, parapets etc.	↓	These factors reduce the exposure rating of the wall
Recessed mortar joints	↓	Consider only in *Sheltered* or *Very sheltered* areas

Table 4 Factors that effect the exposure rating of the wall

Reproduced from 'Thermal insulation: avoiding risks' by permission of BRE.

Guidance

Areas of *severe* exposure to frost attack

The tinted areas have a frost incidence over 60 days a year, rainfall over 1000mm per year and an elevation over 90m above sea level.

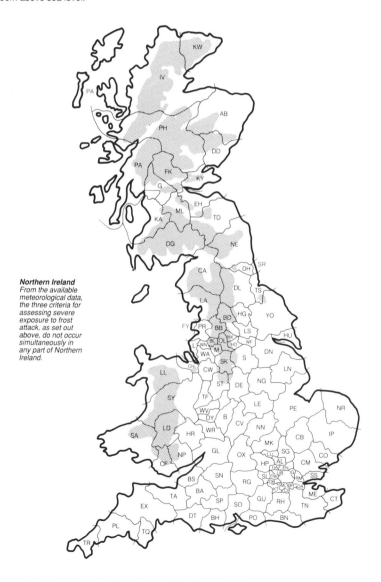

Northern Ireland
From the available meteorological data, the three criteria for assessing severe exposure to frost attack, as set out above, do not occur simultaneously in any part of Northern Ireland.

Map reproduced by permission of the London Brick Company Ltd.

External masonry walls | 6.1

Guidance

The following list identifies the postal areas within which the three criteria for severe exposure to frost attack are met.

Only in a few instances is the whole of the post code district within the area of severe frost exposure.

AB	BB	BD	BL	CA	CF	CH	DD	DE	DG	DH	DL	EH	FK	G	HD	HG	HR	HX	IV	KA
3	1	13	0	5	8	7	8	4	1	8	8	14	1	62	3	3	2	2	1	1
5	2	15	1	6	37	9	6		2		11	23	8	63	4		3	4	3	3
	3	.20	2	7	39				3		12	26	11	64	7		5	6	4	4
	4	21	7	8	40				4		13	27	12	65	8			7	5	5
	5	22	8	9	41				6			28	13	72					6	6
	6	23	9	10	42				7			43	14	74					7	16
	7	24		11	43				8			44	15	75					12	17
	8			12	44				10			45	16	76					13	18
	9			13	45				11			46	17	77					14	19
	10			16	46				12			47	18	81					15	26
	11			17	47				13			48	19	82					16	
	12			19	48				14			55	20	83					17	
				20									21	84					18	
				22									47						19	
				23															22	
																			23	
																			24	
																			25	
																			26	
																			27	
																			28	
																			40	
																			54	

KW	KY	LA	LD	LL	M	ML	NE	NP	OL	PA	PH	PH	S	SA	SK	ST	SY	TD	TS	YO
3	13	2	1	11	24	1	19	1	1	23	1	22	6	9	6	10	10	1	9	6
5	6	2	2	15		2	46	2	2	24	2	23	11	10	10	13	16	2		18
6	8	3	3	16		3	47	3	3	25	3	25	11	11	11		17	5		21
7	9	4	4	20		6	48	4	4	26	4	26	30	13	12		18	8		22
8	10	5	5	21		7	49	5	5	27	5	30		19	13		19	11		
9	12	6	6	22		8	66	6	6	32	6	31		20	14		20	71		
10	20	7	7	23		9	71	7	7	33	7	32		32	15		21			
11	21	8	8	24		10		8	8	34	8	33		33	16		22			
12	22			25		11		44	9	35	9	34		39	17		23			
13	23			26		12			10	36	10	35		40			24			
14				27					11	37	11	36		44			25			
				28					12	38	15	37		48						
				32					13	40	16	38								
				33					14	41	17	39								
				40					15		18	40								
				41					16		19	41								
				54							20									
				55							21									
				57																

▓ partly within   ░ wholly within   Reproduced by permission of the London Brick Company Ltd.

APPENDIX 6.1-D

Guidance

Mortar mixes

Unless recommended otherwise by the brick manufacturer, the mixes in the table below should be used for clay bricks.

In the case of concrete or calcium silicate bricks, particular attention should be paid to manufacturers' recommendations.

Mortar mixes using ordinary Portland or sulphate-resisting cements where required (see also Design clauses 6.1 - D5(b) and (c)).

Location		Recommended cement : lime : sand mix	Recommended cement : sand mix with plasticiser
General wall area above dpc	in areas of *Severe* or *Very severe* exposure	1 : ½ :4 ½	1 : 3 or 4
	other exposure categories	1 : 1 : 5 or 6	1 : 5 or 6
Below dpc level and in chimney stacks		1 : ½ : 4 to 4½	1 : 3 or 4
Cappings, copings and sills		1 : 0 to ¼ : 3	-

As an alternative to the above mortar mixes, the following can be used:
1 : 1 : 5½, cement : lime : sand, with plasticiser, or
1 : 1 : 5½, cement : lime : sand, with plasticiser, using sulphate-resisting cement, where required.

Retarded mortar
Retarded mortar and most pre-mixed mortars can be used over a longer period of time than site mixed, cement : lime : sand mortars. The timescale of use is defined by the manufacturer, whose advice should be followed:
- avoid using during very cold weather as setting times can be seriously delayed
- do not use retarded mortar beyond the time for which it is effective
- because of delayed setting, temporary bracing of larger walls, for example gable peaks and long walls, may be necessary.

Additives
Where plasticisers or other additives are to be used, follow manufacturers' instructions:
- do not overdose, 'more is not better'
- an air entraining agent can help reduce frost damage but it is not an anti-freeze
- do not use unauthorised additives.

Guidance

Dpcs and cavity trays

Some positions where dpcs and cavity trays should be provided:

Location	Provision of dpcs and cavity trays
Base of walls, piers, etc	A dpc should be provided a minimum 150mm above adjoining surfaces and linked with the dpm in solid floors.
Base of partitions built off oversite where there is no integral dpm	Dpc should be full width of partition.
Base of wall built off beam, slab, etc	Detail to prevent entry of damp by driving rain.
Parapet	(1) Beneath coping, and (2) 150mm above adjoining roof surface to link with the roof upstand.
Chimney	(1) Beneath coping, and (2) Between 150mm and 300mm above highest point of intersection with roof. In the case of steeply-pitched roofs, a second dpc should be provided between 150mm and 300mm above the lowest point of the intersection. *For Severe exposure conditions: as for normal conditions but with a dpc tray.*
In cavity walls over openings, air bricks and the like	A cavity tray should be provided to direct to the outside any water that enters the cavity. The cavity tray should extend 150mm each side of the opening.

Guidance

Dpcs and cavity trays (continued)

Location	Provision of dpcs and cavity trays
At *the horizontal abutment* of all roofs over enclosed areas and balconies to walls	A cavity tray should be provided 150mm above the adjoining roof or balcony surface. The tray should be lapped over any roof upstand or flashing to ensure water penetrating into the cavity does not enter the enclosed area.
At *sloping abutments* of all roofs over enclosed areas to cavity walls	A stepped cavity tray should be provided above the roof surface and linked to any roof upstand or flashing to ensure any water penetrating into the cavity does not enter the enclosed area.
Doorsteps	A dpc should be provided behind a doorstep where it is higher than a wall dpc.
Sills	Where precast concrete or similar sills incorporate joints or are of a permeable material, a dpc should be provided beneath them for the full length and be turned up at the back and the end of the sill.
Jambs in cavity	The reveal should be protected throughout its width by a continuous dpc. The width of the dpc should be sufficient to be fixed to, or overlap, the frame and fully protect the reveal. *For Severe exposure conditions: rebated reveal construction, with or without closed cavity and dpc.*

dpm behind doorstep links with dpc

level of wall dpc

doorstep

Durability classification of bricks

BS 3921 classifies clay bricks according to their frost resistance and soluble salt content as follows:

Durability	Frost resistance	Soluble salt content
FL	Frost resistant (**F**), durable in all	Low (**L**)
FN	building situations	Normal (**N**) no limit on soluble salt content
ML	Moderately frost resistant (**M**), durable except when saturated	Low (**L**)
MN	and subject to repeated freezing and thawing	Normal (**N**) no limit on soluble salt content
OL	Not frost resistant (**O**), liable to be damaged	Low (**L**)
ON	by freezing and thawing	Normal (**N**) no limit on soluble salt content

Calcium silicate and concrete bricks contain no soluble salts. Information on their durability is given in Materials clause 6.1 - M2(b).

BUILDMARK™

informing the industry

NHBC STANDARDS

External timber framed walls and wall panels

(FORMERLY PRACTICE NOTE 5)

Introduction

This Practice Note sets out what designers, certifiers and builders must do to meet NHBC technical requirements.

Its purpose is to ensure that design detailing and erection is done so that timbers and wood products will stay dry after completion of the dwelling, that timber in vulnerable places is preservative treated and that the dwelling is structurally stable.

Dates of coming into effect

This Practice Note applies to all timber frame dwellings where the foundations are concreted on or after the dates shown below:

1st April 1983 — All clauses except those for preservative treatment

1st September 1983 — Section 5 for preservative treatment.

Effect on Costs

Nothing for many builders who already treat the frame, and use fibre board sheathing. About £30 — £40 on an average sized house for most of the remainder. Possibly £100 for the few whose present standards are minimal.

Why Necessary

The new energy saving regulations, coupled with the rapid growth in timber frame, combined to create potential risks if no precautions were taken. North American and Scandinavian practice were taken into account but could not be a complete guide here because (a) of differences in methods of construction; (b) differences in climate.

This Practice Note applies to:

Any dwelling which has external walls of load bearing timber work, or dwellings where the upper storeys are timber frame supported on lower storeys of different construction.

Masonry cross wall dwellings do not require certification, but the construction of any external timber frame wall panels must follow the principles of this Practice Note.

This Practice Note is based on the traditional concept of timber frame construction being cladding, wall cavity, sheathing with or without breather membrane, insulated stud work, vapour check and dry lining. Other methods of construction may be permitted if the principles of this Practice Note are met and written acceptance is obtained from the NHBC before use.

Note: Scottish Building Regulations limit the use of timber frame to houses of not more than 3 storeys.

The specifications apply throughout the UK unless a sub-clause is marked as follows:

NE — Not applicable in England and Wales
NS — Not applicable in Scotland
NNI — Not applicable in Northern Ireland

NOTE: ALL DRAWINGS ARE ILLUSTRATIONS OF THE POINT MADE IN THE TEXT AND ARE NOT THE ONLY SOLUTION.

What designers, certifiers and builders must do:

1 DESIGN TO MEET NHBC TECHNICAL REQUIREMENTS

This Practice Note must be read in conjunction with the NHBC Registered House-Builders Handbook: Part 2A: Technical Requirements for the design and construction of dwellings.

The following requirements taken from the Registered House-Builders Handbook must be met:

Rq 1
Building legislation

EVERY DWELLING SHALL COMPLY WITH ALL RELEVANT BUILDING LEGISLATION AND THE REGULATIONS OF STATUTORY UNDERTAKINGS AND OTHER PROPER AUTHORITIES.

Rq 2
Materials, products and building systems

Suitability of Materials
(a) All materials, products and building systems shall be suitable for the purpose for which they are used. Proper account shall be taken of the conditions for their use including their position within the structure and the geographical location of the dwelling.

Testing and use of materials
(b) To comply with these Technical Requirements the quality of materials, products and building systems must be clearly shown to be suitable for the purpose for which they are to be used by testing or other means of verification as set out in paragraph (c) below. They shall be used strictly in accordance with manufacturers' recommendations unless an alternative standard is laid down in the Technical Specifications printed in blue.

Acceptability of Materials: Critical Functions
(c) Unless notified in writing to the contrary, the following will be acceptable as complying with clauses (a) and (b) above:
(1) Where the function is critical to the performance of the dwelling ie. structure, weatherproofing, thermal and sound insulation, services (including heating appliances and flues) and fire resistance:
a. Materials, products and building systems which comply with a standard set by the Council in the Technical Requirements;
b. Where there is no Technical Requirement set by the Council;
i. Materials, products and building systems shall be of a quality not lower than that defined in any relevant British Standard specification provided their use is covered by, and is carried out in accordance with recommendations contained in a relevant British Standard Code of Practice, Practice specification, or in the opinion of the Council they are suitable for their use; or
ii. Their quality and use is satisfactorily assessed by an appropriate independent authority acceptable to the Council including British Board of Agrément and Building Research Establishment. Where there is no technical requirement set by the Council or standard as referred to in b. i or b ii. above, the quality and use of materials, products and building systems shall be in accordance with established satisfactory custom and practice provided that such custom and practice is acceptable to the Council.

Acceptability of Materials: Non Critical Functions
(2) Where the function is critical to the performance of the dwelling:
a. Materials complying with (1) above; or
b. Materials made for a specific use and used strictly in accordance with the manufacturers' recommendations for that use.

Third Party Certification
(d) Third party certification for materials, products and building systems shall be obtained if required by the Technical Specifications printed in blue.

Imported Materials
(e) Imported materials, products and building systems shall comply with the requirements of clauses (a) to (d) above.

Tests
(f) If required by the Council, the builder shall provide written proof from manufacturers of compliance with (a) to (e) above and shall permit the Council to take samples for tests to verify compliance. British Standards tests shall be used where applicable. The costs of any test shall be met by the builder if they prove non-compliance and by the Council if they prove compliance.
Materials proved not to comply shall, if necessary, be removed from the site.

Preservative Treatment
(g) Timbers shall be pretreated against decay and attack as laid down in the Technical Specifications printed in blue. Evidence of treatment shall be provided to the council if required.

Reclaimed Materials
(h) Materials recovered from older buildings may only be re-used with the agreement of the Council on site. Independent certification of suitability may be required.

Proprietary Building systems
(i) Proprietary building systems shall where there is no standard set by the Council comply with clause (c) (1)b.ii.

Rq 3
Facilities and services

Facilities and services shall be provided in accordance with the Schedule to these Requirements and shall be installed in accordance with the deemed-to-satisfy Specifications given hereafter or alternative specifications giving a not lower quality.

Rq 4
Structure and finish

Structure and finish shall be in accordance with the deemed-to-satisfy Specifications given hereafter or alternative specifications giving a not lower quality.

Rq5
Structural design for special conditions

(a) The Requirement shall apply to special conditions which shall include:

foundations on hazardous ground where the hazard makes special consideration necessary;

the foundations and superstructure of every dwelling over three storeys in height;

certain types of foundations and retaining walls as laid down in the Specifications hereafter;

any superstructure element which is not based on specific design criteria as laid down in the Specifications hereafter;

any dwelling not constructed in accordance with UK traditional design.

April 1989

(b) Where required by NHBC, all structural designs shall be carried out by an independent chartered civil or structural engineer or other professional person whose qualifications and status (including professional indemnity insurance) are acceptable to NHBC. (Engineers employed by specialist sub contractors will not normally be acceptable).

(c) The design shall comply with all relevant Codes of Practice including, where appropriate:

June 1985	BS 6399: Part 1: 1984	Code of Practice for dead and imposed loads.
August 1986	CP3 Ch 5 Part 2 BS 8110	'Wind loads' 'The structural use of concrete'
February 1988	BS 5268 BS 8004 BS 5950	'The structural use of timber' 'Foundations' 'The use of structural steel in building'
June 1985	BS 5628 Parts 2 & 3	'Use of masonry'

(d) The design shall relate to the site location and conditions.

(e) In all cases the builder shall:

Require the designer to issue clear instructions for site personnel; and

not permit departure from the design without the designer's written consent.

require the designer or his representative to carry out such inspections as may be required by NHBC. | Au|

(f) Upon request by the Council, the builder shall:

produce such design documents, calculations and prescribed forms of certificate as the Council may require for its scrutiny; and

make available design documents and assembly instructions solely for use by the Council's inspectors on site; and

arrange for the Council's inspectors to have access to places where off-site fabrication is taking place.

Rq 6
Workmanship

(a) ALL WORK SHALL BE CARRIED OUT IN A SOUND, NEAT, DURABLE AND WORKMANLIKE MANNER TO THE SATISFACTION OF THE COUNCIL.

(b) Reasonable precautions shall be taken to protect fixed and unfixed materials against any damage likely to affect the finished quality of the dwelling.

(c) Before handover of the dwelling to the purchaser, care shall be taken to ensure that:

all work has been completed and access provided;

services have been tested and are in working order;

sanitary fittings and glass are free from damage and have been cleaned;

splashes of mortar, paint and the like have been removed;

floors have been cleaned;

rubbish and debris have been removed from the dwelling and the garden.

Ca27
Timber Frame Dwellings

(a) The structural design of timber frame dwellings shall be undertaken by a competent person.

(b) Evidence of this (on form HB 353b) shall be held on site for inspection by the Council. **NS**

(c) Evidence of this (on form HB210) shall be forwarded to NHBC Scottish Office. **NE NNI**

(d) The design and construction shall be in accordance with the principles of Practice Note 5: 1982.

OBTAIN A CERTIFICATE PROVING THAT THE DESIGN HAS BEEN CHECKED

2.1 In England, Wales and Northern Ireland   NS

The design of the superstructure of every house type on every site must be checked by a NHBC listed certifier.

a.   What the certifier must do

The certifier will ensure that the drawings and specifications are checked so that any timber is protected from moisture, the superstructure is structurally stable and that detailing and materials are in accordance with NHBC technical requirements and this Practice Note.

If the design is satisfactory a design certificate (Form HB 353b) must be signed and issued by a NHBC registered certifier (See page 32). The certificate or a copy must be given to the builder. The certifier may accept a structural check by a qualified engineer experienced in timber frame if section C is signed by the engineer.

Applications for inclusion on the list of NHBC certifiers must be made on form HB 349a, obtainable from the Technical Department of NHBC at Chiltern Avenue, Amersham, Bucks. Applications will be considered from professionally qualified architects and consulting civil or structural engineers with at least three years timber frame housing experience and covered by adequate professional indemnity insurance for the work of certification. Other persons may be considered for.acceptance if the persons concerned have experience and adequate professional indemnity insurance and, in the opinion of NHBC, are appropriately qualified to undertake certification.

May
1983

b.   What the builder must do

If he is building a timber framed dwelling or dwellings he must say so on the application for inspection form HB 3. On the same form he must also give the name and number of the approved certifier. Lastly he should obtain a design certificate (form HB 353b) from the certifier and hold it on site as proof that the dwellings have been correctly designed.

2.2 In Scotland   NE NNI

a. In Scotland NHBC require that the structural adequacy of the timber framed superstructure must be assessed by an engineer who:—

i.   Is professionally qualified as a structural or civil engineer.

ii. Is in private practice, or is otherwise approved by the Council in Scotland.

iii. Has at least three years practical experience of timber framed house design.

iv. Carries adequate professional indemnity insurance.

b. The engineer's certification of adequate design must be confirmed on form HB 210 (see page 33) which also provides a facility to advise the Council of:—

i.   The location of the dwelling.

ii. The type of dwelling.

iii. The prefabricator of the dwelling.

iv. The designer of the dwelling.

v.   The builder of the dwelling.

IT IS THE BUILDERS RESPONSIBILITY TO ARRANGE SUBMISSION OF THE HB 210 FORM TO THE NHBC'S SCOTTISH OFFICE PRIOR TO BUILDING COMMENCING.

3 PROVIDE DRAWINGS FOR USE ON SITE

3.1 Drawings

Provide good size assembly drawings showing frame connections, weathering and damp-proofing details and, where critical, erection sequence for use by site personnel.

It is recommended that approximately 1:5 scale be used for details and approximately 1:50 scale be used for plans, elevations and sections.

Manufacturer's drawings are to be made available to NHBC on request.

PREPARE DRAWINGS TO TAKE SPECIAL ACCOUNT OF THE FOLLOWING:—

a.   Structural stability:—

Take account of ground hazards. (SEE HANDBOOK CLAUSE Fo 3).

Ensure that the loads from the structure are transferred to properly constructed foundations.

Construct the ground floor to prevent undue settlement and movement.

Design the frame and roof with adequate racking resistance for structural stability and to resist wind forces.

Anchor the frame to the substructure.

b.   Damp and weather protection to keep timber dry in completed dwellings:—

Control rising damp by protection below the frame.

Control rain penetration by protection around door and window openings and at cavity barriers and by providing a cavity between claddings and sheathings.

Control interstitial condensation by vapour checks and permeability of insulation, sheathing and breather membrane.

Ventilate roofs.

Ventilate cavities between cladding and sheathing.

c.   Details for sound insulation (when applicable).

d.   Details for thermal insulation.

e.   Details to control spread of fire.

f.   Details of any flues.

3.2 **Erection instructions and material specifications**

a. Provide clear instructions to persons responsible for ordering materials and site fixing so they can undertake the work correctly.

b. Keep a copy of drawings, specifications and erection and fixing instructions on site even if the frame erection is carried out by a specialist sub-contractor.

c. The fixing instructions must give the sequence of operations together with any special precautions for temporary support.

d. The instructions must include: —

    i. **Specifications for all materials for critical functions including: —**

Dpms	Cladding
Dpcs	Wall ties
Anchoring to foundations	Cavity ventilation
Timber preservation	Roof ventilation
Structural timber	Cavity barriers
Sheathing	Fire stopping
Breather membrane	Sarking
Insulation	Decking
Vapour check	Acoustic requirements
Nails and staples	Roof trusses

    ii. **Site nailing schedule**

The nailing schedule must allow for every structural connection made on site including fixing details for framing, wall ties, breather membrane, sheathing and vapour checks, and must show as appropriate:

1. Number and spacing of nails or staples;

2. Size and type of nail including material and corrosion protection;

3. Method of nailing (eg skew, end etc.)

COPIES OF THE NAILING SCHEDULE MUST BE GIVEN TO THE MAN DOING THE JOB.

    iii. **Limitations on notching and drilling**

Notching and drilling must comply with NHBC Handbook clause Se 7 unless engineer designed and clearly shown on drawings or in a schedule.
COPIES OF NOTCHING DETAILS MUST BE GIVEN TO THE MAN DOING THE JOB.

KEEP TIMBER DRY

Take the following precautions in detailing and during storage and erection to keep the moisture content of timber below that at which rot can occur.

4.1 Avoid wetting during storage and erection

Protect stored timber and wood products from the weather.

4.2 Do not seal moisture into the frame

Do not fix the vapour check when the moisture content of framing is above 20%.

4.3 Stop rising damp

a. Fit dpcs below all ground floor walls including internal partitions to protect all timber from rising damp. (A dpm is not acceptable by itself.)

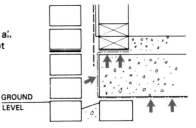

GROUND
LEVEL

Prevent damp rising to timber

b. The void below suspended timber floors shall be ventilated and constructed to meet NHBC Handbook clause Fo 37.

4.4 Stop rain penetration

a. **Dpcs**

i. Fit dpcs, waterbars or equivalent around all openings. A breather membrane is not equivalent to a dpc.

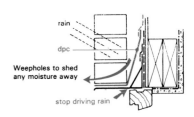

rain

dpc

Weepholes to shed
any moisture away

stop driving rain

Prevent rain penetrating at
heads of openings

4.4 **Stop rain penetration (cont)**

a. **Dpcs (cont)**

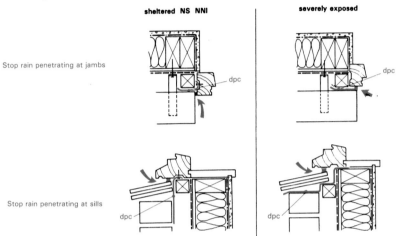

Stop rain penetrating at jambs

Stop rain penetrating at sills

ii. Overlap dpcs etc. so that each joint is
protected and moisture drains outwards.

b. **Breather Membranes**
Always use a breather membrane except with bitumen impregnated
fibre building board when the joints are closely butted and when it
is not in a severely exposed location (see BRE Digest 127).
Plywood panel joints should not be closely butted.

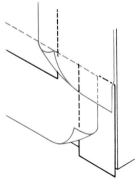

i. Fix the breather membrane to shed
water away from the sheathing and
below the lowest timber.

4.4 **Stop rain penetration (cont)**

b. **Breather Membranes (cont)**

ii. When a breather membrane is not required make sure that the bottom members are protected.

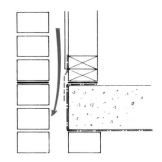

c. **Cavities**

i. Provide a minimum clear vertical cavity between claddings and sheathings: —

Masonry	—	50mm nominal (– 15mm)
Render on unbacked lathing	—	50mm nominal (– 10mm)
Render on backed lathing	—	25mm nominal (–6mm)
Vertical tile hanging without underlay	—	no vertical cavity required when a breather membrane is fitted to the sheathing
Other cladding	—	10mm

January 1985

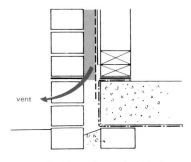

vent

Provide a cavity to reduce risk of rain penetration to the frame. Drain and vent the cavity to remove moisture.

ii. Extend the cavity at least 150mm below dpc, to form drainage to the cavity. Keep this drain clear. Provide weep holes and other measures where necessary to ensure the cavity drains freely.

May 1983

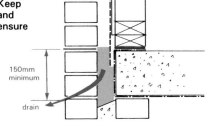

150mm minimum

drain

Provide cavities with a drain at least 150mm below the lowest timber.

4.4 **Stop rain penetration (cont)**

c. **Cavities (cont)**

iii. Ventilate the cavity below dpc level and at eaves and verge level with the equivalent of an open brick perpend every 1.5m.

Avoid mortar blocking ventilation. Make certain that ventilation slots are placed so they are protected from ingress of rain or are below the lowest timber.

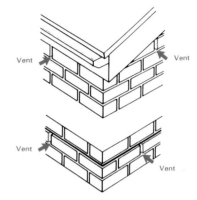

iv. Slope wall ties down from the sheathing and keep them clear of mortar droppings.

v. Protect horizontal cavity barriers (except under eaves) with a dpc tray. The upstand must be a minimum of 100mm.

When a polythene encased cavity barrier is used which provides a minimum 100mm upstand no extra dpc tray is required.

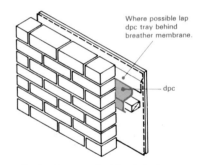

Use dpcs to cover horizontal cavity barriers to shed moisture away from sheathings.

vi. Protect timber cavity barriers with a dpc between the cladding and the timber.

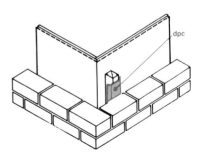

d. **Floor decks**
Protect floor deckings from moisture until the dwelling is substantially weathertight unless the decking is resistant to occasional wetting.

4.5 Control interstitial condensation

a. Fit a vapour check on the warm side of the external wall insulation between the insulation and the plasterboard. The vapour check must cover the external wall including bottom rails, head rails, studs, lintels and window reveals. Any holes shall be repaired.

b. Cut holes closely and neatly around services and seal any gaps.

A vapour check is essential to stop moisture getting into timber frame walls

* 4.6 Limit the risks of high levels of humidity occurring within the dwelling

a. **Fully ventilated tiled or pitched roofs with insulation at ceiling level.**
Do not install a vapour check at ceiling level unless an alternative means for water vapour to escape has been provided.

b. **Roofs with an impervious covering or requiring a vapour check.**
Provide a means for water vapour to escape.

c. **Doors and windows giving a high degree of air tightness (ie air permeability above 150pa when measured in accordance with BS 6375 : Part I : 1983).**
Provide controllable trickle ventilation or other background ventilation.

d. **Bathrooms, kitchens and washing rooms.**
On exposed sites provide a means of ventilation which can be used during inclement weather.

January 1984

4.7 Provide roof ventilation

Ventilate the roof space in accordance witn building regulations and NHBC requirements.

4.8 Protect from accidental spillage or floor washing

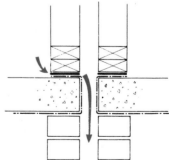

a. Provide drainage between attached dwellings to prevent moisture passing from one dwelling to another.

b. With fully reinforced raft foundations which are continuous across separating walls a barrier must be provided.

c. Prevent moisture from being retained adjacent to timber.

Prevent any moisture which is spilt onto floors from seeping into adjacent property

* 4.9 Prevent condensation from occurring on pipework within timber framed walls

January 1984

Keep service pipework on the warm side of the wall insulation.

* See revision list on back page.

5 DECIDE ON PRESERVATIVE TREATMENT

EXTERNAL WALLS

5.1 Timber framing

a. Timbers rated moderately durable or better and containing no sapwood do not require preservative treatment (See BRE: Princes Risborough Laboratory Technical Note No. 40 — ''The natural durability classification of timber''). Other external wall timbers shall be preserved against decay and insect attack as recommended by British Wood Preserving Association Standard C9 in accordance with Table 1 below or equivalent.

b. Any timber treated with preservative to meet the above requirement and cut after treatment shall be given two liberal applications of a suitable colour tinted preservative to the cut surfaces.

January
1985

Table 1 PRESERVATIVE TREATMENT

Timber Component	Treatment group in Table 1 of BWPA C 9	Acceptable processes
Studs, rails, lintels or binders: floor zone perimeters (timber forming the outer face of the timber frame)	1	CCA Vacuum/pressure OS Double vacuum. Boron diffusion
Timber in cavities between sheathing and cladding: sole plates and bottom rails acting as a sole plate (see also below)	3	CCA Vacuum/pressure OS Double vacuum
Wall fixings: sole plates set below upper surface of screed	4	CCA Vacuum/pressure
Timber cladding	See Building Regulations (as specified in BWPA Standard C6)	

NOTE: At the time of publication BWPA Standard C9 shall be used. Other standards may be developed which are acceptable to NHBC as providing equivalent protection. The advice of BWPA should be sought.

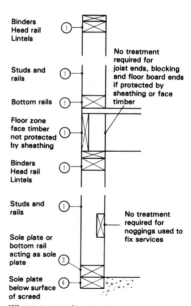

No treatment required for joist ends, blocking and floor board ends if protected by sheathing or face timber

No treatment required for noggings used to fix services

What to treat and treatment group

5.2 Plywood sheathing (In abeyance, see Clause 5.4)

Plywood with moderately durable or better outer veneers can be used without treatment (see BRE: Princes Risborough Laboratory Technical Note No. 40 — "The natural durability classification of timber").

Otherwise all plywood shall be preservative treated either:

a.   at the veneer stage before boards are made up or

b.   as boards treated by either

    i.   10 minute dip, or

    ii.   OS double vacuum to a minimum solution retention of 40 litres/m^3.

5.3 Other sheathings

Medium board and bitumen impregnated fibre building board are acceptable without preservative treatment. All other sheathings must be satisfactorily assessed by an independent authority and be durable for the life of the building. Wood product sheathings shall have a durability not less than plywood treated with preservatives to the above standard.

5.4 Date of coming into force

The requirements for treatment of timber frame will come into force on 1st September 1983 (see clause 5.1).

The requirements for preservative treatment of plywood sheathing (clause 5.2) will not be required from 1st September 1983. Further research into the effect of treatment on plywood, and the need for it, is still in progress Further advice will be given early in 1984. Adequate notice of preservative treatment of plywood, if any, will be given.

May
1983

USE ACCEPTABLE MATERIALS

All materials used for the following critical functions shall meet the specifications given below or have been satisfactorily assessed in accordance with NHBC Handbook requirement Rq 2. Written proof of compliance may be required. Otherwise written acceptance by NHBC shall be obtained prior to use for new materials, traditional materials used in a new way or novel constructions.

6.1 Breather membranes

Breather membranes shall:—

a. be a continuous membrane to protect the sheathing during construction and from water crossing the cavity after construction while allowing water vapour from within the frame to pass out into the cavity.

b. be durable.

c. have a vapour resistance less than 0.6MNs/g when calculated from the results of tests carried out in accordance with BS 3177 at 25°C and relative humidity of 75%.

d. have adequate wet strength to resist site damage.

e. fixing and laps shall be in accordance with Section 12.3 a page 29.

6.2 Cavity barriers and fire stops

Materials listed in the Building Regulations are acceptable. Other materials which comply with the building regulations can be used but proof of compliance may be required.

6.3 Floor decking

a. Shall comply with NHBC Handbook clauses Ca 14 to Ca 18 inclusive.

b. The decking thickness shall be to the manufacturers recommendations or the dimensions in this table, whichever is greater:—

| | Joist Centres | | |
	400mm	450mm	600mm
T & G softwood boarding	16	16	19
Wood chip board	18	18	22
Plywood	12	12	16

6.4 Damp proof courses

Shall comply with NHBC Handbook clause Br 4.

6.5 Damp proof membranes

Shall comply with NHBC Handbook clause Fo 26.

6.6 Holding down

Use austenitic stainless steel, phosphor bronze, silicon bronze or mild steel with zinc coating for holding the frame down to the substructure.

6.7 Nails and staples

a. All staples for fixing sheathing and breather membranes shall be austenitic stainless steel or other material of equivalent strength and corrosion resistance.

b. Nails for fixing breather membranes and sheathing shall be galvanised, sherardised or austenitic stainless steel, phosphor bronze or silicon bronze.

c. Nails for fixing timbers which have been treated by CCA shall comply with b. above.

6.8 Preservation

For timbers and board materials requiring preservation and the treatments required see section 5 of this Practice Note.

6.9 Roof Trusses

a. Design in accordance with BS 5268 parts 2 and 3.

b. Proprietary jointing systems used in roof trusses shall meet Handbook requirement Rq 2.

c. Bracing shall be provided in accordance with clause Ca 37 unless designed in accordance with Rq 5.

6.10 Sheathing

a. Plywood suitable for structural sheathing with bonding equivalent to WBP of BS 1455 and BS 1203.

b. Medium board in accordance with FIDOR Technical Bulletin TB/002.

c. Bitumen impregnated fibre building board in accordance with FIDOR Technical Bulletin TB/001.

d. Any material that has been satisfactorily assessed for the purpose by the Agrément Board.

6.11 Timber

a. All structural timber shall be designed in accordance with BS 5268 parts 2 & 3. | **Feb 1988**

b. All structural timber shall be of a grade suitable for the design.

6.12 Vapour Check

a. Use minimum 500 gauge polythene or vapour check plasterboard. Vapour checks made from re-cycled materials are not acceptable. | **September 1984**

b. Fixing and laps shall be in accordance with Section 12.3 c page 30.

c. The use of foil backed plasterboard or the integral backing of insulation to form the vapour check is not permitted.

6.13 Wall insulation

Must be of a type that breathes eg mineral wool (rock or glass).

Insulation with an integral backing is permitted provided that the backing is on the warm side of the insulation but the backing shall not form the vapour check.

Insulation in the cavity between sheathing and cladding is not permitted.

6.14 Wall ties and their fixings

Wall ties must be flexible to allow for differential movement.

Acceptable materials are austenitic stainless steel, phosphor bronze, silicon bronze and materials which comply with Handbook requirement Rq 2.

Materials for wall ties and their fixings shall be compatible with each other. Any combination of stainless steel, phosphor bronze and silicon bronze is acceptable. | **May 1983**

7 ENSURE THE CONSTRUCTION IS STABLE

7.1 Provide foundations

a. Foundations shall comply with the Foundation Section of NHBC Handbook.

b. Slab thickening is not acceptable as a foundation unless it forms part of an engineer designed foundation.

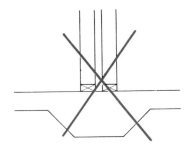

Do not use slab thickening as a foundation to load bearing walls or separating walls unless part of an engineer designed foundation.

7.2 Set out substructure accurately

The substructure must be correctly set out to line level and square to fit the timber frame which is to be manufactured to close tolerances.

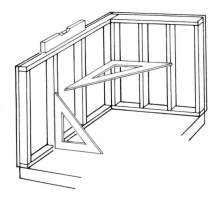

a. Inaccuracies will not be accepted which affect the way the loads from the structure are transmitted to the substructure.

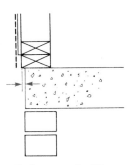

Overhangs exceeding 12mm are not acceptable.

7.2 **Set out substructure accurately (cont)**

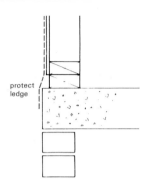

b.   If small ledges occur which might collect moisture, protection must be provided.

protect ledge

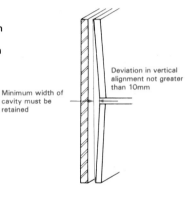

c.   Deviations in vertical alignment greater than 10mm in any storey height will not be permitted and in any event the cavity width must remain within the limits of clause 4.4 c.i. (page 10).

Deviation in vertical alignment not greater than 10mm

Minimum width of cavity must be retained

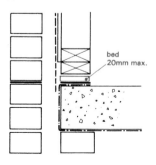

d.   Ensure that any bed between the frame and the substructure:

    i.   does not exceed 20mm in thickness and is the full width of the frame;

    ii.   is durable and does not deform under load;

    iii.   fully supports each stud so that no deformation of the frame will occur.

bed 20mm max.

7.3 **Anchor the frame to the substructure**

a. Anchor frame to resist both lateral movement and uplift of the frame.

b. Do not shot fire close to edges that may spall.

c. When shotfiring into masonry special density blocks must be provided.

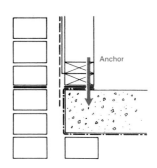

Anchor

7.4 **Design all structural timber in accordance with B.S. 5268**

Feb
1988

7.5 **Bind the wall panels together**

Securely fix wall panels together and to floor and roof framing.

In Scotland
Where there are joints between panels in walls, sole plates and head binder plates shall be provided to bind the panels together. The joints in sole plates and head binder plates may not coincide with those of the panels.

In England, Wales and Northern Ireland
If head plates are not provided, joists and roof trusses must bear directly over studs. **NS**

7.6 **Provide studs to transfer loads**

November
1984

a. Individual studs shall be 38mm nominal thickness and not less than 37mm thick, at maximum 600mm centres, unless other adequate support is provided for wall boards and fixings and agreed by NHBC.

b. Provide a lintel and cripple studs to any opening in load-bearing panels except when the opening does not affect the stud spacing or where the supported loads are redistributed by a perimeter joist.

c. Unless otherwise clearly specified by the designer multiple studs are to be included to support multiple joists.

d. Avoid, wherever possible, creating narrow, inaccessible gaps which are difficult to insulate.

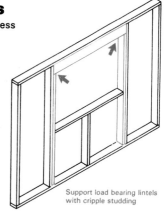

Support load bearing lintels
with cripple studding

7.7 **Notching and drilling**

Notching and drilling must comply with
NHBC Handbook clause Se 7 unless
engineer designed and clearly shown on
drawings or in a schedule.

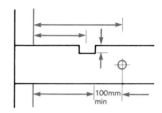

7.8 **Prevent undue movement of floors**

a.   Ensure that floors are strutted in accordance with NHBC Handbook clause
Ca 12.

Ca 12
Strutting (from Registered House-Builders Handbook)

*(a)   This clause shall apply to every floor,
including those designed in
accordance with Rq 5, page 10.*

*(b)   Intermediate strutting shall be
provided as follows:*

Joist span (m)	Rows of strutting
Up to 2.5	*None*
2.5 - 4.5	*1*
Over 4.5	*2*

*(c)   Where necessary, a row of strutting
shall be provided adjacent to bearings
on steelwork and the like.*

*(d)   Herringbone strutting shall be at least
38mm x 38mm and shall be located
clear of the top and bottom edges of
joists.*

*(e)   Solid strutting shall be at least 38mm
thick.*

*(f)   The depth of solid strutting shall be at
least three-quarters of the depth of
the joists.*

*(g)   Strutting shall be blocked to walls at
ends.*

b.   Block between ends of joists on external walls.

c.   Ensure that multiple joists are securely fixed together as specified by
the engineer.

7.9 **Support claddings**

a.   Masonry cladding must not be supported on timber.

b.   Wall ties must be flexible and fixed to studs.

c.   Battens supporting lightweight claddings must be fixed to studs.

7.10 **Securely fix partitioning**

a. The head, and ends of partitions are to be securely fixed to stud work, joists or noggings.

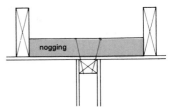

Firmly fix heads of partitioning.

b. At the base of partitions, noggings or extra joists are to be used to transfer the loads unless the engineer can show that the floor deck will transfer the load without undue deflection. Securely fix partitions to supports.

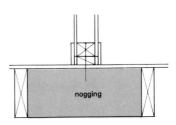

Firmly fix foot of partitions. Support on noggings or extra joists unless the deck is designed to avoid undue deflection.

7.11 **Securely fix plasterboard**

Securely fix or clip plasterboard and dry linings in accordance with NHBC Handbook clauses Wf 12 and Wf 15.

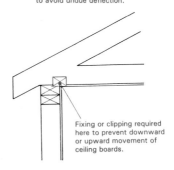

Fixing or clipping required here to prevent downward or upward movement of ceiling boards.

7.12 **Prevent roof distortion**

a. Roofs must be braced to prevent distortion.

b. Brace the roof in accordance with Ca 37 unless designed in accordance with Rq 5.   Feb 1988

c. Ensure that gable end panels are adequately restrained.

d. Roofs of traditional construction shall be properly triangulated.

e. Loads from water cisterns must be transferred to the node points of trussed rafters, in accordance with BS 5268 Part 3.   Feb 1988

Transfer load from cisterns back to node points.

8 ALLOW FOR DIFFERENTIAL MOVEMENT

Allow for movement between dissimilar materials such as masonry cladding and timber framing.

Prevent transfer of load from framing to cladding by making allowances for shrinkage of the timber.

NOTE: Most timber shrinkage occurs in the cross grain, ie in joists, base and head plates.

8.1 Make allowance for movement as follows:

a. For balloon construction which uses dwelling height studs to which the floor is attached follow manufacturers recommendations.

b. For platform construction which uses storey height panels normally separated by floor joists follow manufacturers recommendations or table 2.

Table 2   Typical shrinkage allowance for platform construction.

	Suspended timber ground floor when panels are supported on ground floor joists or perimeter joists	Other ground floor construction
Allowances for ground floor openings	5mm	3mm
Allowances for first floor openings	12mm	9mm
Allowances for second floor openings	18mm	15mm
Eaves and verges	Add 3mm to the allowance for openings on that floor	

8.2 Where to make allowance with masonry cladding

a. **At eaves**
Leave a gap above the masonry which can close as the timber shrinks. Sealing of the gap is not required if it is protected by the eaves overhang.

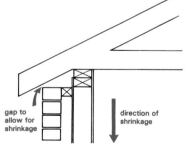

gap to allow for shrinkage

direction of shrinkage

Allow for shrinkage of the frame at eaves

8.2 Where to make allowance with masonry cladding (cont)

b. **Around joinery rigidly fixed to the timber frame**

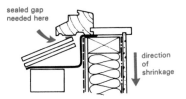

Allow for shrinkage of frame at sills

    i. At sills of openings leave a gap sealed with a compressible sealant.

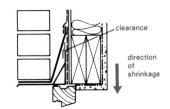

Allow for shrinkage of frame at heads of openings

    ii. At heads of openings allow for a gap to open. This must be sealed by an expandable sealant or well weathered. Do not fix lintels supporting outer leaf masonry rigidly to the timber frame. Allow space between the lintel and its clips for differential movement.

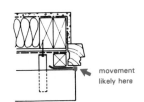

Allow for shrinkage of frame at jambs

    iii. At jambs of openings allow for shear between masonry and joinery.

c. **Around joinery rigidly fixed to the masonry**
Joinery should normally be fixed to the timber frame unless specially provided for by the designer. Make sure that differential movement will not distort the internal finishing to reveals of openings.

8.3 Where to make allowance with lightweight cladding

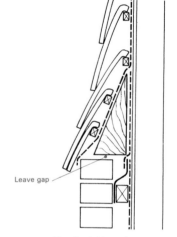

a. Allowances are not required around openings or at eaves and verges.

b. Leave a gap at horizontal junctions with masonry claddings. Ensure it is protected against rain penetration.

Leave gap

Allow for shrinkage of the frame at horizontal junctions

c. Allow for shear movement at vertical junctions between masonry and lightweight cladding.

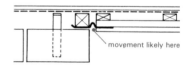

movement likely here

Allow for movement of frame at vertical junctions

8.4 Make allowance for movement at flues

Ensure that timber shrinkage will not affect the performance of, or transfer loads to any flues.

8.5 Use flexible wall ties to allow for movement

a. Wall ties must be flexible to allow for shrinkage. They must slope down from the sheathing.

b. Maximum wall tie spacing: 600mm horizontally, 450mm vertically (or equivalent).

c. At jambs of openings maximum spacing 300mm vertically within 300mm of brick reveal.

CONTROL SPREAD OF FIRE

9.1 Comply with all statutory requirements

9.2 Control the spread of fire through walls, floors and cavities

Ensure that the elements have adequate fire resistance as required by building regulations.

9.3 Control the spread of fire through cavities

Provide cavity barriers and firestops to comply with building regulations making sure they close the cavity.

Generally this is where cavities must be closed by cavity barriers and firestops for two storey houses. Additional requirements must be met for flats and stairwells in dwellings over two storeys.

a. Cavity barriers

VERTICALLY
i. Every 8m, not necessarily at corners of dwelling.
ii. At junctions of separating or compartment walls and at 8m intervals within the separating wall.

HORIZONTALLY
iii. Every 8m and at floor levels (except at ground floor).
iv. At eaves.

ELSEWHERE
v. Around openings.
vi. At ceiling level of top storey, or at verges (but gable wall must have the appropriate fire resistance).

b. **Fire stops**
vii. At junctions of separating walls compartment walls, separating floors and compartment floors.
viii. At junctions of separating walls with roof.

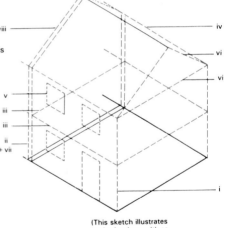

(This sketch illustrates cavity barrier positions for a 2 storey dwelling only.)

9.4 Services

Do not route service mains through any separating wall cavity.

Ensure that service outlets do not impair the fire resistance of walls and floors.

In Scotland
No services are permitted within a separating wall cavity.

CONTROL SOUND TRANSMISSION

a. Meet the requirements of building regulations for reduction of sound through separating and compartment walls and floors.

b. Ensure any substantiating test data applies to the construction being used and that evidence is available to NHBC inspectors on request.

c. Construct walls and floors strictly in accordance with the design.

d. Avoid services in separating or compartment walls or floors wherever possible. When installed, the sound insulation integrity must be maintained. (In Scotland services are not permitted in separating walls.)

e. Do not fix any floating floor through the sound deadening quilt. Ensure that the floating floor is completely isolated from the structure.

f. Do not support load-bearing partitions off any floating floor.

g. Ensure that skirtings are not fixed to any floating floor.

MAKE PROVISION FOR SERVICES

Consider the routing of services early in the design.
Services should be kept off external walls and separating walls where possible.
In Scotland services are not permitted in separating walls.
Service installations must comply with the Services section of NHBC Handbook.

Pay special attention to: —

a. Ensuring no electricity cable, other than meter tails, is in the cavity between sheathing and cladding of external walls.

b. Complying with water authority Bye-Laws particularly for access to pipe work.

c. Cutting holes closely and neatly around services and sealing any gaps.

d. Wiring surrounded by insulation shall be rated to take account of the effect of the insulation.

e. Keeping notching and drilling within the requirements of this Practice Note (see clause 7.7).

12 CONTROL SITE WORK
By providing competent supervision and clear instructions

CARELESS WORK CAUSES MORE DEFECTS THAN LACK OF SKILL.

12.1 Tell the operatives what to do

Brief the operatives so they understand the purpose of the job they are doing and why it is important.

Ensure that they have enough information and the right equipment to carry out the job correctly.

12.2 Follow the erection instructions

Carefully follow any special precautions such as temporary support during erection and protection of materials.

12.3 Check the work as it proceeds

Fast build systems such as timber frame require checking as the work proceeds or mistakes critical to the performance could be missed. To assist the checking of the work the site supervisor may wish to use the "NHBC Site Supervisors Checklist" obtainable, free of charge, from local NHBC inspectors or NHBC Information Office, 58 Portland Place, London W1N 4BU.

Pay special attention to:-

   a.   **Breather membranes**
Ensure laps are at least 100mm on horizontal laps and 150mm on vertical laps. Fix upper layers over lower layers to ensure rain runs away from the sheathing. Stagger vertical joints wherever possible. Breather membranes must be secured at regular intervals to prevent damage by wind.

Make sure that the lowest timbers in the wall are protected and that stud positions are marked for wall tie fixing.

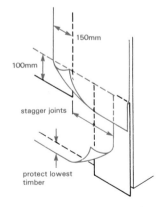

lap breather membranes correctly

12.3 **Check the work as it proceeds (cont)**

b. **Insulation**
Make sure the insulation covers all the
wall area between studs and is tight
against studs and rails. No gaps should
be left at corners, noggings and
junctions with partitions.
Any backing to the insulation must be on
the warm side of the insulation.

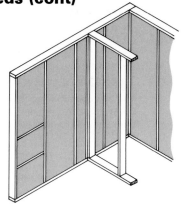

Insulation must completely fill all areas to
be insulated (shaded on diagram)

c. **Vapour Check**
Ensure that the frame is dry (moisture
content below 20%) before vapour check
is fixed.

Make sure that the vapour check is fixed
on the warm side of the insulation and is
either separate minimum 500 gauge polythene or vapour check plasterboard. The
vapour check must cover the external
wall area including rails, studs, window
reveals, lintels and cills. Make sure that
holes are cut neatly and any gaps sealed.

September
1984

i. **Minimum 500 gauge polythene sheet**
  1. Ensure that all joints occur
     on studs or noggings with
     at least 100mm lap.
  2. Fix the polythene securely
     to the top and bottom of
     the frame, at laps and
     around openings (approx.
     250mm centres).
  3. All tears must be repaired.

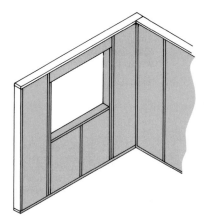

Vapour check must completely cover all
external wall framing (shaded on diagram)

ii. **Vapour check plasterboard**
Ensure that all joints occur at
studs or noggings and that they
are filled, taped and finished.
When cutting avoid pushing the
vapour check off the board.

12.3 **Check the work as it proceeds (cont)**

d.   **Claddings**
Ensure that wall ties are fixed to studs within the maximum spacing
and that the ties slope down from the sheathing.

Make sure that movement allowances have been made around
openings and at eaves.

Make sure that no horizontal cladding batten is next to the sheathing,
except with tile hanging.

Ensure that the cavity is provided with ventilation.

Ensure that nothing obstructs the cavity or its drainage.

12.4 **Prevent damage by providing good storage**

Keep site storage to a minimum.

Store panels on level bearers, sheathing side up with cross laths to give an
air gap between panels.

Roof trusses should be stored vertically for long term storage, otherwise
horizontally on level bearers.

Ensure that storage areas are well drained.

Cover materials.

12.5 **Repair damaged materials**

Replace or repair   —   torn breather membranes
and vapour checks.

—   damaged sheathing.

—   twisted or misaligned studs.

—   studs with excessive wane.

—   any other damaged material.

Replace the entire panel if badly damaged.

Breather membranes and vapour checks are easily damaged by wind,
carelessness, or vandalism. Neither of them should be left uncovered for
longer than is necessary.

12.6 **Do not modify designs or change material specifications** without the agreement of the designer and certifier

12.7 **If in doubt — Ask**

HB353B CERTIFICATE FOR TIMBER FRAME DWELLINGS
ENGLAND, WALES AND N. IRELAND

A

NHBC

serving the home buyer

This form is to be issued to the registered house-builder and made available to the NHBC inspector on site.

Builder's Name ....

Address ....

Site Address				
Dwelling or Plot Numbers	No. of Units	Frame/House Type	Drawing Number	Other means of Specification (if applicable)

SPECIMEN

B

Designer .... Prefabricator ....

Address .... Address ....

C CERTIFICATION THAT DRAWINGS & SPECIFICATIONS HAVE BEEN CHECKED

THIS SECTION CAN BE COMPLETED BY A QUALIFIED ENGINEER EXPERIENCED IN TIMBER FRAME HOUSING

STRUCTURAL CHECK: I have checked that items (b), (c), (d) & (e) overleaf have been met.

Signed .... Name ....

Position .... Date ....

Address ....

D THIS SECTION MUST BE SIGNED BY A NHBC LISTED CERTIFIER:–

I have been engaged to certify the design of the dwelling listed by ....

who is a Registered House-Builder (or person acting on his behalf).

All conditions covered by the NHBC timber frame certifiers' list of checks (see over) have been met and I confirm that the dwelling is of conventional timber frame construction in compliance with NHBC requirements.

Signed .... Date ....

Name .... NHBC Ref. No. of Certifier: TF ....

N.B. If the dwelling is of novel timber frame construction, or if materials are used which do not

---

ABSTRACT FROM NHBC TIMBER FRAME CERTIFIERS' LIST OF CHECKS

I hereby undertake to NHBC that as a condition of being an NHBC listed certifier I will ensure that the drawings and specifications have been checked by competent persons. In particular in issuing a certificate I certify that:-

a The construction detailing has been checked to ensure adequate resistance to rising damp, rain penetration and interstitial condensation in accordance with Chapter 6.2 (previously known as Practice Note 5) and that preservative treatment as required by Chapter 2.3 has been specified.

b Nothing is required which is contrary to good building practice or the requirements of NHBC's Chapter 6.2 (previously known as Practice Note 5) . If any novel design approach or detail is incorporated written acceptance from NHBC will be obtained before a certificate is issued.

c Structural calculations have been carried out to establish that the dwellings comply with:-
- 'Building Regulations
- 'British Standard Code of Practice CP 3: Chapter V: Part2 "Wind Loads"
- 'British Standard BS 5268 "Structural use of timber"
- 'British Standard BS 6399 "Code of Practice for dead and imposed loads"
- 'NHBC Requirements.

d Arithmetic calculations have been independently checked.

e Proper consideration has been given to all the details of construction in accordance with Chapter 6.2 (previously known as Practice Note 5) to give adequate:-
- anchorage to sub-structure
- sizing, jointing and nailing of structural members and sheathing
- resistance to racking
- construction of lintels and provision of additional studs at openings
- fixing and relationship of ground and upper floor joists to the wall framings
- framing and holding down of the roof

f Full certified information on design detail has been given to the builder in a form suitable for use by operatives on site.

g All materials specified meet NHBC's requirements especially those materials which perform a critical function. The following is an extract of Technical Requirement R3

Technical Requirement	Performance Standard	Performance Standard
The Builder shall ensure that	Proper account shall be taken of the use and location of materials, products and building systems in relation to: o geographical location o a position on the site o position within the structure and construction works o durability	Code of Practice, or (iii) compliance with standards not lower than those defined in a relevant British Standard specification or equivalent, provided their use is accepted by the NHBC, or (iv) satisfactory assessment by an appropriate independent technical approvals authority accepted by the NHBC, including:
R3 Materials Requirement		British Board of Agrément (BBA), Building Research Establishment (BRE), Wimpey Laboratory Assessment Service (WIMLAS), or a body authorised under Annex A to the Construction Products Directive, or
All materials, products and building systems shall be suitable for their intended purpose	Materials, products and building systems will normally be acceptable if they comply with the following:	(v) use of materials and products in accordance with well established satisfactory custom and practice, provided that such custom and practice is acceptable to NHBC, or
	(a) MATERIALS AND PRODUCTS USED FOR CRITICAL FUNCTIONS Functions critical to performance are: structure, fire resistance, weatherproofing, thermal and sound insulation and services, including heating appliances and flues.	(vi) acceptance in writing by the NHBC that the quality and use is satisfactory
	Any of the following is acceptable:	**(b) MATERIALS AND PRODUCTS USED FOR NON CRITICAL FUNCTIONS** Compliance with the above acceptance criteria for critical functions or strictly in accordance with manufacturers' recommendations for the specific use.
	(i) Performance in accordance with standards set by the NHBC, or (ii) where no NHBC standard is set, compliance with the relevant British Standard or equivalent European Technical Specification approved by a Committee for Standardisation, provided it is used in accordance with the relevant	

A CERTIFIER IS NOT PERMITTED TO DELETE ANY OF THESE CONDITIONS

(SCOTLAND)

serving the home buyer

TIMBER FRAME CONSTRUCTION

One Form Should Be Completed in Respect of Each Site.

To Be Delivered To:-

NHBC (Scotland)
5 Manor Place, Edinburgh, EH3 7DH
14 Days Prior To Site Erection Starting

PANEL 1	REGISTERED BUILDER OR DEVELOPER
NAME	
NHBC REG. NO.	

PANEL 2	SITE LOCATION
ADDRESS	
PLOT NOS.	

PANEL 3	KIT MANUFACTURER
NAME	
CONTACT	
PHONE NO.	
SCOTFI REG. NO.	

PANEL 4	HOUSE TYPE NAMES OR DRAWING NUMBERS

SPECIMEN

PANEL 5	CERTIFICATION BY INDEPENDENT CONSULTING ENGINEER

I confirm that I have assessed the timber frame superstructure of the dwelling types listed in Panel 4, taking account of all relevant British Standards, and have found them to be structurally adequate for the location shown in Panel 2. I am satisfied that the manufacturer is able to supply the registered builder or developer identified in Panel 1 with erection instructions in specification and drawing form suitable for use by site operatives.

I accept that I have a Duty of Care to the NHBC (Scotland) who will rely upon this certification.

Signature _____

Date _____

PANEL 6	CERTIFYING ENGINEER
Name	
Qualifications	
Organisation	
Address	
Phone No.	

New Requirements (January 1984)

*4.6 page 12   Limit the risks of high levels of humidity occurring within the dwelling.

*4.9 page 12   Prevent condensation from occurring on pipework within timber frame walls.

* At the date of going to press, this clause, recommended by the Joint Technical Committee of England/Wales, Northern Ireland and Scotland, had not been formally ratified by the Executive Committees of NHBC. However, readers of this document may assume it will take effect for all dwellings whose foundations are concreted on or after 1st January 1984, unless they have been previously notified to the contrary.

Revisions May 1983

2.1 page 5   Reworded with last paragraph added.

4.4 page 10   Cavity fill level modified in sketches and clause c. ii reworded.

5.2 page 14
5.4   Requirement for treatment of plywood sheathing in abeyance pending further research.

6.7 page 16   Materials other than austenitic stainless steel acceptable provided they have equivalent strength and corrosion resistance.

6.14 page 17   Materials for wall ties and their fixings must be compatible with each other.

7.6 page 20   Stud size relaxed to permit 38mm nominal, 35mm minimum if planed and 37mm minimum if regularised.

General:—   Minor editorial and typographical revisions.

Revisions March 1984

6.12 page 17   Increase in vapour check specification.

7.6 page 20   Stud size requirements changed to 38mm nominal (37mm minimum).

Revisions March 1985

4.4 page 10   Clause c(i); modifications to tolerances.

5.1 page 13   Requirement that colour tinted preservative for cut ends be used.

Revisions February 1988

General page 4   New clause Rq 2 incorporated. British Standard references revised in clause Rq 5

6.9 page 16

6.11 page 17   Reference made to BS 5268 for trussed rafter design and Ca 37 for bracing.

7.4 page 20

7.12 page 22

BUILDMARK™

informing the industry

CI/SfB	81	(22)	
CAWS	F10	K31	

Operative from January 1992

NHBC STANDARDS

Internal walls

This Chapter gives the Technical Requirements and recommendations for internal walls, including separating walls, compartment walls, flues and chimneys.

LIST OF CHAPTERS

THE STANDARDS

The NHBC Standards give:
● Technical Requirements in red
● Performance Standards in dark blue
● Guidance   in light blue
for the design and construction of dwellings
acceptable to NHBC.

Diagrams may contain text in red. This is to highlight
points but has no mandatory significance.

The Standards come into effect for every NHBC
registered home whose foundations are concreted on
or after the publication date shown on the cover of
each Chapter and apply throughout the UK, unless
otherwise stated.

COMPOSITION OF THE STANDARDS

The Standards are divided into 10 Parts, each
containing one or more Chapters covering
a particular aspect. The Parts follow the usual
construction process.

In general, each Chapter is made up of sections
dealing with Design, Materials and Sitework.
In some cases one or more of these aspects
may not be included.

TECHNICAL REQUIREMENTS

Each Chapter (except former Practice Notes) contains
the five mandatory Technical Requirements which
MUST be met by the Builder.

The Technical Requirements are printed in red.
Chapter 1.1 'Introduction to the Standards and
Technical Requirements' contains full details.

PERFORMANCE STANDARDS

Most Chapters consist of detailed Performance
Standards printed in dark blue, normally in the left-
hand column of each Design, Materials or Sitework
page, subdivided into Clauses designated D, M or S,
respectively.

Alternative standards of performance will be
acceptable ONLY if, in the opinion of NHBC, the
Technical Requirements are met and the standard
achieved is not lower than the stated Performance
Standard.

GUIDANCE

Guidance on how the Performance Standard may be
met is normally shown, printed in light blue, in the
right-hand column opposite the relevant Performance
Standard. Some Chapters contain pages which are
all Guidance.

Guidance is based on normal procedures and
recommended practices shown by experience to be
satisfactory and acceptable. NHBC will consider
alternative methods to meet specific requirements,
subject to prior consultation and evaluation.

SCOPE

This Chapter gives the Technical Requirements and recommendations for internal walls, including separating walls, compartment walls, flues and chimneys.

NHBC Standards do not cover aspects of health and safety relating to building operations and to the handling and use of certain building materials. Such matters are covered by statutory requirements.

FINDING INFORMATION

To find information on a particular subject, the following procedure is recommended:

1 Identify the **Part** most appropriate for the subject.

2 Identify the **Chapter** which deals with the particular element of construction.

3 Decide whether the information required relates to the Design, Materials or Sitework **Section** of the Chapter.

4 Decide from the Contents list the **heading** under which the required information is most likely to be found.

5 Review the **clauses** listed against the heading to see which has the relevant Performance Standard.

6 Review the **items** under the Performance Standards and decide which is relevant.

7 Review the guidance in the right-hand column opposite the item most relevant to the subject. If a clause number is known, use the above procedure to find the clause.

For example: **6.3 - S4(c)** means:

6	Part 6	Superstructure (excluding roofs)
3	Chapter 3	Internal walls
S	Section	SITEWORK
4	Clause 4	Timber stud partitions
(c)	Item (c)	support and fixings.

CONTENTS

Clause

Technical Requirements	Performance Standards

R1 Statutory requirements

Work shall comply with all relevant Building Regulations and other statutory requirements

R2 Design requirement

Design and specification shall provide satisfactory performance

R3 Materials requirement

All materials, products and building systems shall be suitable for their intended purpose

R4 Workmanship requirement

All work shall be carried out in a proper, neat and workmanlike manner

R5 Structural design requirement

Structural design shall be carried out by suitably qualified persons in accordance with British Standards and Codes of Practice

Chapter 1.1 gives the detailed Performance Standards which relate to these Technical Requirements.

DESIGN STANDARD

6.3 - D1   Design shall meet the Technical Requirements

Design that follows the guidance below will be acceptable for internal walls, including separating walls, compartment walls, flues and chimneys.

STATUTORY REQUIREMENTS

6.3 - D2   Design shall comply with all relevant statutory requirements

A list of statutory references applicable to this Chapter is given in Appendix 6.3-A.

LOADBEARING MASONRY WALLS

6.3 - D3   Loadbearing masonry internal walls shall be designed to support and transfer loads to foundations safely and without undue movement

Structural design of masonry walls should be in accordance with BS 5628.

Items to be taken into account include:

(a) provision of foundations

Any loadbearing wall should be provided with either:

● a foundation, or

● a means of support that transfers the load safely to a foundation.

Sleeper walls should be designed and constructed as described in Chapter 4.4 'Strip and trench fill foundations' (each section).

Where necessary, oversite concrete should be protected against sulphate attack by the use of a polyethylene sheet dpm, not less than 1000 gauge (0.25mm), properly lapped.

Loadbearing walls built off a concrete ground bearing slab are acceptable only if the concrete forms part of a foundation which is designed by an Engineer in accordance with Technical Requirement R5.

Foundation design should take account of any site investigation or ground hazards.

DESIGN

Performance Standards	Guidance

LOADBEARING MASONRY WALLS (continued)

6.3 - D3 (b) structural elements

Bricks and blocks should be selected in accordance with their intended use. The table below gives recommended strengths of bricks and blocks to be used in buildings up to 3 storeys high:

Height of wall	Minimum compressive strength of brick or block unit
1 or 2 storeys	blocks - 2.8N/mm² bricks - 5.0N/mm²
Lowest storey of a 3 storey wall or where individual storeys exceed 2.7m	blocks - 7.0N/mm² bricks - 7.0N/mm² (unless calculations show that lower strengths are suitable)
Upper storeys of 3 storey wall	blocks - 2.8N/mm² bricks - 5.0N/mm²

(c) lateral restraint

Loadbearing walls, including separating walls should be provided with lateral restraint:

● at each floor level, and
● at the ceiling level below a roof.

Statutory references for lateral restraint are listed in Appendix 6.3-A.

Concrete floors provide adequate restraint if:

● they have a minimum 90mm bearing onto the wall, or
● they abut each side of the wall (provided that both floors are at, or about, the same level).

Restraint straps should be provided at 2m centres to each floor when:

● floors are not at, or near, the same level, and
● the floor span is parallel to the wall, and
● the floor is not built into the wall.

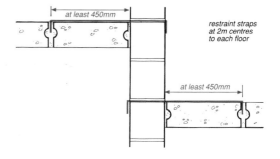

at least 450mm

restraint straps at 2m centres to each floor

at least 450mm

Performance Standards

Guidance

Timber joists with a minimum of 90mm bearing normally provide adequate lateral restraint.

Where timber joists are *not* built into a masonry wall, restraint should be provided at 2m centres by means of either:
- restraint type joist hangers to BS 5628 : Part 1, or
- restraint straps with a cross section of at least 30mm x 5mm.

Where restraint is required and restraint-type hangers are not used, straps should be:
- at least 300mm long on each joist
- fixed with four fixings to each joist
- not more than 2m apart.

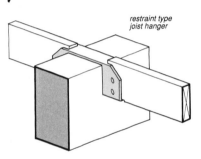

restraint type joist hanger

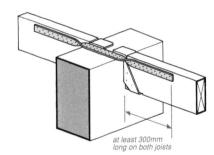

at least 300mm long on both joists

In England and Wales, timber joists should *not* be built into masonry separating walls. The shrinkage cracks which occur between the timber joists and masonry walls provide paths for sound transmission and fire.

In Scotland, Northern Ireland and the Isle of Man, joists can be built into separating walls, but spaces around joist ends should be adequately filled with mortar.

Performance Standards	Guidance

LOADBEARING MASONRY WALLS (continued)

6.3 - D3 **(d) bonding and tying**

Where masonry walls abut and use the same type of block, they may be fully bonded or tied together. Where materials are dissimilar, eg where a separating wall made with dense concrete blocks meets a partition wall of lightweight blocks, a tied joint is preferable as this will avoid random cracking.

Tied joints should be formed using expanded metal strip, wall ties or equivalent fixings, at maximum 300mm vertical centres.

Where the separating wall uses denser blocks than the inner leaf of the external wall, the separating wall should be carried through to the cavity and the inner leaf of the external wall tied to it. This is to prevent a reduction in the sound resistance of the wall.

Where the inner leaf of the external wall is of insulated masonry and the separating wall uses denser or uninsulated blocks, a cold bridge may be formed. Extra insulation may be required at the junction of separating and external walls.

(e) movement joints

For guidance on the design of movement joints, reference should be made to Clause D8.

(f) wall ties for cavity separating walls

Normally, the two leaves of cavity separating walls should be tied together to provide structural stability. However, the ties should be kept to a minimum as they provide paths for sound transmission across the cavity. Reference should be made to Clause D9 for details.

LOADBEARING TIMBER WALLS

6.3 - D4 **Loadbearing timber internal walls shall be designed to support and transfer loads to foundations safely and without undue movement**

Structural design of loadbearing timber walls should be in accordance with BS 5268.

Structural timber should be specified according to the strength classes in BS 5268 : Part 2, eg SC3 or SC4. When using the BS 4978 grading rules, the timber species should be included. The strength classes can then be determined from BS 5268.

Items to be taken into account include:

(a) provision of foundations

Foundations should be provided as for structural masonry walls (see Clause D3(a)).

Performance Standards

Guidance

(b) structural elements

Normally, individual studs, sills and headplates should be 38mm x 75mm. Larger timber section sizes may be required in order to achieve an adequate level of fire resistance. Studs should be spaced at maximum 600mm centres.

A lintel and cripple studs should be provided to any opening except when the stud spacing is unaffected. Normally, multiple studs should be provided to support multiple joists.

Where internal walls are made up of panels, structural continuity should be maintained, for example by the use of a continuous top binder.

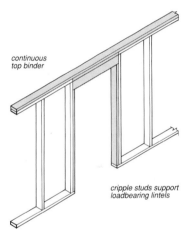

continuous
top binder

cripple studs support
loadbearing lintels

Framing joints should be secured with not less than two nails per joint.

**(c) wall ties for cavity
separating walls**

For timber framed separating walls, ties should be specified in accordance with the system designer's recommendations to ensure structural stability.

To limit sound transmission, metal tie straps should be:
● not more than 14 gauge (2.0mm) or 16 gauge (1.6mm)
● fixed below ceiling level
● spaced at least 1.2m apart horizontally.

Thicker ties, fixed at ceiling level or more closely spaced will increase sound transmission across the cavity.

DESIGN

Performance Standards	Guidance

BEAMS AND LINTELS

6.3 - D5 **Beams and lintels shall be adequate for their purpose**

Items to be taken into account include:

(a) loads and spans

Loads and spans should be either in accordance with manufacturers' recommendations or designed by an Engineer in accordance with Technical Requirement R5.

(b) materials

Concrete or steel lintels are suitable for use in masonry walls. Timber lintels should not be used to support masonry.

Lintels should extend beyond each end of openings in masonry as follows:

Span [m]	Minimum length of bearing [mm]
Up to 1.2	100
Over 1.2	150

Where structurally necessary, padstones should be provided under the bearings of lintels and beams. Reference should be made to Chapter 6.5 'Steelwork support to upper floors and partitions'.

NON-LOADBEARING INTERNAL PARTITIONS

6.3 - D6 **Non-loadbearing partitions shall have adequate strength and be adequately supported**

Items to be taken into account include:

(a) partition construction

The following constructions are acceptable:

- partitions of brick or block construction
- timber stud partitions using studs, sills and headplates nominally 63mm x 38mm. Studs should be spaced to suit the thickness of plasterboard used, as follows:
  - not more than 450mm spacing for 9.5mm boards
  - not more than 600mm spacing for 10mm to 20mm boards
- proprietary partitions of plasterboard, strawboard or other material, detailed and constructed in accordance with manufacturers' recommendations.

(b) movement joints

Reference should be made to Clause D8.

Performance Standards

Guidance

(c) method of supporting partition

Walls and partitions should be supported by the structural floor, *not* by a floating floor that incorporates a compressible layer.

Preferably, masonry partitions should be supported on:
- other masonry partitions or walls (wherever possible the design of dwellings should be such that first floor masonry partitions are a continuation of those on the ground floor)
- concrete floors
- steel or concrete beams.

Where steel or concrete beams are to be used, it may be necessary to use padstones at bearings.

Masonry partitions should not be supported by timber joists or beams, unless they have been designed by an Engineer in accordance with Technical Requirement R5.

The design should make allowance for the relatively flexible nature of the timber and the relatively rigid nature of masonry.

Where stud partitions or proprietary plasterboard partitions are supported by a timber floor, extra noggings or joists should be specified, unless it can be shown that the deck can transfer the load without undue movement.

Allowance should be made for the possible deflection of floors at the head of partitions to prevent the partition becoming loadbearing.

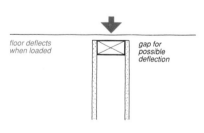

floor deflects when loaded *gap for possible deflection*

DESIGN

Performance Standards   **Guidance**

FIRE RESISTANCE

6.3 - D7 **Internal walls shall, where necessary, have adequate resistance to the spread of fire**

The guidance below applies in England, Wales, Northern Ireland and the Isle of Man. In Scotland, reference should be made to statutory requirements.

Items to be taken into account include:

(a) fire resistance of internal walls

In houses up to 2 storeys, the following walls should be fire-resisting:

- loadbearing walls (half-hour minimum)
- separating walls (one hour minimum)
- walls between a house and an integral or attached garage (half-hour minimum).

In houses of 3 or more storeys, in addition to the above, the walls enclosing the staircase should have half-hour fire resistance.

For flats, the following walls should be fire-resisting:

- loadbearing walls within the flat (half-hour for up to 2 storeys, one hour for 3 or more storeys)
- separating walls, compartment walls and walls enclosing protected shafts, such as staircases (normally one hour)
- walls enclosing hallways to second floor (and above) flats (half-hour for up to 2 storeys, one hour for 3 or more storeys).

Statutory references for fire resistance and cavity barriers are listed in Appendix 6.3-A.

(b) firestopping

Fire-resisting walls should be firestopped or constructed to resist fire spread:

- at their perimeter
- at junctions with other fire-resisting walls, floors and roofs
- where openings are formed for doors, pipes, etc.

The following details should be designed carefully:

- the junction between a separating or compartment wall and a pitched roof or a flat roof
- where pipes and cables penetrate a fire-resisting wall (reference should also be made to Chapter 8.1 'Internal services' (Design and Sitework).

The wall dividing an integral or attached garage and the floor above should act together to provide adequate resistance to fire spread. If there is either no ceiling or no floor to the space above the ceiling to the garage, vertical fire separation may be required.

When firestopping against timber construction, it is important to specify compressible material, such as mineral wool, to allow timber shrinkage to take place without affecting the firestopping.

Performance Standards	Guidance

(c) provision of cavity barriers

Statutory references for the location of cavity barriers are listed in Appendix 6.3-A.

All internal walls of hollow or cavity construction, whether fire-resisting or not, should have cavity barriers installed at their perimeter and at junctions with fire-resisting floors and walls. For cavity separating walls of masonry construction, the top of the wall needs to be closed for fire resistance.

Timber framed separating walls should be specified with cavity barriers of wire reinforced mineral wool at junctions with floors and ceilings. Reference should be made to Chapter 6.2 'External timber framed walls and wall panels' for further information.

MOVEMENT JOINTS

6.3 - D8 Masonry walls shall, where necessary, be provided with movement joints

Movement joints should be provided in straight unbroken lengths of wall as shown in the following table:

Type of brick or block	Joint width [mm]	Normal spacing
Clay bricks	16	12m (15m max)
Calcium silicate brick	10	7.5m to 9m
Concrete block and brick	10	6m

Movement joints in foundations should be continued through the superstructure.

SOUND INSULATION

6.3 - D9 Internal walls shall, where necessary, have adequate resistance to the transmission of sound

Items to be taken into account include:

(a) separating walls

Statutory references for the sound insulation of separating walls are listed in Appendix 6.3-A.

For details of separating walls in timber frame construction, reference should be made to Chapter 6.2 'External timber framed walls and wall panels'.

DESIGN

Performance Standards

Guidance

SOUND INSULATION (continued)

6.3 - D9(a) (continued)

To ensure an adequate level of sound insulation for masonry separating walls:

- perforated bricks or hollow bricks should not be specified. The weight of the wall should comply with the relevant statutory regulations as detailed above
- if plasterboard is not used, wet plaster should be specified to seal air paths in masonry walling
- if plasterboard is used, joints should be staggered
- in England and Wales, joist ends should not be built into separating walls as timber shrinkage creates gaps for sound transmission. Joist hangers should be used or joists run parallel to walls
- avoid any reduction in the thickness of masonry, but where this is unavoidable, eg to accommodate electrical sockets, positions on opposite sides of the separating wall should be staggered.

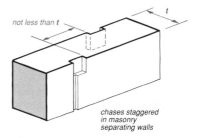

not less than t

t

chases staggered in masonry separating walls

Care should be taken when specifying a dry lining to masonry separating walls. The thickness of plasterboard layers and the method of fixing may be critical. For details, reference should be made to BS 8212.

(b) cavity separating walls

Cavity separating walls should be constructed so that any external cavity wall insulation placed by blown or pumped methods, where permitted, cannot enter the separating wall cavity.

In masonry cavity separating walls, where the cavity is up to 75mm, flexible wall ties should be used, such as:

- butterfly type ties to BS 1243, or
- ties assessed for the purpose.

Where structural design permits, the omission of ties will enhance sound insulation.

Ties should be spaced 900mm horizontally and 450mm vertically. Closer spacing will increase sound transmission. Wider spacing may impair structural stability. Rigid ties transmit sound more readily than flexible ties.

Performance Standards

Guidance

(c) flanking transmission

The position of openings, such as windows, doors, air bricks, etc, in adjacent dwellings can affect flanking sound transmission. The requirements of the statutory regulations should be followed.

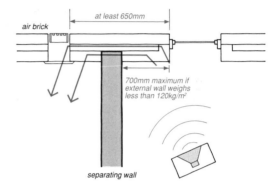

air brick

at least 650mm

700mm maximum if external wall weighs less than 120kg/m²

separating wall

(d) partitions to rooms containing a WC

PARTITION PERFORMANCE

Any partition between a room containing a WC and a living room, dining room, study or bedroom should have a weighted sound reduction index of not less than 38dB over the frequency range 100-3150Hz, when tested in accordance with BS 2750. This does not apply to a partition between a WC and a bedroom where the WC forms an en-suite facility to the bedroom.

The following methods of construction will achieve the performance level stated above.

BLOCKWORK PARTITIONS

Blocks having a density of not less than 600kg/m³ finished on both sides with 13mm of plaster are acceptable.

Blockwork should be tied in every course to adjoining walls, with the joints filled solid.

For details of bonding and tying, reference should be made to Sitework clause 6.3 - S3(d).

Performance Standards   **Guidance**

SOUND INSULATION (continued)

6.3 - D9(d) (continued)

TIMBER STUDWORK

Timber studwork is acceptable if used with one of the following combinations of materials:

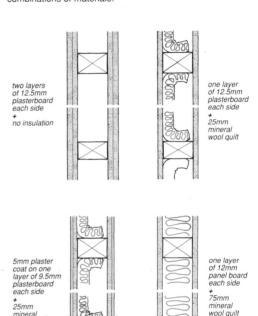

two layers
of 12.5mm
plasterboard
each side
+
no insulation

one layer
of 12.5mm
plasterboard
each side
+
25mm
mineral
wool quilt

5mm plaster
coat on one
layer of 9.5mm
plasterboard
each side
+
25mm
mineral
wool quilt

one layer
of 12mm
panel board
each side
+
75mm
mineral
wool quilt

Other forms of timber studwork construction will be acceptable provided the criteria given under PARTITION PERFORMANCE is achieved and independent evidence of performance is available at the request of NHBC.

Where two thicknesses of board are used, the joints should be staggered and the joints in the outer layer properly filled.

Top plates, bottom plates and end studs should be secured and sealed to the adjoining structure so that sound paths cannot develop following shrinkage and/or deflection of the timber.

PROPRIETARY PARTITIONS

Certain proprietary partition systems meet the required standard. The partition manufacturer should have independent test evidence of the system's performance.

Performance Standards

Guidance

DAMP-PROOFING

6.3 - D10 Internal walls shall be designed to provide adequate resistance to moisture from the ground

Loadbearing walls built off foundation walls should have a dpc at their base at least the width of the wall. The dpc should link with any adjoining dpm.

Where steps are necessary in the ground floor slab, a dpc should be incorporated as a continuous link between the upper and lower dpcs. The vertical part of the dpc should be protected from damage during construction.

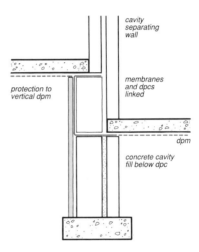

cavity separating wall

membranes and dpcs linked

protection to vertical dpm

dpm

concrete cavity fill below dpc

Performance Standards

Guidance

DAMP-PROOFING (continued)

6.3 - D10 (continued)

Dpcs should be included below the following:

● non-loadbearing partitions built off an in-situ ground slab with a dpm applied to the top of the slab

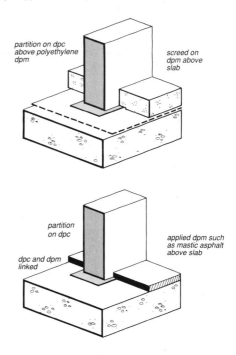

partition on dpc
above polyethylene
dpm

screed on
dpm above
slab

partition
on dpc

applied dpm such
as mastic asphalt
above slab

dpc and dpm
linked

● partitions that may be adversely affected by residual damp (eg stud partitions) built off any type of concrete floor.

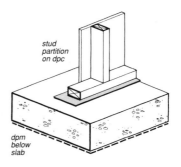

stud
partition
on dpc

dpm
below
slab

Performance Standards   Guidance

FLUES AND FIREPLACES

6.3 - D11 Flues and fireplaces shall be in accordance with relevant standards and statutory requirements

Items to be taken into account include:

(a) statutory requirements

Statutory references relating to flues and fireplaces are listed in Appendix 6.3-A.

Reference should be made to the following Chapters for information on other statutory requirements associated with flues and fireplaces:

8.1 'Internal services' (Design and Materials) - ventilation

7.2 'Pitched roofs' (Design and Materials) - chimneys above roof level.

Combustible materials should be protected against heat from appliances or flues either by providing sufficient separation or by being shielded by non-combustible materials in accordance with the relevant Building Regulations. The method of providing protection should be indicated, including thickness and type of materials, dimensions, etc.

(b) fireplace openings

Fireplace openings for solid fuel appliances should follow the recommendations of BS 6461 and the Solid Fuel Advisory Service.

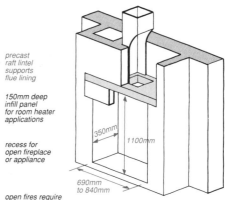

precast raft lintel supports flue lining

150mm deep infill panel for room heater applications

recess for open fireplace or appliance

350mm

1100mm

690mm to 840mm

open fires require additional units within the recess

DESGIN

Performance Standards	Guidance

FLUES AND FIREPLACES (continued)

6.3 - D11 (c) chimney construction

Chimneys should be constructed of:

● materials listed in the relevant statutory regulations, or

● proprietary factory-made units that have been assessed in accordance with Technical Requirement R3.

For details of weatherproofing where chimneys pass through pitched roofs, reference should be made to Chapter 7.2 'Pitched roofs' (Sitework).

Flue blocks to BS 1289 are acceptable only for use with conventional gas fires. Decorative gas fires with a coal or log effect should have a flue suitable for a solid fuel appliance or a flue approved by British Gas for use in this situation.

When specifying an open fire the designer should:

● specify a chimney and fireplace opening that can be used with any type of domestic heating appliance, or

● (if there are limitations) ensure that information on any limitation is passed on to the home owner.

Flues should:

● be vertical, where possible

● not have more than two bends.

Bends should not make an angle of more than 45° to the vertical and should be formed from manufactured components, not cut on site.

The gather at the base of the flue should be shaped and sealed to ensure the efficient passage of flue gases.

Liners should be fixed 'socket up'. Proprietary flue blocks should be jointed in accordance with the manufacturer's recommendations.

Voids between lining and surrounding masonry should be filled in accordance with BS 6461.

Performance Standards

Guidance

PROVISION OF INFORMATION

6.3 - D12 Designs and specifications shall be produced in a clearly understandable format and include all relevant information

Drawings should give full information, including:

- wall layout, with all dimensions shown
- position and size of openings and lintels
- details at junctions, indicating firestopping where applicable
- details of wall constructions and materials, ties and restraints
- construction of hearths and fireplace recesses, with relevant dimensions
- details of foundations where required
- construction of flues and chimneys giving details of appliance connection to flue
- method of protecting combustible materials against heat from appliances and flues.

6.3 - D13 All relevant information shall be distributed to appropriate personnel

Ensure that design and specification information is issued to site supervisors and relevant specialist subcontractors and/or suppliers.

Where proprietary components are to be used, manufacturers usually have specific requirements for fixing and/or assembly of their products. This information should also be made available for reference on site so that work can be carried out satisfactorily in accordance with the design and specification.

Performance Standards	Guidance

MATERIALS STANDARDS

6.3 - M1 All materials shall:
(a) meet the Technical Requirements
(b) take account of the design

Materials that comply with the design and the guidance below will be acceptable for internal walls, including separating walls, compartment walls, flues and chimneys.

Materials for internal walls should comply with all relevant standards, including those listed below. Where no standard exists, Technical Requirement R3 applies (see Chapter 1.1 'Introduction to the Standards and Technical Requirements').

References to British Standards and Codes of Practice include those made under the Construction Products Directive (89/106/EEC) and, in particular, appropriate European Technical Specifications approved by a European Committee for Standardisation (CEN).

MASONRY MATERIALS

6.3 - M2 Masonry shall comply with relevant standards

Items to be taken into account include:
(a) precast concrete blocks

Concrete blocks should comply with BS 6073.

When used in loadbearing partitions, blocks should have the minimum compressive strength required by the design. The table below gives recommended strengths of blocks to be used in specific cases:

Height of wall	Minimum compressive strength of block unit
1 or 2 storeys	blocks - 2.8N/mm^2
Lowest storey of a 3 storey wall or where individual storeys exceed 2.7m	blocks - 7.0N/mm^2 (unless calculations show that lower strengths are suitable)
Upper storeys of 3 storey wall	blocks - 2.8N/mm^2

Where buildings are more than 3 storeys in height, masonry should be designed in accordance with Technical Requirement R5 using the block strength specified by the designer.

Performance Standards | **Guidance**

MASONRY MATERIALS (continued)

6.3 - M2(a) (continued)

The maximum loadbearing capacity of the wall should not exceed the recommendations of the manufacturer.

In some partitions to WC compartments and all separating walls, blocks should have at least the *minimum density* required by the design in order to achieve the required sound insulation.

Where special blocks/pipes are used for flues, the manufacturer's recommendations should be checked. Special materials may be required around the blocks/pipes.

(b) bricks

Bricks should comply with the relevant British Standards:
● clay bricks should comply with BS 3921
● calcium silicate bricks should comply with BS 187
● concrete bricks should comply with BS 6073.

When used in a separating wall, bricks should have at least the *minimum density* required by the design. A lighter brick may not provide a suitable level of sound resistance.

For bricks suitable for use in chimney stacks above roof level, reference should be made to Chapter 6.1 'External masonry walls' (each section).

(c) mortar

A mortar of 1 : 1 : 5½, cement : lime : sand, with plasticiser is suitable for both internal and external walls.

Unless otherwise specified by the brick or block manufacturer, ordinary Portland cement to BS 12 may be used. Sulphate-resisting Portland cement should be used, where necessary (see Chapter 6.1 'External masonry walls' (Materials)).

Admixtures, retarded mortars and pre-mixed mortars may be used in accordance with the manufacturer's recommendations, provided those of the masonry manufacturer agree.

WALL TIES AND RELATED ITEMS

6.3 - M3 **Walls ties and related items shall be of the appropriate type and strength and shall have adequate durability**

WALL TIES FOR SEPARATING WALLS

Wall ties should either:
● be butterfly type to BS 1243, or
● be approved in accordance with Technical Requirement R3.

Performance Standards

Guidance

HANGERS, STRAPS, ETC

Joist hangers, restraint straps, bond ties, etc should be protected against corrosion. Ferrous metals with the following levels of protection are acceptable:

● post-galvanizing to BS 729, or

● pre-galvanizing to BS 2989.

Restraint straps for use in masonry construction should have a minimum cross section of 30mm x 5mm.

TIMBER

6.3 - M4 **Timber shall be of the appropriate grades and sizes to support the imposed loads**

Preferably, regularised timber should be used for stud partitions. Structural timber should be specified according to the strength classes in BS 5268 : Part 2, eg SC3 or SC4. When using the BS 4978 grading rules, the timber species should be included. The strength class can then be determined from BS 5268.

Statutory references which give information about timber grades and sizes are listed in Appendix 6.3-A.

Finger joints should comply with BS 5291 and timber for dry lining with BS 8212.

6.3 - M5 **Timber shall have a suitable moisture content**

To minimise drying shrinkage, timber should have a moisture content not greater than 21%.

PLASTERBOARD

6.3 - M6 **Plasterboard shall be of a suitable thickness for its intended use**

Plasterboard should be to BS 1230. Plasterboard thickness should be:

● 9.5mm for stud spacing up to 450mm

● 12.5mm for stud spacing up to 600mm.

For sound-resisting walls (separating walls and walls to WC compartments), the correct thickness and number of layers of plasterboard sheets should be specified (see Design clause 6.3 - D9).

Tapered edge boards should be used where the plasterboard is to be jointed only before decoration.

Dry lining systems should comply with BS 8212. Reference should be made to Chapter 8.2 'Wall and ceiling finishes' (each section) for further details.

Performance Standards	Guidance

PROPRIETARY SYSTEMS

6.3 - M7 Prefabricated proprietary partition systems shall be suitable for their purpose

Proprietary partitions should be specified in accordance with the manufacturer's recommendations.

DAMP-PROOF COURSES

6.3 - M8 Materials for damp-proofing shall adequately resist the passage of moisture

Materials which are acceptable for use as dpcs include:
- bitumen to BS 6398
- polyethylene to BS 6515
- proprietary materials assessed in accordance with Technical Requirement R3.

Dpcs should be not less than the width of the wall or partition.

SOUND INSULATION MATERIALS

6.3 - M9 Materials used for sound insulation shall be of a suitable thickness

Normally, mineral wool quilt should be used for acoustic insulation in partitions. The thickness should be as required by the design.

FIRESTOPPING MATERIALS

6.3 - M10 Firestopping materials shall be suitable to resist the passage of fire

Suitable firestopping materials include:
- mineral wool
- cement mortar
- gypsum plaster
- intumescent mastic or preformed strip
- proprietary sealing systems (particularly those designed for service penetrations) assessed in accordance with Technical Requirement R3 to maintain the fire resistance of the wall.

FIREPLACES AND FLUES

6.3 - M11 Fireplaces and flues shall be constructed of materials which ensure adequate discharge of combustion products to the outside air and reduce the risk of the building catching fire

FIREPLACES

Fireplaces, firebacks and throat lintels should be to BS 1251.

It is recommended that the area behind firebacks or solid fuel appliances (such as room heaters) be filled in with vermiculite concrete. Vermiculite concrete can be made by mixing 4 parts vermiculite : 1 part lime with water.

Guidance

CHIMNEYS AND LININGS

Linings which are acceptable include:

● clay flue liners to BS 1181, or

● clay pipes to BS 65, or

● part of a flue block system either complying with BS 6461 or assessed in accordance with Technical Requirement R3

● flue blocks to BS 1289 (suitable only for gas fires or similar appliances).

Insulated metal chimneys should comply with BS 4543. Check that the chimney is suitable for the appliance being served.

Suitable materials for flue pipes are given in the statutory references listed in Appendix 6.3-A.

Performance Standards   **Guidance**

SITEWORK STANDARDS

6.3 - S1 **All sitework shall:**
  (a) meet the Technical
      Requirements
  (b) take account of the
      design
  (c) follow established
      good practice and
      workmanship

Sitework that follows the design and the guidance below will be acceptable for internal walls, including separating walls, compartment walls, flues and chimneys.

DAMP-PROOF COURSES

6.3 - S2 **Damp-proof courses shall**
      be installed to prevent
      moisture entering the
      building

A dpc should be provided below all loadbearing walls built off foundation walls. The dpc should be linked with any adjoining dpm.

The dpm may be either continuous or formed by two separate overlapping pieces.

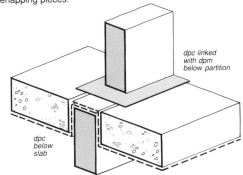

dpc linked with dpm below partition

dpc below slab

Dpcs should be provided below timber partitions where directly fixed to floor slabs, even if there is a dpm beneath the slab. This is to prevent residual moisture in the concrete affecting the timber.

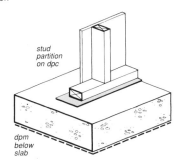

stud partition on dpc

dpm below slab

Performance Standards   **Guidance**

DAMP-PROOF COURSES (continued)

6.3 - S2 (continued)

A dpc should be provided below all internal walls where the dpm is applied to the top surface of the slab.

The dpcs should be at least the width of the partition. Where dpcs join, the lap should be at least 150mm.

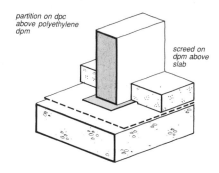

partition on dpc above polyethylene dpm

screed on dpm above slab

MASONRY PARTITIONS

6.3 - S3   Construction of masonry internal walls shall ensure adequate stability

Items to be taken into account include:

(a) setting out and workmanship

Partitions should be accurately set out in accordance with the design.

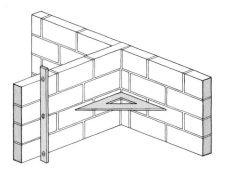

All work should be reasonably plane and true. Walls should be plumbed and courses levelled by using lines and spirit levels.

Openings should be formed to the correct size and shape. Templates should be used, where necessary.

Performance Standards   **Guidance**

(b) construction sequence

Walling should be constructed in lifts/stages to prevent distortion of wall panels during construction.

(c) mortar mix and joints

MIX
Make sure the correct mix is used. A mortar of 1 : 1 : 5½, cement : lime : sand, with plasticiser is suitable for both internal and external walls.

Unless otherwise specified, ordinary Portland cement may be used. Sulphate-resisting Portland cement should be used, where necessary (see Chapter 6.1 'External masonry walls' (Sitework)).

Mixers should be maintained and cleaned to function properly.

Mortar should be used within 2 hours, unless it is a retarded mortar. Mortar should not be re-tempered after setting has commenced.

RETARDED MORTAR
Retarded mortar should not be used beyond the time specified by the supplier.

Retarded mortar should not be used during cold weather.

ADDITIVES
Where plasticisers or other additives are to be used, the manufacturer's instructions should be followed. An air entraining agent can help reduce frost damage but it is not an anti-freeze. The recommended quantity of air entraining agent should be carefully measured for each batch in accordance with the manufacturer's instructions.

MORTAR JOINTS
All bricks and blocks should be laid on a full bed of mortar. All perpends should be solidly filled.

If walls are to be finished with wet plaster, joints should be raked out square to a shallow depth to provide a key. For dry lining, mortar joints should be struck off flush.

For information on dry lining masonry walls, reference should be made to Chapter 8.2 'Wall and ceiling finishes' (Sitework).

Performance Standards   **Guidance**

MASONRY PARTITIONS (continued)

6.3 - S3   (d) bondling and tying

A regular bonding pattern should be maintained. All masonry walls and partitions should be fully bonded or tied, as required by the design.

Either:

● tooth every alternate course, or

● tie with expanded metal or equivalent, at centres not exceeding 300mm vertically.

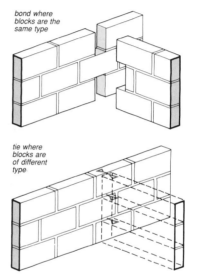

bond where blocks are the same type

tie where blocks are of different type

Joist filling should be brick or blockwork, without excessive mortar joints. Bricks and blocks should not be mixed.

To avoid cracking, bricks and blocks or blocks of different types should not be mixed in the same wall.

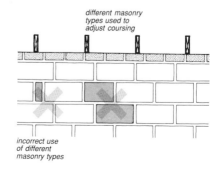

different masonry types used to adjust coursing

incorrect use of different masonry types

Performance Standards

Guidance

(e) chasing for services

Chases can reduce the sound insulation value of a wall and should be cut only where required by the design. Impact power tools that can damage the wall should not be used.

The depth of horizontal chases should not exceed one-sixth the thickness of the single leaf, and vertical chases, one-third the thickness. Hollow blocks should not be chased, unless specifically permitted by the manufacturer.

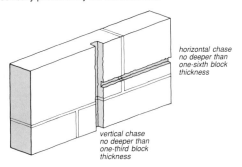

horizontal chase no deeper than one-sixth block thickness

vertical chase no deeper than one-third block thickness

(f) size, location and support of lintels and beams

Lintels should be the correct size for the opening and have the correct bearing at each end:

Span [m]	Minimum bearing [mm]
Up to 1.2	100
Over 1.2	150

Long lintels may require padstones. Lintels should bear on a full block where possible and be installed level on a solid bed of mortar. Soft or non-durable packing should not be used. Small pieces of cut bricks or blocks should not be used around lintel bearings. Concrete lintels should be the right way up.

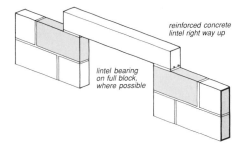

reinforced concrete lintel right way up

lintel bearing on full block, where possible

Where steel beams are to be used, reference should be made to Chapter 6.5 'Steelwork support to upper floors and partitions' (Sitework) for guidance on steel beam sizes and the need for padstones.

Performance Standards | **Guidance**

MASONRY PARTITIONS (continued)

6.3 - S3 **(g) restraint strapping**

Joists built into masonry walls provide adequate lateral restraint.

Restraint straps may be required by the design. If so, they should be fitted before new masonry is built above.

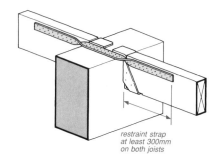

restraint strap
at least 300mm
on both joists

TIMBER STUD PARTITIONS

6.3 - S4 **Construction of timber stud internal walls shall ensure adequate stability**

Items to be taken into account include:

(a) setting out and workmanship

Partitioning should be correctly positioned, square and plumb.

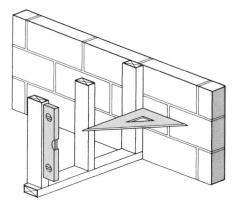

Studs should be spaced at centres to suit the plasterboard thickness. Extra studs should be provided at openings, as required by the design.

Performance Standards

Guidance

(b) size of timber members

Loadbearing timber partitions should be constructed in accordance with the design. Unless designed otherwise, the minimum specification for all partitions should be:

- sill and head plates 63mm x 38mm
- studs 63mm x 38mm at maximum 600mm centres
- framing joints secured with not less than 2 nails per joint
- blocking/nogging for support of plasterboard 43mm x 38mm
- blocking/nogging for other purposes 63mm x 38mm.

(c) support and fixings

Partitions should be fixed at head and base to noggings or joists.

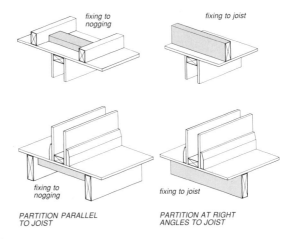

fixing to nogging

fixing to joist

fixing to nogging

fixing to joist

PARTITION PARALLEL TO JOIST

PARTITION AT RIGHT ANGLES TO JOIST

Partitions should be firmly fixed to each other and to abutting walls. Noggings or extra studs should be used, where necessary.

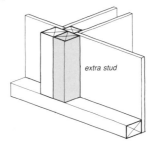

extra stud

Performance Standards

Guidance

TIMBER STUD PARTITIONS (continued)

6.3 - S4(c) (continued)

Internal partitions should not be wedged against ceiling joists or roof trusses. This does not allow for ceiling deflection/ movement and can damage the ceiling boards.

Partitions should not be over-wedged at floor level. This could damage floor boarding.

Noggings should be provided to support fittings, such as radiators, wall mounted boilers, sanitary fittings, kitchen units, etc.

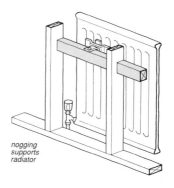

nogging supports radiator

Fixing and finishing plasterboard partitions should be in accordance with Chapter 8.2 'Wall and ceiling finishes' (Sitework).

PROPRIETARY PARTITIONS

6.3 - S5 **Proprietary partitions shall be erected in accordance with manufacturers' recommendations**

Partitioning should be correctly positioned, square and plumb. The manufacturers' recommended construction sequence should be followed.

Timber or other additional fixings should be provided for radiators, electrical outlets, switches and the like.

Performance Standards

Guidance

SEPARATING WALLS

6.3 - S6 **Construction of separating walls shall ensure adequate sound insulation**

MASONRY SEPARATING WALLS

The correct density of block should be used. Holes, voids, even hairline cracks, can significantly reduce the effectiveness of a sound-insulating wall.

To maintain sound insulation:

- fully fill all mortar beds and perpends
- lay bricks frog up and ensure all voids are filled
- use only butterfly or other approved wall ties for cavities up to 75mm wide
- space wall ties 900mm minimum horizontally and 450mm minimum vertically
- stagger the positions of electrical socket outlets on opposite sides of separating walls
- tie in or tooth bond to adjoining walls to improve rigidity of separating wall.

Solid separating walls should be taken through the inner leaf of a cavity external wall using metal ties to provide rigidity. However, if the same blocks are used for both walls, tooth bonding is preferable.

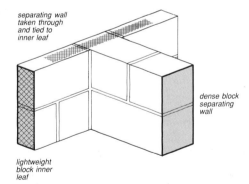

separating wall taken through and tied to inner leaf

dense block separating wall

lightweight block inner leaf

TIMBER SEPARATING WALLS

The design details should be carefully followed. There should be no gaps in the:

- mineral wool quilt
- plasterboard layers
- firestopping.

Services should not penetrate the plasterboard layer. They should be fixed in front of the plasterboard.

Performance Standards

Guidance

PARTITIONS TO ROOMS CONTAINING A WC

6.3 - S7 **Partitions to rooms containing a WC shall provide adequate sound insulation, where required by the design**

A partition between a room containing a WC and a living room, dining room, study or bedroom (except where the WC is en-suite) should have adequate sound insulation.

The design should be checked to see how sound insulation is to be achieved.

Most masonry partitions provide adequate sound insulation without additional treatment.

Some methods of providing adequate sound insulation with a timber stud partition are shown below:

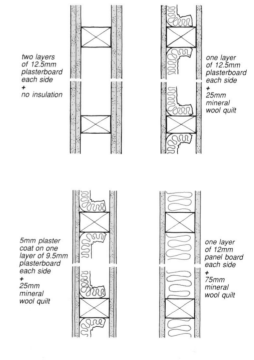

two layers
of 12.5mm
plasterboard
each side
+
no insulation

one layer
of 12.5mm
plasterboard
each side
+
25mm
mineral
wool quilt

5mm plaster
coat on one
layer of 9.5mm
plasterboard
each side
+
25mm
mineral
wool quilt

one layer
of 12mm
panel board
each side
+
75mm
mineral
wool quilt

Where two layers of plasterboard are used, the joints should be staggered and the joints in the outer layer properly filled.

Proprietary plasterboard partitions usually need an additional layer of plasterboard to one or both sides of the partition to provide adequate sound insulation.

Performance Standards   Guidance

WALLS PROVIDING FIRE RESISTANCE

6.3 - S8   **Internal walls shall, where required, have adequate resistance to fire spread**

Items to be taken into account include:

(a) separating wall construction

Junctions between separating walls and roofs should be firestopped to the underside of the tiling to prevent fire spreading between dwellings.

The separating wall should stop about 25mm below the top of adjacent roof trusses.

Soft packing, such as mineral wool, should be used above and below the roofing underlay, to allow for movement in roof timbers and prevent 'hogging' of the tiles.

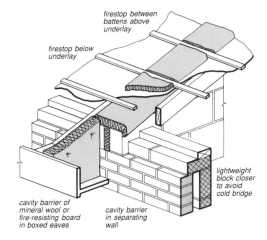

firestop between battens above underlay

firestop below underlay

lightweight block closer to avoid cold bridge

cavity barrier of mineral wool or fire-resisting board in boxed eaves

cavity barrier in separating wall

It is important that a cavity barrier is provided within boxed eaves. The cavity barrier should be wire reinforced mineral wool blanket, at least 50mm thick, nailed to the rafter and carefully cut to shape to fully seal the boxed eaves.

(b) penetration of fire-resisting walls by services

Pipes, cables and ducting should be firestopped where they pass through fire-resisting walls, including:

● separating walls

● compartment walls

● walls to ducts serving flats.

The design requirements for firestopping should be checked and making good completed neatly.

Performance Standards

Guidance

CHIMNEYS, FLUES AND LININGS

6.3 - S9 Construction of chimneys, flues and linings shall comply with relevant standards and safety requirements

It is recommended that the area behind firebacks or solid fuel appliances (such as room heaters) be filled in with vermiculite concrete. Vermiculite concrete can be made by mixing 4 parts vermiculite : 1 part lime with water.

Flue pipes and liners should be fixed 'socket up' and correctly aligned. Patent flue blocks should be fixed according to manufacturers' instructions, normally 'socket up'. 'Socket up' joints prevent condensation and tar from seeping out through the joints.

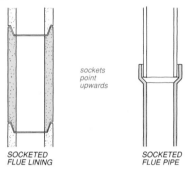

sockets point upwards

SOCKETED FLUE LINING

SOCKETED FLUE PIPE

Flue pipes and liners should be surrounded in accordance with the design or manufacturers' recommendations with proper material of the correct thickness. Timber and other combustible material should be spaced away from chimneys and flues.

Special mortar mixes should be used for flue joints when specified by the manufacturer. Each joint should be fully filled and all surplus mortar cleared from the inside at each joint as the flue is built. Flue blocks should be coursed and bonded or tied to a wall to provide stability.

Flue pipes should be supported at maximum 1.8m centres and have support directly below each socket.

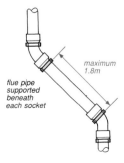

maximum 1.8m

flue pipe supported beneath each socket

Guidance

Statutory references

The following table lists references to building legislation and associated documents applicable at August 1990.

Clause	Subject	Statute			
		Building [1] Regulations	Building [2] Standards (Scotland)	Building [3] Regulations (N Ireland)	Isle of Man [4] Bye-laws
D3(b)	Structural design	A1/2	Part C	Part D	Part D
D3(c)	Lateral restraint	A1/2	Part C	Part D	Part D
D7(a)	Fire resistance	B2/3/4	Part D Part E	Part E	Part E
D7(c)	Cavity barriers	B2/3/4	Part D	Part E	Part E
D9(a)	Separating walls	E1/2/3	Part H	Part G	Part G
D11	Flues and fireplaces	J1/2/3	Part F	Part L	Part L
		Associated documents			

[1] Approved Documents to the Building Regulations 1985 for England and Wales (and 1990 edition).
[2] Building Standards (Scotland) Regulations 1981 and all published amendments.
[3] Building Regulations (Northern Ireland) 1990.
[4] Isle of Man Bye-laws 1976, amended 1980 and 1987.

BUILDMARK™

informing the industry

CI/SfB	81	(23)		
CAWS	G20	E60		

Operative from January 1992

Chapter **6.4**

NHBC STANDARDS

Timber and concrete upper floors

This Chapter gives the Technical Requirements and recommendations for the construction of timber and concrete upper floors (in houses) and separating floors (in flats).

LIST OF CHAPTERS

THE STANDARDS

The NHBC Standards give:
● Technical Requirements in red
● Performance Standards in dark blue
● Guidance   in light blue
for the design and construction of dwellings
acceptable to NHBC.

Diagrams may contain text in red. This is to highlight
points but has no mandatory significance.

The Standards come into effect for every NHBC
registered home whose foundations are concreted on
or after the publication date shown on the cover of
each Chapter and apply throughout the UK, unless
otherwise stated.

COMPOSITION OF THE STANDARDS
The Standards are divided into 10 Parts, each
containing one or more Chapters covering
a particular aspect. The Parts follow the usual
construction process.

In general, each Chapter is made up of sections
dealing with Design, Materials and Sitework.
In some cases one or more of these aspects
may not be included.

TECHNICAL REQUIREMENTS
Each Chapter (except former Practice Notes) contains
the five mandatory Technical Requirements which
MUST be met by the Builder.

The Technical Requirements are printed in red.
Chapter 1.1 'Introduction to the Standards and
Technical Requirements' contains full details.

PERFORMANCE STANDARDS
Most Chapters consist of detailed Performance
Standards printed in dark blue, normally in the left-
hand column of each Design, Materials or Sitework
page, subdivided into Clauses designated D, M or S,
respectively.

Alternative standards of performance will be
acceptable ONLY if, in the opinion of NHBC, the
Technical Requirements are met and the standard
achieved is not lower than the stated Performance
Standard.

GUIDANCE
Guidance on how the Performance Standard may be
met is normally shown, printed in light blue, in the
right-hand column opposite the relevant Performance
Standard. Some Chapters contain pages which are
all Guidance.

Guidance is based on normal procedures and
recommended practices shown by experience to be
satisfactory and acceptable. NHBC will consider
alternative methods to meet specific requirements,
subject to prior consultation and evaluation.

SCOPE

This Chapter gives the Technical Requirements and recommendations for the construction of timber and concrete upper floors (in houses) and separating floors (in flats).

NHBC Standards do not cover aspects of health and safety relating to building operations and to the handling and use of certain building materials. Such matters are covered by statutory requirements.

FINDING INFORMATION

To find information on a particular subject, the following procedure is recommended:

1 Identify the **Part** most appropriate for the subject.

2 Identify the **Chapter** which deals with the particular element of construction.

3 Decide whether the information required relates to the Design, Materials or Sitework **Section** of the Chapter.

4 Decide from the Contents list the **heading** under which the required information is most likely to be found.

5 Review the **clauses** listed against the heading to see which has the relevant Performance Standard.

6 Review the **items** under the Performance Standards and decide which is relevant.

7 Review the guidance in the right-hand column opposite the item most relevant to the subject. If a clause number is known, use the above procedure to find the clause.

For example: **6.4 - D14(b)** means:

6	Part 6	Superstructure (excluding roofs)
4	Chapter 4	Timber and concrete upper floors
D	Section	DESIGN
14	Clause 14	FLOOR DECKING
(b)	Item (b)	resistance to moisture.

CONTENTS

TECHNICAL REQUIREMENTS

Technical Requirements	Performance Standards

R1 Statutory requirements
Work shall comply with all relevant Building Regulations and other statutory requirements

Chapter 1.1 gives the detailed Performance Standards which relate to these Technical Requirements.

R2 Design requirement
Design and specification shall provide satisfactory performance

R3 Materials requirement
All materials, products and building systems shall be suitable for their intended purpose

R4 Workmanship requirement
All work shall be carried out in a proper, neat and workmanlike manner

R5 Structural design requirement
Structural design shall be carried out by suitably qualified persons in accordance with British Standards and Codes of Practice

Performance Standards | Guidance

DESIGN STANDARD

6.4 - D1 Design shall meet the Technical Requirements

Design that follows the guidance below will be acceptable for timber and concrete upper floors.

STATUTORY REQUIREMENTS

6.4 - D2 Design shall comply with all relevant statutory requirements

A list of statutory references applicable to this Chapter is given in Appendix 6.4-A.

UPPER FLOOR DESIGN

6.4 - D3 Upper floors shall be designed to support and transmit loads safely to the supporting structure without undue deflection

Items to be taken into account include:

(a) dead and imposed loads

The dead loads should include the weight of the following:
- floor decking and finishes
- ceilings and applied finishes
- walls and partitions supported by the floor
- permanent fixtures such as boilers, water tanks, etc.

Imposed loads are the variable loads imposed when the building is in use. They include the weight of furniture and people. BS 6399 : Part 1 recommends an imposed loading allowance of $1.5kN/m^2$ for self contained dwellings. Where the design includes communal areas serving flats or maisonettes, refer to BS 6399 : Part 1 for recommended imposed loads.

Information concerning balconies is given in Chapter 7.1 'Flat roofs and balconies' (Design and Sitework).

(b) supporting structure

The floor structure should have an adequate bearing on the supporting structure. Timber joists and hangers should normally have a minimum bearing of:
- 90mm on masonry walls (75mm if the wall is separately restrained), or
- 75mm if onto a wall plate.

Concrete floors should normally have a minimum bearing of 90mm.

Joists may be built into the inner leaf of an external cavity wall or supported on joist hangers. Where they are built into solid external walls, joists should be pre-treated with preservative in accordance with Chapter 2.3 'Timber preservation (natural solid timber)' (Design).

DESIGN

Performance Standards	Guidance

STRUCTURAL TIMBER

6.4 - D4 **Structural timber shall be adequate for the spans and imposed loads**

Items to be taken into account include:

(a) strength class

Structural timber is normally specified as strength Class SC3 or SC4. Tables giving the permitted clear span for joists of strength Class SC3 and SC4 are reproduced in Appendix 6.4-B.

(b) timber joist sizes

Joist sizes are given in the span tables in Appendix 6.4-B. Where the tables do not apply or where there are concentrated loads, floor joists should be designed by an Engineer in accordance with Technical Requirement R5.

Regularised timber is recommended for floor joists. The tables reproduced in Appendix 6.4-B are for sawn sizes. If regularised timber is used, either use the next larger sawn size or use tables produced by authoritative organisations for that purpose.

(c) joist spacing

Timber joists should not be spaced at centres greater than 600mm.

When planning joist spacings, allow a clearance of 25mm to 75mm between the first joist and the wall face. This helps when installing services and fixing floorboards.

(d) support of lightweight partitions

Multiple joists supporting lightweight non-loadbearing partitions running parallel to the joists should be suitably fixed together (see Sitework clause 6.4 - S7).

(e) support of masonry partitions

Where first floor masonry partitions cannot be built over ground floor masonry walls, steel or reinforced concrete beams should be specified to avoid the effects of shrinkage and long term deflection which can occur with timber beams. It is not acceptable to support masonry partitions on timber joists, unless they are designed by an Engineer in accordance with Technical Requirement R5.

(f) heavy loads

Bearers should be specified under heavy loads, such as hot water cylinders and bath feet. This helps to spread the load over two or more joists.

(g) adverse effects of shrinkage and moisture

Timber that is excessively wet is more susceptible to rot and drying shrinkage. Timber adjacent to heat sources, such as flues, boilers and hot water cylinders, is more susceptible to drying shrinkage. To minimise drying shrinkage, joists and carcassing timber specifications should state a maximum moisture content of 21%.

Performance Standards

Guidance

TRIMMERS

6.4 - D5   Adequately sized trimmers shall be provided around floor openings

Trimmed openings may be needed around staircase openings and chimneys. Trimmed joists may be supported using either:
- joist hangers
- notches
- support battens (light loading only)
- tusked tenon joints.

The following guidelines on increasing the width of trimmer joists relative to the standard joists should be observed:

No of joists carried by trimmer	Increase in width
1 joist only, positioned nearer to the end than one-fifth of the span	no extra width
1 to 4 joists	minimum of 12mm
5 to 8 joists	minimum of 25mm
More than 8 joists	designed in accordance with Technical Requirement R5

Further information concerning staircases is given in Chapter 6.6 'Staircases' (Design and Sitework).

STRUTTING

6.4 - D6   Strutting shall be adequate to limit twisting of joists

Herringbone strutting or blocking should be provided at the ends of joists where they:
- bear onto steelwork
- bear onto intermediate walls
- are supported on joist hangers.

Where joists span over 2.5m, additional strutting should also be specified as follows:

Joist span [m]	Rows of strutting
Up to 2.5	none needed
2.5 to 4.5	1 (at centre of span)
Over 4.5	2 (at equal spacing)

As blocking can be affected by shrinkage (of both blocking and joists), it is recommended that herringbone strutting is used wherever possible.

Metal strutting systems are also acceptable if assessed in accordance with Technical Requirement R3.

DESIGN

Performance Standards | Guidance

JOIST HANGERS

6.4 - D7 **Joist hangers shall be suitable for the joist width and depth, the strength of masonry and the required load**

Manufacturers usually make joist hangers in a range of sizes to suit the commonly available joist sizes.

If low strength masonry is used, the loading on the top flange of the joist hanger should not be greater than the compressive strength of the masonry.

6.4 - D8 **Adequate end bearings shall be provided for joists and joist hangers**

The design should detail the type of support to be used for joists, trimmers and trimming joists.

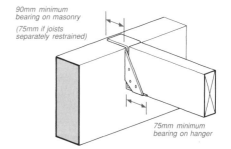

90mm minimum
bearing on masonry

(75mm if joists
separately restrained)

75mm minimum
bearing on hanger

JOIST SUPPORT AT SEPARATING WALLS

6.4 - D9 **Joists shall be correctly supported at masonry separating walls**

In England and Wales, timber joists should not be built into masonry separating walls. The shrinkage cracks which occur between the timber joists and masonry walls provide paths for sound transmission and fire.

Joists should either run parallel to masonry separating walls or be supported by joist hangers.

In Scotland, Northern Ireland and the Isle of Man, joists can be built into separating walls but spaces around joist ends should be adequately filled with mortar.

Performance Standards | Guidance

RESTRAINT STRAPPING

6.4 - D10 Adequate restraint strapping shall be provided

Restraint straps and/or joist hangers suitable for taking tensile forces may be required to tie the walls and upper floors together.

BS 8103 : Part 1 (Clause 4.4) gives details of the connections between structural elements.

The position and size of restraint straps should be shown on drawings.

STRUCTURAL STEEL IN FLOORS

6.4 - D11 Steelwork in floors shall be designed by an Engineer

Structural steelwork should be in accordance with Chapter 6.5 'Steelwork support to upper floors and partitions' (each section), or should be designed by an Engineer in accordance with Technical Requirement R5.

Where steelwork supports timber joists, the timber joists should be notched at both top and bottom to allow for shrinkage of the timber.

at least 12mm projection

at least 2mm projection

Care should be taken to ensure that structural discontinuity does not result from the use of transverse steel joists, particularly in cross wall dwellings, for example by the use of continuous decking fixed to joists on both sides of the steel.

Steel sizes should allow adequate bearing for timber joists, where required.

FIRE SPREAD

6.4 - D12 Floors shall be designed to provide the appropriate fire resistance

For houses, except in Scotland, with up to 2 storeys and no basement, the fire resistance may be modified half-hour, except over a garage where full half-hour fire resistance of upper floors should be provided (see Appendix 6.4-A).

Other constructions may be acceptable if assessed in accordance with Technical Requirement R3.

Performance Standards

Guidance

FIRE SPREAD (continued)

6.4 - D13 Structural timber shall be located away from heat sources

Combustible material should be kept away from heat sources as described in Chapter 8.1 'Internal services' (Sitework). In particular, structural timber should be at least 40mm from the outer surface of a masonry chimney or fireplace recess. Floorboards may be closer than 40mm from the chimney wall.

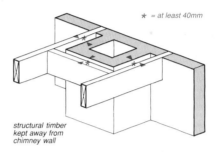

★ = at least 40mm

structural timber kept away from chimney wall

FLOOR DECKING

6.4 - D14 Floor decking shall be suitable for the intended use

Items to be taken into account include:

(a) decking and joist centres

The correct thickness of decking should be specified for the joist centres used. Thicknesses should be not less than those shown in this table for normal domestic loads, ie 1.5kN/m².

	Thickness of decking [mm]		
	Joist centres		
	400mm	450mm	600mm
T and G softwood boarding	16	16	19
Chipboard	18	18	22
Plywood	12	12	16

Other decking materials not listed in the table should comply with Technical Requirement R3.

(b) resistance to moisture

Chipboard for flooring should be moisture-resistant flooring Type C4 to BS 5669 throughout the dwelling.

(c) fixing

Adequate support and correct fixings should be specified in accordance with the manufacturer's recommendations. All butt joints should be supported by joists or noggings. Nail length should be 2½ times the thickness of the decking material.

Performance Standards	Guidance

CONCRETE FLOORS

6.4 - D15 Concrete floors shall be designed to transmit loads to the supporting structure without undue movement

Design should be in accordance with Clause D3.

Design of in-situ or precast concrete floors should be in accordance with BS 8110 and Technical Requirement R5. Proprietary concrete elements will be acceptable, if assessed in accordance with Technical Requirement R3.

FLOORS BETWEEN DWELLINGS

6.4 - D16 Floors between dwellings shall be designed to provide adequate fire resistance

Materials and constructions should comply with Technical Requirement R3 and statutory requirements (see Appendix 6.4-A).

6.4 - D17 Floors between dwellings shall be designed to adequately limit sound transmission

Floor designs will be acceptable if they comply with statutory requirements (see Appendix 6.4-A).

Floating floors should be designed to be structurally separate from the supporting floor and all walls.

Floors should be designed so that there are no airpaths, especially at the perimeter. This limits the transfer of airborne sound and avoids flanking transmission. Examples of suitable floor designs are given in relevant statutory references (see Appendix 6.4-A).

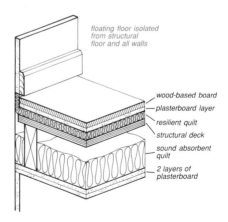

floating floor isolated from structural floor and all walls

wood-based board

plasterboard layer

resilient quilt

structural deck

sound absorbent quilt

2 layers of plasterboard

For details of floor finishes and related insulation, reference should be made to Chapter 8.3 'Floor finishes' (each section).

DESIGN

Performance Standards | Guidance

PROVISION OF INFORMATION

6.4 - D18 Designs and specifications shall be produced in a clearly understandable format and include all relevant information

The design should ensure compatibility with other drawings, especially with respect to services.

For upper floors, the drawings should show:
- direction of floor span and size and spacing of joists or concrete components
- size of trimmers and trimming joists
- openings in the floor
- supporting walls below
- walls and partitions above
- positions of restraint straps
- positions of large service penetrations, eg chimneys, SVPs
- position of insulation
- details at all junctions.

6.4 - D19 All relevant information shall be distributed to appropriate personnel

Ensure that design and specification information is issued to site supervisors and relevant specialist subcontractors and/or suppliers.

Where proprietary components are to be used, manufacturers may have specific requirements for fixing and/or assembly of their products. This information should also be made available for reference on site so that work can be carried out satisfactorily, in accordance with the design and specification.

Performance Standards	Guidance

MATERIALS STANDARDS

6.4 - M1   All materials shall:
(a) meet the Technical Requirements
(b) take account of the design

Materials that comply with the design and the guidance below will be acceptable for timber and concrete upper floors.

Materials for timber and concrete upper floors should comply with all relevant standards, including those listed below. Where no standard exists, Technical Requirement R3 applies (see Chapter 1.1 'Introduction to the Standards and Technical Requirements').

References to British Standards and Codes of Practice include those made under the Construction Products Directive (89/106/EEC) and, in particular, appropriate European Technical Specifications approved by a European Committee for Standardisation (CEN).

STRUCTURAL TIMBER

6.4 - M2   Structural timber shall be of the appropriate grades and sizes to support the imposed loads

Structural timber should be specified according to the strength classes in BS 5268 : Part 2. It is insufficient to specify timber using the BS 4978 grading rules (eg GS, M50) unless the timber species is also specified. The strength class can then be determined from Table B1 in Approved Document A1/2 to the Building Regulations or Table 3 of BS 5268 : Part 2.

Finger joints should comply with BS 5291.

Where possible, regularised timber should be used for joists.

6.4 - M3   Structural timber shall be of suitable durability, particularly in conditions where it could become damp

Timber that is built into solid external walls or embedded should be pre-treated with preservative. Reference should be made to Chapter 2.3 'Timber preservation (natural solid timber)' (each section) for recommended methods of preservative treatment.

Any timber treated with preservative and cut after treatment should be given two liberal applications of a suitable colour tinted preservative to the cut surfaces.

6.4 - M4   Structural timber shall have a suitable moisture content

To minimise drying shrinkage, joists and carcassing timber should have a maximum moisture content of 21%. The moisture content should be measured 600mm from the ends of the timber.

Performance Standards | Guidance

JOIST HANGERS AND RESTRAINT STRAPS

6.4 - M5 **Hangers and straps shall be of appropriate types and strength and shall have adequate durability**

Joist hangers to BS 6178 are acceptable. It is important that joist hangers are the correct size for the timber joist or trimmer.

Where joist hangers are required to take tensile forces, a joist hanger complying with the requirements of BS 5628 : Part 1 : Appendix C should be used.

Restraint straps should be in accordance with the requirements of BS 5628 : Part 3. Tables 1 and 14 list suitable materials and protective finishes (see Appendix 6.4-C). Nails or screws should be specified for fixing restraint straps to joists.

STRUTTING

6.4 - M6 **Strutting shall ensure adequate rigidity of the floor structure**

Timber strutting should be either:

● herringbone strutting at least 38mm x 38mm, or

● solid strutting at least 38mm thick and at least three-quarters the depth of the joist.

Proprietary metal strutting should have been assessed in accordance with Technical Requirement R3.

Thin metal strip is not acceptable as strutting.

FLOOR DECKING

6.4 - M7 **The type and thickness of the decking material shall have adequate strength and moisture resistance**

The following materials are acceptable:

● softwood boarding in accordance with BS 1297

● moisture-resistant chipboard, Type C4 to BS 5669. Ring shank nails (length 2½ x decking thickness) or screws should be specified for fixing chipboard

● plywood in accordance with BS 6566. Fixings and support should be as recommended by the manufacturer

● floor decking materials not covered by a British Standard should have been assessed in accordance with Technical Requirement R3.

SOUND INSULATION

6.4 - M8 **Materials for floating floors, including insulation materials, shall be of a type that will provide adequate sound insulation**

Details of materials for floating floors should be in accordance with Chapter 8.3 'Floor finishes' (each section).

Performance Standards	Guidance

STRUCTURAL STEEL

6.4 - M9 **Steelwork shall be suitably durable and be of the appropriate section to support the imposed loads**

Structural steel should be in accordance with Chapter 6.5 'Steelwork support to upper floors and partitions' (each section), or be designed by an Engineer in accordance with Technical Requirement R5.

Steel beams should be protected by a suitably durable paint coating as detailed in Chapter 8.5 'Painting and decorating' (each section).

CONCRETE AND REINFORCEMENT

6.4 - M10 **Concrete shall have appropriate reinforcement and be of a mix design that is suitable for the location and intended use**

For guidance on the specification and use of concrete, concrete additives and reinforcement, reference should be made to Chapter 2.1 'Concrete and its reinforcement' (each section).

PROPRIETARY SYSTEMS

6.4 - M11 **Proprietary flooring systems shall have adequate strength and durability**

Proprietary concrete flooring systems should be designed in accordance with BS 8110, or should have been assessed in accordance with Technical Requirement R3.

Performance Standards

Guidance

SITEWORK STANDARDS

6.4 - S1 All sitework shall:

(a) **meet the Technical Requirements**

(b) **take account of the design**

(c) **follow established good practice and workmanship**

Sitework that complies with the design and the guidance below will be acceptable for timber and concrete upper floors.

TIMBER FLOORS

6.4 - S2 Timber joists shall be selected, located and supported as detailed in the design

Items to be taken into account include:

(a) **timber grades and sizes**

Check materials on delivery to site for conformity with the drawings and specification.

Structural timber should be marked to show its strength class (normally SC3 or SC4). Alternatively, evidence of species and grade should be available to determine the equivalent strength class.

Where timber is graded to BS 4978, it should also be marked with identification of the company responsible for the grading.

Storage time may be minimised by phasing deliveries to suit the work programme. When storage is required, timber should be stored on bearers or in racks and be protected.

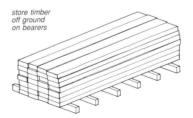

store timber off ground on bearers

(b) **moisture content**

Joists and general carcassing timber should have a moisture content of 21%. The moisture content should be measured 600mm from the ends of timber.

Performance Standards

Guidance

TIMBER FLOORS (continued)

6.4 - S2   (c) timber quality

Timber should be rejected if it:
- is excessively bowed, twisted or cambered
- has large edge knots or shakes
- has a wany edge more than half the thickness
- has any sign of rot
- has been damaged.

(d) bearing

Bearings for joists should be 90mm on masonry (75mm if the wall is separately restrained). Bearings for joists, where they are nailed to a timber plate, should be 75mm minimum. Bearings should be level. If joists are not laid level, the floor will be springy and uneven. Where bearings are uneven, joists should be levelled using hard packing, eg tiles or slates bedded in mortar. Loose or soft packing should not be used. For further information concerning timber framed construction, reference should be made to Chapter 6.2 'External timber framed walls and wall panels'.

(e) levelling

Where possible, regularised timber should be used. The tables reproduced in Appendix 6.4-B are for sawn sizes. If regularised timber is used, the next larger sawn size should be used unless advised otherwise.

The floor should be levelled from the staircase trimmer and trimming joist.

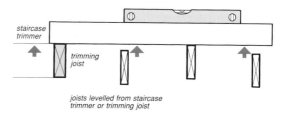

joists levelled from staircase
trimmer or trimming joist

(f) joist spacings

Joist spacing should be as shown on the drawings. If the joist spacing is not shown, the designer should provide spacing details. Do not increase the spacing. Joists should not be spaced at more than 600mm centres. The decking material to be used should be taken into account.

(g) clearance from the wall

When placing joists, a clearance of 25mm to 75mm should be allowed between the first joist and the wall face. This helps when installing services and fixing floor decking.

Performance Standards

Guidance

(h) building into cavity walls

Joists should not be allowed to project into the cavity as the ends may catch mortar droppings and get damp.

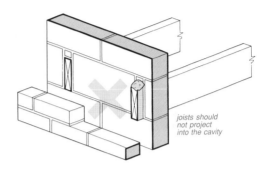

joists should not project into the cavity

JOIST HANGERS

6.4 - S3 **Hangers shall be of the correct size and properly built in**

It is important that the joist hanger is the correct size for the timber joist or trimmer.

Where joist hangers are supported on lightweight blockwork, the suitability of the hanger should be checked. Joist hangers which meet BS 6178 are stamped on the base or gusset with the minimum compressive strength of block for which they are suitable, eg 2.8N/mm^2 or 3.5N/mm^2.

Joist hangers should be supported on level beds and should be tight to the wall.

The masonry course to carry the joist hangers should be checked for level and height. Hangers should not be cut into the walling.

Restraint type hangers should be used where specified.

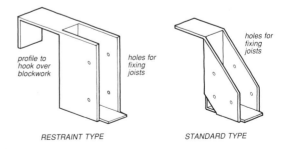

profile to hook over blockwork *holes for fixing joists* *holes for fixing joists*

RESTRAINT TYPE *STANDARD TYPE*

Performance Standards

Guidance

JOIST HANGERS (continued)

6.4 - S4 **Joists shall be properly cut to length and fitted to joist hangers**

Joists should be accurately cut to length for a tight fit. The joist should be notched into the hanger to keep the ceiling line level.

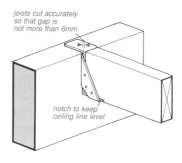

joists cut accurately so that gap is not more than 6mm

notch to keep ceiling line level

Joist hangers should be fully nailed.

When joist hangers are used at both ends of a joist, measuring, marking and cutting should be accurate to ensure the joist fits properly at both ends.

TRIMMED AND TRIMMING JOISTS

6.4 - S5 **Trimmed and trimming joists shall be properly supported**

Trimmed and trimming joists should be used as detailed in the design.

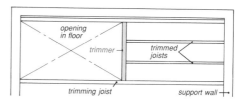

opening in floor

trimmer

trimmed joists

trimming joist

support wall

The thickness and depth of trimmed and trimming joists should be as detailed in the design.

Performance Standards

Guidance

The ends of trimmed joists may be supported using joist hangers or notches. When using hangers, 'timber-to-timber' hangers should be used, *not* wall hangers.

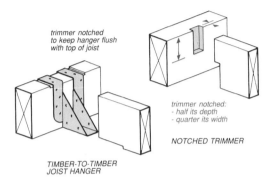

trimmer notched to keep hanger flush with top of joist

trimmer notched:
- half its depth
- quarter its width

NOTCHED TRIMMER

TIMBER-TO-TIMBER JOIST HANGER

For lightly loaded trimmed joists, support battens (plates) may be used.

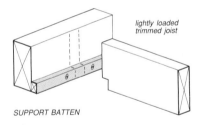

lightly loaded trimmed joist

SUPPORT BATTEN

6.4 - S6 Joists shall be properly trimmed into steelwork

Joists trimmed into steelwork should be notched at both top and bottom to allow for timber shrinkage.

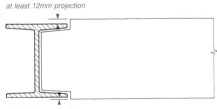

at least 12mm projection

at least 2mm projection

Performance Standards

Guidance

MULTIPLE JOISTS

6.4 - S7   Multiple joists shall be securely fixed together

Joists may be doubled up to support a non-masonry partition or to form trimmers.

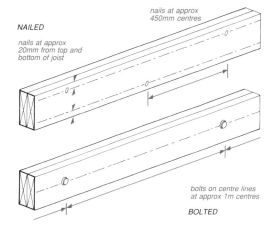

Fixings should be to the Engineer's specification and should be given a second check for tightness just before fixing the ceiling.

Toothed plate, split ring and shear plate connectors should be used in strict accordance with manufacturers' recommendations.

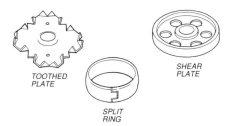

Washers, or single faced connectors, should be used with bolts. Check whether toothed connectors are required between the timber faces. Ensure that all washers, etc are provided.

Bolts should be checked for tightness (fixing bolts should not be used for tightening). Make sure that timber is not damaged by over-tightening.

Performance Standards	Guidance

STRUTTING

6.4 - S8   **Appropriate strutting shall
be provided, where required**

Items to be taken into account
include:

(a) span of the floor

Strutting should be provided before laying floor decking as
follows:

Joist span [m]	Rows of strutting
Up to 2.5	none needed
2.5 to 4.5	1 (at centre of span)
Over 4.5	2 (at equal spacing)

Either herringbone strutting (38mm x 38mm timber) or minimum
38mm thick solid strutting should be used, for not less than
three-quarters the depth of the joist. Strutting should not project
beyond the top and bottom edges of joists. At the end of each
run of strutting the last joist should be firmly blocked to the wall.

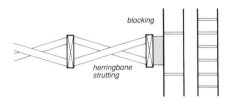

blocking

*herringbone
strutting*

(b) bearings onto steelwork

Joists should be strutted where they bear on, or are notched
into, steelwork to prevent rotation.

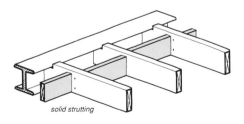

solid strutting

Performance Standards

Guidance

STRUTTING (continued)

6.4 - S8 (c) joists supported by hangers

Solid blocking should be used at all joist bearings where they are not built into brickwork or blockwork. This includes some forms of timber frame construction. The blocking may be used for fixing plasterboard and floor decking.

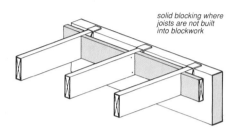

solid blocking where joists are not built into blockwork

NOTCHING AND DRILLING

6.4 - S9 Notching and drilling shall be carried out within recognised limits

Timber joists and studs should only be notched and drilled within the limits shown in the table below:

Item	Location	Maximum size
Notching joists up to 250mm depth	Top edge 0.1 to 0.2 of span	0.15 x depth of joist
Drilling joists up to 250mm depth	Centre line 0.25 to 0.4 of span	0.25 x depth of joist

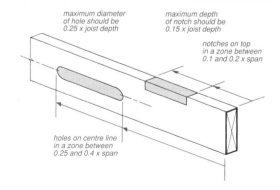

maximum diameter of hole should be 0.25 x joist depth

maximum depth of notch should be 0.15 x joist depth

notches on top in a zone between 0.1 and 0.2 x span

holes on centre line in a zone between 0.25 and 0.4 x span

Performance Standards

Guidance

Notches and drillings in the same joist should be at least 100mm apart horizontally.

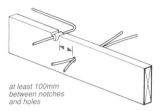

at least 100mm between notches and holes

Special instructions should be obtained from the designer when and drilling:

● is required in joists deeper than 250mm

● does not meet the above guidelines, or

● is needed close to heavy loads, such as those from partitions, cisterns, cylinders and stair trimming.

If structural strength is impaired by notching or drilling, the element should be replaced or correctly repaired.

RESTRAINT STRAPPING

6.4 - S10 Restraint strapping shall be provided where specified in the design details

When the external wall is to be stabilised by connection to the floor, straps may be required. They may be fixed to the top or bottom of the joist, depending on how the masonry is coursed.

Where joists run parallel to the wall, straps should be supported on noggings fixed between the joists. Packing should be provided between the wall and the first joist. Noggings should be at least ¾ the depth of the joists. Straps should be placed at a maximum of 2 metres apart.

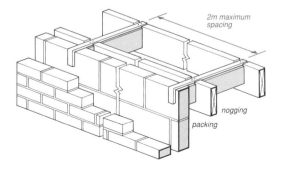

2m maximum spacing

nogging

packing

Performance Standards	Guidance

RESTRAINT STRAPPING (continued)

6.4 - S10 (continued)

Straps will not normally be required at the ends of joists if there is at least 90mm bearing (eg if they are built into blockwork). If joist hangers are not designed to provide restraint, separate straps should be fitted in addition to joist hangers.

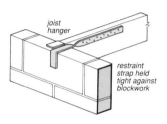

joist hanger

restraint strap held tight against blockwork

6.4 - S11   Straps shall be located to provide adequate restraint for the masonry

Straps should bear on the centre of bricks or blocks, not on mortar joints.

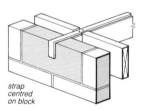

strap centred on block

6.4 - S12   Straps shall be fixed with suitable screws or nails

Straps should be notched into at least two joists and fixed with 2 screws or nails into each joist.

Performance Standards	Guidance

OVERLAPPING JOISTS

6.4 - S13 Overlapping joists shall be properly fixed to prevent disruption of finishes

Where joists overlap on loadbearing intermediate walls, they should be nailed together and cut so that they will not project beyond the supporting wall by more than 100mm. This is to prevent the floor decking being pushed up or the ceiling being cracked when the cantilevered part of the joist moves upwards.

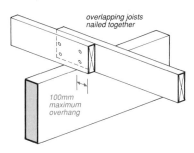

overlapping joists nailed together

100mm maximum overhang

FLOOR DECKING : GENERAL

6.4 - S14 Flooring shall only be fixed when the dwelling is substantially weathertight

All timber-based materials swell when they become wet. Wet timber-based floor decking may twist and bow producing large gaps when drying out. To avoid these problems, floor decking should be kept dry at all times and damp or damaged materials replaced.

When floor decking has to be stored, it should be stored on a hard base, under cover, if possible indoors.

6.4 - S15 Floor decking shall be securely fixed to the floor joists

Before fixing floor decking, a check should be made that all noggings, blocking and strutting are in place and fixed securely.

The length of nails should be 2½ times the thickness of the decking.

The ends of adjacent boards should be square. Joints should be staggered and supported on noggings or joists. Reference should be made to Clause S22 for fixing floating floors.

Temporary wedges and packings at the perimeter should be removed after the floor decking is complete.

Performance Standards   **Guidance**

FLOOR DECKING : GENERAL (continued)

6.4 - S16 Completed floor decking shall not be overloaded and shall be protected against damage

Floors should not be overloaded, especially with materials stored during construction. Where necessary, fixed flooring and/or floor decking should be protected against damp (for example from plaster splashes) and damage.

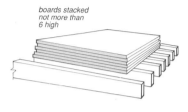

boards stacked not more than 6 high

SOFTWOOD BOARDING

6.4 - S17 Softwood boarding shall be securely fixed

End (butt) joints should be made on joists and staggered, ie the joints of adjacent boards should not be on the same joist.

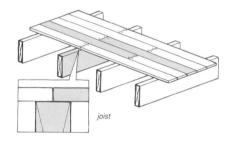

joist

Board thickness should not be less than the following for the joist spacings indicated:

Board thickness [mm]	Maximum joist centres [mm]
16	450
19	600

Boards should be cramped up and either double nailed or secret nailed to each joist. Nails should be of a length 2½ times the thickness of the decking and should be punched well below the surface.

Performance Standards	Guidance

CHIPBOARD FLOORING

6.4 - S18 Chipboard flooring shall be of the type and thickness specified

Only moisture-resistant, Type C4 chipboard to BS 5669 should be used for flooring. This can be recognised by the red/green stripe on the chipboard edge and an identifying stamp on the back of the boards.

Board thicknesses should be not less than the following for the joist spacings indicated:

Board thickness [mm]	Maximum joist centres [mm]
18/20	450
22	600

6.4 - S19 Chipboard flooring shall be securely fixed

ALL TYPES OF CHIPBOARD

Chipboard should be supported and fixed in accordance with manufacturers' instructions, using either:

- flat-headed ring shank nails of length 2½ times the thickness of the chipboard, or
- screws.

Edges at room perimeters should be supported on joists or noggings.

Fixing centres to joists should be:

- 200mm to 300mm centres around the board perimeter
- 400mm to 500mm centres on intermediate supports.

An expansion gap of at least 10mm should be allowed at room perimeters between chipboard and walls.

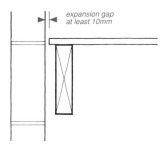

expansion gap
at least 10mm

6.4 | Timber and concrete upper floors

Performance Standards

Guidance

CHIPBOARD FLOORING (continued)

6.4 - S19 (continued)

SQUARE EDGED BOARDS AND BOARDS WITH LOOSE TONGUES

Boards should be supported on all sides on joists or noggings.

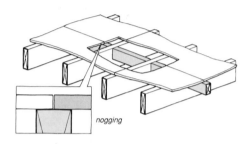

nogging

TONGUED AND GROOVED BOARDS

Boards should be laid with long edges at right angles to joists.

Short edges should be supported on joists or noggings.

Projecting ends of boards should be cut back to form a butt joint on a joist.

To prevent squeaking, tongued and grooved joints between boards should be glued with adhesives complying with BS 4071.

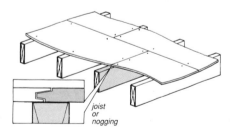

*joist
or
nogging*

Performance Standards	Guidance

PLYWOOD FLOORING

6.4 - S20 Plywood decking shall be securely fixed

Plywood should be laid with the face grain at right angles to the supports. All butt joints and joints with loose tongues should be supported on joists or noggings. All end joints should occur over joists (38mm minimum thickness) or noggings.

Board thickness should be not less than the following for the joist spacings indicated:

Board thickness [mm]	Maximum joist centres [mm]
12	450
16	600

Nails for fixing plywood should be either:
- plain wire nails
  - minimum diameter 3.35mm
  - minimum length 65mm
  - with penetration not less than 40mm, *or*
- annular-ring shank nails
  - minimum diameter 3mm
  - minimum length 50mm
  - penetration not less than 32mm.

Fixings should be at 150mm centres (max) around the perimeter and 300mm centres (max) on intermediate supports.

An expansion gap of at least 10mm should be allowed at room perimeters between plywood and walls.

OTHER FLOOR DECKING

6.4 - S21 Proprietary flooring materials shall be securely fixed

Other proprietary floor decking should have been assessed in accordance with Technical Requirement R3 and should be fixed in accordance with any certification requirements.

FLOORS BETWEEN DWELLINGS

6.4 - S22 The floating part of a floor shall be completely separated by a quilt or other resilient layer from the main structure and surrounding walls

The structural component of floors between dwellings may be concrete, steel, timber or a combination of these materials.

The floor finish should be completely separated from the structure.

Performance Standards   Guidance

FLOORS BETWEEN DWELLINGS (continued)

6.4 - S22 (continued)

Where specified, support battens should be located immediately above the joists. Battens should not be nailed to joists through insulation. Boards should be fixed securely to battens with nails no longer than the combined thickness of board and batten.

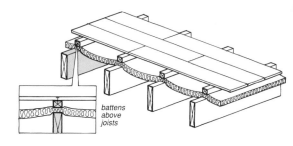

battens above joists

All joints should be glued where boards are laid loose over insulation, without battens.

Proprietary floating floor systems should be fixed strictly in accordance with the manufacturer's, and any relevant certification, requirements.

Where board materials are laid loose, all joints in tongued and grooved boards should be glued.

The gap between the floating floor and the wall or skirting should be sealed to prevent sound and vibration transmission. A sealant or neoprene strip should be used. Skirtings should not be fixed to the floating floor.

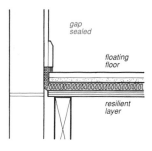

gap sealed

floating floor

resilient layer

Performance Standards	Guidance

CONCRETE FLOORS

6.4 - S23 Concrete upper floors shall be constructed/ erected reasonably level and smooth

Care should be taken to ensure that concrete floors are reasonably level and smooth. Particular care should be taken at doorways and junctions.

6.4 - S24 Appropriate measures shall be taken when concreting or screeding in cold weather

Reference should be made to Chapter 1.4 'Cold weather working'.

IN-SITU CONCRETE

6.4 - S25 Reinforced concrete upper floors shall be constructed in accordance with design details

All concrete work should be in accordance with Chapter 2.1 'Concrete and its reinforcement' (each section).

The Builder should not depart from the design without the Engineer's written consent.

PRECAST CONCRETE

6.4 - S26 Precast concrete upper floors shall be erected in accordance with design details

Items to be taken into account include:

(a) manufacturer's assembly instructions

A copy of the manufacturer's assembly instructions (and BBA Certificate, if applicable) should be on site and the recommendations should be followed.

The Builder should not depart from the design without the Engineer's written consent.

(b) bearings

Bearings onto masonry should be 90mm minimum. Bearings onto steelwork should be 75mm minimum.

Bearings should be solid and level. Any open frogs in brickwork should be filled.

Performance Standards	Guidance

PRECAST CONCRETE (continued)

6.4 - S26 (c) setting out of beams

When setting out beam and block floors, use the infill blocks as spacers to ensure correct spacing between beams.

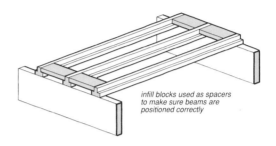

infill blocks used as spacers to make sure beams are positioned correctly

Beam layout drawings should always be followed. Doubled beams usually support concentrated loads, such as partitions.

(d) propping of beams and planks during construction

Where floors rely on structural topping or in-situ make-up sections, propping may be needed until the in-situ concrete has reached its design strength.

(e) grouting of joints

Most precast floors rely on a grout to ensure composite action of the units and provide adequate strength, as well as fire and sound resistance.

The manufacturer's specification should be checked for the grout mix.

(f) restraint straps and ties

Restraint straps should be shown on the drawings. They are usually necessary where the beams run parallel with the wall.

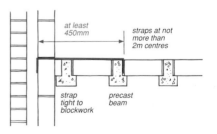

at least 450mm

straps at not more than 2m centres

strap tight to blockwork

precast beam

Metal ties may be required to provide a structural link across internal and separating walls.

Performance Standards | Guidance

(g) position of holes for services

Where holes are required for services, blocks should be omitted or cut where necessary. Infill blocks should be cut carefully and neatly without damage. Using a hammer and bolster to cut blocks may cause significant damage.

(h) trimmed openings

Large openings for staircases and chimneys may require openings to be trimmed. Specifications and drawings should be followed.

Steel trimmer shoes may be used to trim openings.

Doubled beams are common around trimmed openings, and should be propped until all voids have been solidly concreted and the concrete has reached its design strength.

(i) cracked or broken components

Beams, planks or infill blocks that are cracked should not be used.

(j) clips for suspended ceiling

Some designs include metal ceiling clips inserted between the planks or blocks so that timber battens can be fixed below.

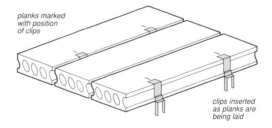

planks marked
with position
of clips

clips inserted
as planks are
being laid

FIRESTOPPING

6.4 - S27 Service penetrations shall be firestopped in floors between dwellings

The specified method of firestopping should be carried out. There should be no holes or gaps for smoke to penetrate once the firestopping has been installed.

Guidance

Statutory references

The following table lists references to building legislation and associated documents applicable at August 1990.

Clause	Subject	Statute			
		Building [1] Regulations	Building [2] Standards (Scotland)	Building [3] Regulations (N Ireland)	Isle of Man [4] Bye-laws
D3	Joist sizes/span tables	A1/2	Part C	Part D	Part D
D10	Restraint strapping	A1/2	Part D	Part D	Part D
D12	Fire spread within dwellings	B2/3/4	Part D	Part E	Part E
D16	Fire resistance between dwellings	B2/3/4	Part D	Part E	Part E
D17	Sound insulation	E1/2/3	Part H	Part G	Part G
Associated documents					

[1] Approved Documents to the Building Regulations 1985 for England and Wales (and 1990 edition).
[2] Building Standards (Scotland) Regulations 1981 and all published amendments.
[3] Building Regulations (Northern Ireland) 1990.
[4] Isle of Man Bye-laws 1976, amended 1980 and 1987.

Guidance

Span tables for timber floor joists

Tables 1 and 2 in this Appendix are taken from Tables B3 and B4 in Approved Document A1/2. The tables assume an imposed floor loading of 1.5kN/m^2, but no allowance has been made for partition loads.

The sizes given are minimum sizes. If regularised timber joists are used, use the next nominal size up.

For upper floors with a 22mm thick floor decking and 12.5mm plasterboard ceiling, a dead load of between 0.25kN/m^2 and 0.5kN/m^2 may be assumed. Use the centre three columns from the tables.

For timber separating floors, the dead load of the constructions given in Approved Document E1/2/3 is about 0.6kN/m^2 to 0.7kN/m^2, therefore use the three right-hand columns.

Table 1 - Span table for timber floor joists - strength Class SC3

Table **B3**   **Floor joists**

Timber of strength class **SC3** (see Table B1)

	Dead load† [kN/m²]								
	Not more than 0.25			More than 0.25 but not more than 0.50			More than 0.50 but not more than 1.25		
	Spacing of joists [mm]								
	400	450	600	400	450	600	400	450	600
Size of joist [mm × mm]	Maximum clear span of joist [m]								
38 × 75	1.22	1.09	0.83	1.14	1.03	0.79	0.98	0.89	0.70
38 × 89*	1.62	1.47	1.12	1.50	1.36	1.06	1.26	1.15	0.91
38 × 100	1.91	1.78	1.38	1.80	1.64	1.28	1.49	1.36	1.09
38 × 125	2.54	2.45	2.01	2.43	2.30	1.83	2.01	1.85	1.50
38 × 140*	2.85	2.74	2.40	2.72	2.59	2.17	2.33	2.15	1.76
38 × 150	3.05	2.93	2.56	2.91	2.76	2.40	2.50	2.35	1.93
38 × 175	3.55	3.40	2.96	3.37	3.19	2.77	2.89	2.73	2.36
38 × 184*	3.73	3.56	3.10	3.53	3.34	2.90	3.03	2.86	2.48
38 × 200	4.04	3.85	3.35	3.82	3.61	3.13	3.27	3.09	2.68
38 × 225	4.53	4.29	3.73	4.25	4.02	3.50	3.65	3.44	2.99
47 × 75	1.41	1.33	1.02	1.35	1.24	0.96	1.16	1.06	0.84
47 × 100	2.11	2.00	1.67	2.00	1.90	1.54	1.74	1.60	1.29
47 × 125	2.73	2.63	2.38	2.61	2.51	2.17	2.33	2.15	1.76
47 × 150	3.27	3.14	2.84	3.13	3.01	2.66	2.78	2.62	2.24
47 × 175	3.80	3.66	3.28	3.64	3.50	3.07	3.21	3.03	2.63
47 × 200	4.33	4.17	3.71	4.15	3.99	3.48	3.63	3.43	2.98
47 × 225	4.81	4.67	4.13	4.65	4.45	3.88	4.04	3.82	3.32
50 × 75	1.45	1.37	1.08	1.39	1.30	1.01	1.22	1.11	0.88
50 × 100	2.18	2.06	1.76	2.06	1.95	1.62	1.82	1.67	1.35
50 × 125	2.79	2.68	2.44	2.67	2.56	2.28	2.40	2.24	1.84
50 × 150	3.33	3.21	2.92	3.19	3.07	2.75	2.86	2.70	2.33
50 × 175	3.88	3.73	3.38	3.71	3.57	3.17	3.30	3.12	2.71
50 × 200	4.42	4.25	3.82	4.23	4.07	3.58	3.74	3.53	3.07
50 × 225	4.88	4.74	4.26	4.72	4.57	3.99	4.16	3.94	3.42
63 × 100	2.41	2.29	2.01	2.28	2.17	1.90	2.01	1.91	1.60
63 × 125	3.00	2.89	2.63	2.88	2.77	2.52	2.59	2.49	2.16
63 × 150	3.59	3.46	3.15	3.44	3.31	3.01	3.10	2.98	2.63
63 × 175	4.17	4.02	3.66	4.00	3.85	3.51	3.61	3.47	3.03
63 × 200	4.73	4.58	4.18	4.56	4.39	4.00	4.11	3.95	3.43
63 × 225	5.15	5.01	4.68	4.99	4.85	4.46	4.62	4.40	3.83
75 × 125	3.18	3.06	2.79	3.04	2.93	2.67	2.74	2.64	2.40
75 × 150	3.79	3.66	3.33	3.64	3.50	3.19	3.28	3.16	2.86
75 × 175	4.41	4.25	3.88	4.23	4.07	3.71	3.82	3.68	3.30
75 × 200	4.92	4.79	4.42	4.77	4.64	4.23	4.35	4.19	3.74
75 × 225	5.36	5.22	4.88	5.20	5.06	4.72	4.82	4.69	4.16

* North American surfaced size
† Dead load is the load supported by the joist, excluding the mass of the joist

Reproduced from Approved Document A1/2 by permission of HMSO.

Guidance

Table 2 - Span table for timber floor joists - strength Class SC4

Table **B4**   **Floor joists**

Timber of strength class **SC4** *(see Table B1)*

Size of joist [mm × mm]	Not more than 0.25			More than 0.25 but not more than 0.50			More than 0.50 but not more than 1.25		
	400	450	600	400	450	600	400	450	600
	Maximum clear span of joist [m]								
38 × 75	1.34	1.26	1.09	1.29	1.22	1.05	1.17	1.11	0.93
38 × 89*	1.72	1.62	1.40	1.64	1.55	1.34	1.47	1.39	1.21
38 × 100	2.02	1.91	1.66	1.92	1.82	1.58	1.70	1.62	1.42
38 × 125	2.65	2.55	2.28	2.53	2.43	2.15	2.25	2.14	1.89
38 × 140*	2.96	2.85	2.59	2.83	2.72	2.47	2.54	2.44	2.18
38 × 150	3.17	3.05	2.77	3.03	2.91	2.65	2.72	2.62	2.37
38 × 175	3.69	3.55	3.22	3.53	3.39	3.08	3.17	3.05	2.76
38 × 184*	3.87	3.73	3.39	3.71	3.57	3.24	3.33	3.20	2.90
38 × 200	4.20	4.04	3.68	4.02	3.87	3.52	3.62	3.48	3.15
38 × 225	4.70	4.54	4.13	4.52	4.35	3.95	4.07	3.91	3.54
47 × 75	1.49	1.41	1.22	1.43	1.35	1.17	1.29	1.23	1.07
47 × 100	2.23	2.12	1.84	2.11	2.00	1.75	1.87	1.77	1.56
47 × 125	2.84	2.73	2.48	2.72	2.61	2.37	2.44	2.34	2.07
47 × 150	3.40	3.27	2.97	3.25	3.13	2.84	2.93	2.81	2.55
47 × 175	3.95	3.80	3.46	3.78	3.64	3.31	3.41	3.28	2.97
47 × 200	4.50	4.33	3.95	4.31	4.15	3.78	3.89	3.74	3.39
47 × 225	4.94	4.81	4.43	4.79	4.66	4.24	4.36	4.20	3.81
50 × 75	1.54	1.45	1.26	1.47	1.39	1.21	1.33	1.26	1.10
50 × 100	2.30	2.18	1.90	2.17	2.06	1.80	1.92	1.82	1.61
50 × 125	2.90	2.79	2.53	2.77	2.67	2.42	2.50	2.40	2.13
50 × 150	3.46	3.34	3.03	3.32	3.19	2.90	2.99	2.87	2.61
50 × 175	4.03	3.88	3.53	3.86	3.71	3.38	3.48	3.34	3.04
50 × 200	4.59	4.42	4.03	4.40	4.23	3.85	3.97	3.81	3.46
50 × 225	5.02	4.88	4.52	4.86	4.73	4.33	4.45	4.28	3.89
63 × 100	2.51	2.41	2.12	2.40	2.28	2.01	2.11	2.01	1.78
63 × 125	3.12	3.01	2.74	2.99	2.88	2.62	2.69	2.59	2.35
63 × 150	3.73	3.59	3.27	3.58	3.44	3.13	3.22	3.10	2.82
63 × 175	4.33	4.18	3.81	4.16	4.00	3.65	3.75	3.61	3.28
63 × 200	4.86	4.73	4.34	4.71	4.56	4.16	4.28	4.12	3.74
63 × 225	5.29	5.15	4.81	5.13	4.99	4.66	4.76	4.62	4.20
75 × 125	3.30	3.18	2.90	3.16	3.05	2.77	2.85	2.75	2.50
75 × 150	3.94	3.80	3.46	3.78	3.64	3.32	3.41	3.28	2.99
75 × 175	4.57	4.41	4.03	4.39	4.23	3.86	3.97	3.82	3.48
75 × 200	5.06	4.93	4.59	4.91	4.78	4.40	4.52	4.36	3.97
75 × 225	5.51	5.36	5.02	5.34	5.20	4.86	4.96	4.82	4.45

Dead load† [kN/m²]

Spacing of joists [mm]

* North American surfaced size
† Dead load is the load supported by the joist, excluding the mass of the joist

APPENDIX 6.4-C

Timber and concrete upper floors

Guidance

Protection from corrosion of metal components embedded in masonry

Metal components, other than wall ties built into masonry, should be made of a material listed below and protected in the way described in Table 1. Reference should be made to Table 2 for guidance on which category of material and protection to use.

Table 1 - Anchorages, dowels and fixings

Category	Base material	Form	Grade and standard to be complied with	Protective measures to be carried out after fabrication
A	Hot-dip galvanized low carbon steel	Sheet	BS 2989, Z1 or Z2, coating type G 600. Minimum mass of coating 600 g/m² including both sides	All external cut edges to be protected using a one-pack chemical-resistant paint complying with HF1A to HF2F in part 4 of table 4H of BS 5493 : 1977 and modified to give adequate adhesion to the fixing
			BS 2989, Z1 or Z2, coating type G 275. Minimum mass of coating 275 g/m² including both sides	Coating to be applied after fabrication to the external surfaces and consisting of either: (a) bituminous solution complying with types 1 or 2 of BS 3416 and of minimum thickness 25 µm; or (b) a one-pack chemical-resistant paint complying with HF1A to HF2F in part 4 of table 4H of BS 5493 : 1977 and modified to give adequate adhesion to the fixing. Where the zinc is removed on internal surfaces during fabrication, e.g. by welding, further protection should be applied to these areas
B	Low carbon steel	Strip	BS 1449 : Part 1 : 1983 (mechanical requirements in table 11 only)	Post-galvanizing complying with BS 729. Minimum mass of coating 460 g/m² including both sides
			BS 4360 grade 43A	
C	Low carbon steel	Strip	BS 1449 : Part 1 : 1983 (mechanical requirements in table 11 only)	Post-galvanizing complying with BS 729. Minimum mass of coating 940 g/m² including both sides
			BS 4360 grade 43A	
D	Copper		BS 6017	
	Copper alloys		BS 2870 : 1980, grades listed in tables 8 and 12	Material other than phosphor bronze to be formed either: (a) by bending at dull red heat and allowing to cool in still air; or
			BS 2873 : 1969, grades listed in tables 4 and 6	
			BS 2874 : 1968, grades listed in tables 6, 8 and 9 except CA 106	(b) by cold forming and subsequently stress relief annealing at 250 °C to 300 °C for 30 min to 1 h. Effectiveness of stress relieving of cold formed components to be tested by the supplier using the mercurous nitrate test described in clause 11 of BS 2874 : 1969
	Austenitic stainless steel, minimum 18/8 composition and excluding free machining specifications	Strip	BS 1449 : Part 2	
		Bar Rod	BS 970 : Part 1	
		Tube	BS 6323 : Part 8	
		Wire	BS 1554 BS 3111 : Part 2	

Reproduced from BS 5628 : Part 3 by permission of BSI.

Guidance

Table 2 - Protection of metal components (other than wall ties) built into masonry

Type of component	Situation	Category given in table 1 (material and recommended protective measures)	
		Three storeys or less	More than three storeys
Anchorages, bonding ties, slip brick ties and continuous support angles	All	C or D	D
Dowels and restraint straps Joist hangers Reinforcement for non-structural use	Internal walls	A, B, C, D	A, B, C, D
	In contact with or embedded in inner leaf	A, B, C, D	A, B, C, D
	In contact with or embedded in outer leaf or single leaf walls	C or D	D
Lintels	All	As specified in BS 5977 : Part 2 for the appropriate type of lintel i.e. installed with or without d.p.c.	Not normally applicable. If used, special precautions may be necessary
Cavity trays	All	As specified in BS 5977 : Part 2 for lintels installed without d.p.c.	As specified in BS 5977 : Part 2 for lintels installed without d.p.c.

It is an NHBC recommendation that components in contact with, or embedded in, an inner leaf which is damp or exposed to periodic wettings (eg below dpc) should be protected in the same way as components in contact with, or embedded in, an outer leaf.

Reproduced from BS 5628 : Part 3 by permission of BSI.

BUILDMARK™

NHBC, Buildmark House, Chiltern Avenue, Amersham, Bucks HP6 5AP

NHBC, 5 Manor Place, Edinburgh, Scotland EH3 7DH

NHBC, Holyrood Court, 59 Malone Road, Belfast BT9 6SA

informing the industry

CI/SfB	81	(29)	Hh2	
CAWS	G10			

Operative from January 1992

Chapter **6.5**

NHBC STANDARDS

Steelwork support to upper floors and partitions

This Chapter gives the Technical Requirements and recommendations for steelwork to support masonry partitions, timber floors and to trim floor voids.

LIST OF CHAPTERS

THE STANDARDS

The NHBC Standards give:
● Technical Requirements in red
● Performance Standards in dark blue
● Guidance in light blue
for the design and construction of dwellings acceptable to NHBC.

Diagrams may contain text in red. This is to highlight points but has no mandatory significance.

The Standards come into effect for every NHBC registered home whose foundations are concreted on or after the publication date shown on the cover of each Chapter and apply throughout the UK, unless otherwise stated.

COMPOSITION OF THE STANDARDS
The Standards are divided into 10 Parts, each containing one or more Chapters covering a particular aspect. The Parts follow the usual construction process.

In general, each Chapter is made up of sections dealing with Design, Materials and Sitework. In some cases one or more of these aspects may not be included.

TECHNICAL REQUIREMENTS
Each Chapter (except former Practice Notes) contains the five mandatory Technical Requirements which MUST be met by the Builder.

The Technical Requirements are printed in red. Chapter 1.1 'Introduction to the Standards and Technical Requirements' contains full details.

PERFORMANCE STANDARDS
Most Chapters consist of detailed Performance Standards printed in dark blue, normally in the left-hand column of each Design, Materials or Sitework page, subdivided into Clauses designated D, M or S, respectively.

Alternative standards of performance will be acceptable ONLY if, in the opinion of NHBC, the Technical Requirements are met and the standard achieved is not lower than the stated Performance Standard.

GUIDANCE
Guidance on how the Performance Standard may be met is normally shown, printed in light blue, in the right-hand column opposite the relevant Performance Standard. Some Chapters contain pages which are all Guidance.

Guidance is based on normal procedures and recommended practices shown by experience to be satisfactory and acceptable. NHBC will consider alternative methods to meet specific requirements, subject to prior consultation and evaluation.

SCOPE

This Chapter gives the Technical Requirements and recommendations for the size of steelwork to support masonry partitions, timber floors and to trim floor voids.

NHBC Standards do not cover aspects of health and safety relating to building operations and to the handling and use of certain building materials. Such matters are covered by statutory requirements.

FINDING INFORMATION

To find information on a particular subject, the following procedure is recommended:

1 Identify the **Part** most appropriate for the subject.

2 Identify the **Chapter** which deals with the particular element of construction.

3 Decide whether the information required relates to the Design, Materials or Sitework **Section** of the Chapter.

4 Decide from the Contents list the **heading** under which the required information is most likely to be found.

5 Review the **clauses** listed against the heading to see which has the relevant Performance Standard.

6 Review the **items** under the Performance Standards and decide which is relevant.

7 Review the guidance in the right-hand column opposite the item most relevant to the subject. If a clause number is known, use the above procedure to find the clause.

For example: **6.5 - S2(b)** means:

6	Part 6	Superstructure (excluding roofs)
5	Chapter 5	Steelwork support to upper floors and partitions
S	Section	SITEWORK
2	Clause 2	STEELWORK
(b)	Item (b)	bearing.

CONTENTS   Clause

TECHNICAL REQUIREMENTS

DESIGN

MATERIALS

SITEWORK

APPENDIX 6.5-A

APPENDIX 6.5-B

APPENDIX 6.5-C

TECHNICAL REQUIREMENTS

Technical Requirements	Performance Standards

R1 Statutory requirements
Work shall comply with all relevant Building Regulations and other statutory requirements

Chapter 1.1 gives the detailed Performance Standards which relate to these Technical Requirements.

R2 Design requirement
Design and specification shall provide satisfactory performance

R3 Materials requirement
All materials, products and building systems shall be suitable for their intended purpose

R4 Workmanship requirement
All work shall be carried out in a proper, neat and workmanlike manner

R5 Structural design requirement
Structural design shall be carried out by suitably qualified persons in accordance with British Standards and Codes of Practice

Performance Standards   **Guidance**

DESIGN STANDARD

6.5 - D1   Design shall meet the Technical Requirements

Design that follows the guidance below will be acceptable for steelwork supporting either masonry partitions or floors.

STRUCTURAL DESIGN

6.5 - D2   Steelwork shall be designed to support and transmit loads to the supporting structure without undue movement or deflection

Steelwork (including its support and any connections) should be either:

● designed by an Engineer in accordance with Technical Requirement R5, or

● where appropriate, detailed according to the designs shown in this Chapter.

The designs shown in this Chapter are in accordance with BS 5950 using grade 43 steel and therefore meet statutory requirements.

It should be noted that the information given in this Chapter has been prepared primarily to assist Builders in providing proper support to masonry partitions and floors. The designs given will not always be the most economic and an Engineer may be able to design a smaller section beam for a particular situation.

Items to be taken into account include:

(a) support of masonry partitions

Where appropriate, masonry partitions may be supported by steelwork selected in accordance with Appendix 6.5-A.

Care should be taken during construction to avoid the problem of out-of-true masonry being only partly supported by steelwork.

(b) support of floors

Timber floors can be supported by steelwork.

Where appropriate, steelwork should be in accordance with Appendices 6.5-B and 6.5-C.

The timber floor should be in accordance with Chapter 6.4 'Timber and concrete upper floors' (each section), including proper allowance for shrinkage of timber joists supported by steelwork.

at least 12mm projection

at least 2mm projection

Performance Standards	Guidance

STRUCTURAL DESIGN (continued)

6.5 - D2 (c) support of steelwork

Steelwork may need to be supported on padstones to distribute loads safely.

When using this Chapter, padstones should be in accordance with Appendix 6.5-A or Appendix 6.5-B, as appropriate.

Masonry should be in accordance with Chapter 6.1 'External masonry walls' (each section) or Chapter 6.3 'Internal walls' (each section), as appropriate.

(d) steelwork to steelwork connection

Connections between steel beams should be designed.

Where appropriate, steelwork beam-to-beam connections should be in accordance with Appendix 6.5-C.

Appendix 6.5-C uses bolted connections (using black bolts) or welding. Connections requiring the use of other forms of connection (such as high strength friction grip bolts) should be designed by an Engineer in accordance with Technical Requirement R5.

(e) durability

Steelwork should be given a protective coating system to ensure durability. Reference should be made to Sitework clause 6.5 - S3 for details.

(f) fire resistance

Where required by statutory requirements (such as Building Regulations, Bye-laws, etc), steelwork should be provided with protection to give the required level of fire resistance.

Performance Standards	Guidance

MATERIALS STANDARDS

6.5 - M1 All materials shall:
(a) meet the Technical Requirements
(b) take account of the design

Materials that comply with the design and the guidance below will be acceptable for steelwork supporting either masonry partitions or floors.

Materials for steelwork supporting either masonry partitions or floors shall comply with all relevant standards, including those listed below. Where no standard exists, Technical Requirement R3 applies (see Chapter 1.1 'Introduction to the Standards and Technical Requirements').

References to British Standards and Codes of Practice include those made under the Construction Products Directive (89/106/EEC) and, in particular, appropriate European Technical Specifications approved by a European Committee for Standardisation (CEN).

STEELWORK

6.5 - M2 Steelwork shall be of sufficient strength and durability

Steelwork will be acceptable if it complies with Clause M1 above and is based on:

BS 4   Part 1 : Structural steel sections : Specification for hot-rolled sections, or

BS 4360 Specification for weldable structural steels, or

BS 4848 Specification for hot-rolled structural steel sections.

To ensure durability, steelwork should be given a protective coating system. For steelwork which is to be bolted (using black bolts) or not connected, an acceptable coating system is one coat of high build zinc phosphate primer and one coat of bituminous paint. Where welding is to be carried out, use the protective coating system specified by the designer.

PADSTONES

6.5 - M3 Padstones shall distribute point loads safely to the supporting structure

Where a steel beam is supported by masonry, a padstone may be required to spread the load over a sufficiently large area of the masonry to prevent overstressing. A padstone may be necessary (see Table 3, Appendix 6.5-A and Table 5, Appendix 6.5-B for sizes).

Where the inner leaf is used to provide a major contribution to the thermal insulation of a cavity wall, any padstone that is needed should have similar thermal properties to the masonry used for the rest of the inner leaf or precautions should be taken to prevent cold bridging.

For example, if the masonry is built using voided concrete blocks (with insulation in the voids) it would not be acceptable to use an in-situ or precast concrete padstone without the addition of insulation.

MATERIALS

Performance Standards	Guidance

CONNECTIONS

6.5 - M4 **Connections shall be chosen to be capable of supporting and transmitting the intended loads**

Connections should comply with the design. Bolts will be acceptable if they comply with the design and are based on the relevant British Standards, including:

BS 4190 Specification for ISO metric black hexagon bolts, screws and nuts

BS 4395 Specification for high strength friction grip bolts and associated nuts and washers for structural engineering

BS 4604 Specification for the use of high strength friction grip bolts in structural steelwork.

Welded connections should comply with:

BS 5135 Specification for arc welding of carbon and carbon-manganese steels.

Performance Standards	Guidance

SITEWORK STANDARDS

6.5 - S1 **All sitework shall:**
(a) **meet the Technical Requirements**
(b) **take account of the design**
(c) **follow established good practice and workmanship**

Construction that follows the design and the guidance below will be acceptable for steelwork supporting either masonry partitions or floors.

STEELWORK

6.5 - S2 **Steelwork shall be installed to achieve the required structural performance**

Items to be taken into account include:

(a) **the section size and grade detailed in the design**

When materials are delivered to site, check that they conform with either:
● the Engineer's design, or
● the steelwork sizes given in the Appendices to this Chapter.

(b) **bearings**

Bearings for steelwork should be:
● at least 100mm, and
● clean, dry and level.

Padstones may be required in accordance with:
● the Engineer's design, or
● the guidance given in Table 3, Appendix 6.5-A and Table 5, Appendix 6.5-B.

(c) **connections**

Where steelwork-to-steelwork connections are required, follow either:
● the Engineer's design, or
● the guidance given in Appendix 6.5-C.

Only weld, cut or drill steelwork if it is required by the design.

Performance Standards	Guidance

STEELWORK (continued)

6.5 - S3 Steelwork shall be protected to achieve the required durability

To ensure durability, steelwork should be given a protective coating system.

For steelwork which is to be bolted (using black bolts), or not connected, an acceptable coating system is one coat of high build zinc phosphate primer and one coat of bituminous paint.

Guidance on the protection of structural steel is given in BS 5493.

Where steelwork is to be protected by intumescent paint for fire purposes, manufacturers' recommendations should be followed.

STEELWORK - UNGALVANIZED

Internal and external steelwork that has not been galvanized should be protected with at least:

● two coats of zinc phosphate primer, and

● a suitable decorative finish where required.

STEELWORK - GALVANIZED

Unless steelwork is galvanized to a rate of $460g/m^2$, it should be protected as described for ungalvanized.

Guidance

DESIGN TABLES FOR SUPPORT OF MASONRY PARTITIONS (no floor loads)

Steel beams in accordance with the Tables 1, 2 and 3 in this Appendix will be acceptable to NHBC for the support of masonry partitions, if:

- the masonry partition is not more than 2.7m in height, **and**
- steel beams only support the weight of the masonry partition and self weight, **and**
- steel beams span no more than 4.0m, **and**
- the masonry partition is built centrally on the steelwork beam, **and**
- the masonry partition is of one of the types detailed in Table 1, **and**
- padstones are provided, where required, **and**
- the masonry supporting the steel beam is of at least 2.8N/mm² blockwork (workface size 440mm x 215mm) or brickwork and the beam supports do not occur over a door or window opening.

If **any** of the above limitations are not met, steelwork should be designed in accordance with Technical Requirement R5.

Method of applying tables

1 Check that the situation is within all the limitations detailed above.

2 Identify the masonry partition construction and thickness.

3 Use Table 1 to establish the load per metre run.

4 Check the span of the beam(s).

5 Use Table 2 to determine a suitable steel section size.

6 Check whether padstones are required - see Table 3.

(To help in applying the tables, a worked example is given at the end of this Appendix.)

APPENDIX 6.5-A

Guidance

DESIGN TABLES FOR SUPPORT OF MASONRY PARTITIONS (continued)

Table 1 - Load of partition to be supported

Type of masonry for supported partition (not more than 2.7m high and plastered both sides)	Maximum masonry density [kg/m³]	Structural thickness [mm]		
		100	90	75
		load [kN/m run]		
Dense masonry	2000	6.8	6.2	5.4
Medium masonry	1400	5.1	4.8	4.2
Lightweight masonry	800	3.5	3.3	2.9

Table 2 - Size of steel beam supporting partition

Partition load (from Table 1) [kN/m run]	Clear span of beam [m]	Smallest suitable Universal Beam size [mm x mm x kg/m]
Less than 3	up to 4	127 x 76 x 13
	over 4	see Note 2
3 to 5	up to 3	127 x 76 x 13
	3 to 3.5	152 x 89 x 16
	3.5 to 4	178 x 102 x 19
	over 4	see Note 2
5 to 7	up to 2.5	127 x 76 x 13
	2.5 to 3	152 x 89 x 16
	3 to 4	178 x 102 x 19
	over 4	see Note 2

Notes to Table 2

1 For spans up to 4m, Universal Column 152mm x 152mm x 23kg/m, which is the smallest size available, may be used.

2 For spans over 4m, beams should be designed by an Engineer in accordance with Technical Requirement R5.

Guidance

Table 3 - Size of padstone

Type of masonry for supported partition (not more than 2.7m high and plastered both sides)	Thickness of wall supporting beam [mm]						Minimum depth of padstone
	100	125	140	150	190	215	
	Min length of padstone [mm]						[mm]
Dense masonry	215	190	185	180	165	155	150
Medium masonry	155	140	135	130	120	110	150
Lightweight masonry	95	85	80	75	70	70	150

Notes to Table 3

1 Padstones are not necessary where the flange dimension of the beam exceeds the length of the padstone given in this table.

2 When steelwork is in line with the wall supporting it (ie when acting as a lintel over an opening):

● the flange dimension of the beam should not be more than 50mm greater than the thickness of the supporting wall, *and*

● the minimum length of padstone should be 200mm, *and*

● the padstone depth should match the coursing of adjacent masonry, *and*

● the web of the beam should be over the centre of the wall.

3 The minimum length of steel bearing onto padstone should be 100mm.

4 Padstones can be formed from:

● in-situ concrete

● precast concrete

● concrete blocks

● clay bricks.

Padstones should be formed in one unit with a minimum compressive strength of $10N/mm^2$.

For padstone sizes less than 215mm x 100mm, engineering bricks will be suitable.

Guidance

DESIGN TABLES FOR SUPPORT OF MASONRY PARTITIONS (continued)

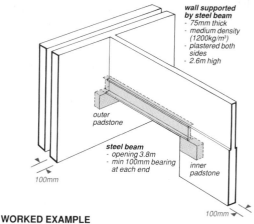

wall supported by steel beam
- *75mm thick*
- *medium density (1200kg/m³)*
- *plastered both sides*
- *2.6m high*

outer padstone

steel beam
- *opening 3.8m*
- *min 100mm bearing at each end*

inner padstone

100mm

100mm

WORKED EXAMPLE

Procedure

1 Using information about the supported wall and Table 1:
- load per metre run   = 4.2kN/m.

2 Using the load per metre run, the span of the beam and Table 2:
- suitable section size   = 178 x 102 x 19 UB

(The alternative 152 x 152 x 23 UC is not suitable as it is too wide for the inner padstone/wall.)

3 Using information about the wall supporting the beam (100mm thick), the walls supported by the beam (medium density block) and Table 3:
- minimum padstone size = 155mm long
                            = 150mm deep
- outer padstone (beam at right angles to wall):
  - minimum length = 155mm (as this is greater than the flange dimension of the steel section obtained in **2** above - 102mm - a padstone is required to distribute the load)
  - minimum depth = 150mm
  - thickness = 100mm, to match blockwork.

  (The actual length and depth of the padstone could be larger to suit masonry coursing.)
- inner padstone (beam in line with the wall):
  - minimum length = 200mm (see Note 2 to Table 3)
  - minimum depth = 150mm
  - thickness = 100mm, to match blockwork.

Note

Beam supports should not occur above window or door openings.

Guidance

DESIGN TABLES FOR SUPPORT OF FLOORS (no masonry partition loads)

Limitations

Steel beams in accordance with Tables 4 and 5 in this Appendix will be acceptable to NHBC for the support of floors, if:

● the floor construction is of decking (softwood boarding, chipboard or plywood) on timber joists with a plasterboard ceiling underneath which is given either a plaster skim coat or a plastic finish (Artex or similar), **and**

● allowance has been made of 0.5kN/m² for self weight (floor and ceiling load)

● the floor does not support masonry partitions, **and**

● any lightweight partition (such as plasterboard on timber studwork or proprietary product) is non-loadbearing, **and**

● padstones are provided, where required, **and**

● clear span of beam does not exceed 4.4m, **and**

● connections between steelwork beams are in accordance with Appendix 6.5-C or are designed by an Engineer, **and**

● the floor support is one of the methods shown in Figure 1.

If **any** of the above limitations are not met, steelwork should be designed by an Engineer in accordance with Technical Requirement R5.

Method of applying tables

1 Check that the situation is within all the limitations detailed above.

2 Using Figure 1, determine the area supported by the beam(s).

3 Check the span of the beam(s).

4 Use Table 4 to determine a suitable steel section size.

5 Check whether padstones are required by Table 5.

6 If steel beam-to-steel beam connections are required, use Appendix 6.5-C.

DESIGN TABLES FOR SUPPORT OF FLOORS (continued)

Figure 1 - Effective areas supported by steel beams

If an area shown as 'void' contains a staircase, add 2m² to the effective area supported by any beam which supports (partially or fully) that staircase.

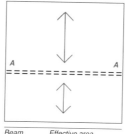

Beam	Effective area
AA	

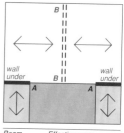

Beam	Effective area
AA	+
BB	

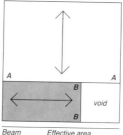

Beam	Effective area
AA	+
BB	

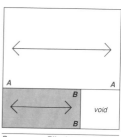

Beam	Effective area
AA	
BB	

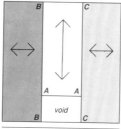

Beam	Effective area
AA	
BB	+
CC	+

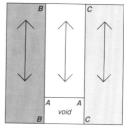

Beam	Effective area
AA	
BB	
CC	

Table 4 - Size of steel beam supporting floor

Effective area supported [m²]	Effective trimmer span = clear span + 100mm [m]	Smallest suitable steel section size [mm x mm x kg/m]	
		Universal beam	Universal column
0 to 20	0 to 2.0	127 x 76 x 13	152 x 152 x 23
0 to 20	2 to 2.5	127 x 76 x 13	152 x 152 x 23
20 to 30		152 x 89 x 16	152 x 152 x 23
0 to 10	2.5 to 3	127 x 76 x 13	152 x 152 x 23
10 to 20		152 x 89 x 16	152 x 152 x 23
20 to 30		178 x 102 x 19	152 x 152 x 23
0 to 10	3 to 3.5	127 x 76 x 13	152 x 152 x 23
10 to 30		178 x 102 x 19	152 x 152 x 23
30 to 40		203 x 133 x 25	152 x 152 x 30
0 to 10	3.5 to 4	152 x 89 x 16	152 x 152 x 23
10 to 20		178 x 102 x 19	152 x 152 x 23
20 to 30		203 x 102 x 23	152 x 152 x 23
40 to 50		203 x 102 x 30	152 x 152 x 30
40 to 50		see Note 1	152 x 152 x 37
0 to 10	4 to 4.5	203 x 102 x 23	152 x 152 x 23
10 to 20		203 x 133 x 25	152 x 152 x 23
20 to 30		203 x 133 x 30	152 x 152 x 30
30 to 40		see Note 1	152 x 152 x 37
40 to 50		see Note 1	203 x 203 x 46

Note to Table 4

1 Beams should be designed by an Engineer in accordance with Technical Requirement R5.

DESIGN TABLES FOR SUPPORT OF FLOORS (continued)

Table 5 - Size of padstone

Effective area supported (as used in Table 4) [m²]	Minimum padstone size [mm]					
	Thickness of wall supporting steel beam [mm]					
	Up to 105		105 to 155		156 to 216	
	length	depth	length	depth	length	depth
Up to 10	95	150	80	150	70	150
10 to 20	185	150	160	150	140	150
20 to 30	275	150	240	150	210	150
30 to 40	365	215	320	150	280	150
40 to 50	455	300	400	215	345	215

Notes to Table 5

1 See limitations listed at the beginning of this Appendix.

2 Padstones are not necessary where the flange dimension of the beam exceeds the length of the padstone given in this table.

3 Where the steelwork is in line with the wall supporting it (ie acting to form a lintel over an opening):
- the steel flange dimension should not be more than 50mm greater than the thickness of the supporting wall, *and*
- the minimum length of padstone should be 200mm, *and*
- the padstone depth should match the coursing of adjacent masonry, *and*
- the web of the beam should be over the centre of the wall.

4 Padstones can be formed from:
- in-situ concrete
- precast concrete
- concrete blocks
- clay bricks.

Padstones should be formed in one unit with a minimum compressive strength of 10N/mm².

For padstone sizes less than 215mm x 100mm, engineering bricks will be suitable.

Guidance

Connection of beams supporting floors

The connection methods shown in this Appendix (determined using Appendix 6.5-B) are suitable for connecting steel beams used to support floor loads.

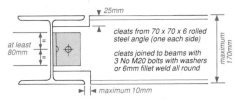

JOINT BETWEEN BEAMS OF SIMILAR SIZE
(neither beam deeper than 170mm)

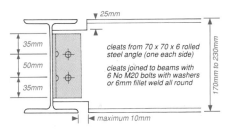

JOINT BETWEEN BEAMS OF SIMILAR SIZE
(beams 170mm to 230mm deep)

Limitations

Limitations on the use of this method are:

● neither beam is to support masonry partitions, **and**
● both beams have been chosen from Table 4 of Appendix 6.5-B, **and**
● beams do not differ in depth by more than 40mm.

The following connections should be designed by an Engineer in accordance with Technical Requirement R5:

● between steel sections which differ in depth by more than 40mm, or
● between steel sections, one of which carries floor loads and one of which carries a masonry partition, or
● between steel sections which have not been derived using Appendix 6.5-B, or
● between steel sections which both carry masonry partitions.

BUILDMARK™

informing the industry

CI/SfB	81	(24)	
CAWS	L30		

Operative from January 1992

Chapter **6.6**

NHBC STANDARDS

Staircases

This Chapter gives the Technical Requirements and
recommendations for staircases.

LIST OF CHAPTERS

THE STANDARDS

The NHBC Standards give:
● Technical Requirements in red
● Performance Standards in dark blue
● Guidance in light blue
for the design and construction of dwellings acceptable to NHBC.

Diagrams may contain text in red. This is to highlight points but has no mandatory significance.

The Standards come into effect for every NHBC registered home whose foundations are concreted on or after the publication date shown on the cover of each Chapter and apply throughout the UK, unless otherwise stated.

COMPOSITION OF THE STANDARDS
The Standards are divided into 10 Parts, each containing one or more Chapters covering a particular aspect. The Parts follow the usual construction process.

In general, each Chapter is made up of sections dealing with Design, Materials and Sitework. In some cases one or more of these aspects may not be included.

TECHNICAL REQUIREMENTS
Each Chapter (except former Practice Notes) contains the five mandatory Technical Requirements which MUST be met by the Builder.

The Technical Requirements are printed in red. Chapter 1.1 'Introduction to the Standards and Technical Requirements' contains full details.

PERFORMANCE STANDARDS
Most Chapters consist of detailed Performance Standards printed in dark blue, normally in the left-hand column of each Design, Materials or Sitework page, subdivided into Clauses designated D, M or S, respectively.

Alternative standards of performance will be acceptable ONLY if, in the opinion of NHBC, the Technical Requirements are met and the standard achieved is not lower than the stated Performance Standard.

GUIDANCE
Guidance on how the Performance Standard may be met is normally shown, printed in light blue, in the right-hand column opposite the relevant Performance Standard. Some Chapters contain pages which are all Guidance.

Guidance is based on normal procedures and recommended practices shown by experience to be satisfactory and acceptable. NHBC will consider alternative methods to meet specific requirements, subject to prior consultation and evaluation.

SCOPE

This Chapter gives the Technical Requirements and recommendations for staircases.

NHBC Standards do not cover aspects of health and safety relating to building operations and to the handling and use of certain building materials. Such matters are covered by statutory requirements.

FINDING INFORMATION

To find information on a particular subject, the following procedure is recommended:

1 Identify the **Part** most appropriate for the subject.

2 Identify the **Chapter** which deals with the particular element of construction.

3 Decide whether the information required relates to the Design, Materials or Sitework **Section** of the Chapter.

4 Decide from the Contents list the **heading** under which the required information is most likely to be found.

5 Review the **clauses** listed against the heading to see which has the relevant Performance Standard.

6 Review the **items** under the Performance Standards and decide which is relevant.

7 Review the guidance in the right-hand column opposite the item most relevant to the subject. If a clause number is known, use the above procedure to find the clause.

For example: **6.6 - S2(a)** means:

6	Part 6	Superstructure (excluding roofs)
6	Chapter 6	Staircases
S	Section	SITEWORK
2	Clause 2	LOCATION AND FIXING
(a)	Item (a)	headroom.

CONTENTS

Clause

Technical Requirements	Performance Standards

R1 **Statutory requirements**
Work shall comply with all relevant Building Regulations and other statutory requirements

Chapter 1.1 gives the detailed Performance Standards which relate to these Technical Requirements.

R2 **Design requirement**
Design and specification shall provide satisfactory performance

R3 **Materials requirement**
All materials, products and building systems shall be suitable for their intended purpose

R4 **Workmanship requirement**
All work shall be carried out in a proper, neat and workmanlike manner

R5 **Structural design requirement**
Structural design shall be carried out by suitably qualified persons in accordance with British Standards and Codes of Practice

Performance Standards	Guidance

DESIGN STANDARD

6.6 - D1   **Design shall meet the Technical Requirements**

Design that follows the guidance below will be acceptable for staircases.

STATUTORY REQUIREMENTS

6.6 - D2   **Design shall comply with all relevant statutory requirements**

A list of statutory references applicable to this Chapter is given in Appendix 6.6-A.

SAFE TRANSMISSION OF LOADS

6.6 - D3   **Design shall ensure that loads are properly supported and transmitted to the supporting structure without undue movement, deflection or deformation**

Generally, all stairs and staircases should be in accordance with BS 5395 : Parts 1 and 2.

Items to be taken into account include:

(a) timber staircase construction

Timber domestic staircases with straight flights and quarter- or half-landings should comply with BS 585. Particular attention should be paid to the performance requirements for strength, deflection and vibration under load, given in BS 585 : Part 2.

There is no British Standard relating to winders and landings. These should be designed to:
● ensure proper support
● minimise deflection
● prevent squeaking.

The method of fixing flights to the surrounding structure should be specified.

(b) concrete staircase construction

Reinforced concrete staircases should be designed to BS 8110 and comply with Chapter 2.1 'Concrete and its reinforcement' (each section) and, where appropriate, designed by an Engineer in accordance with Technical Requirement R5.

(c) steel staircase construction

Steel staircases should be designed to BS 5950.

Performance Standards | Guidance

SAFE TRANSMISSION OF LOADS (continued)

6.6 - D3 **(d) proprietary staircase construction**

Proprietary staircases should:
- comply with an assessment in accordance with Technical Requirement R3
- be suitable for their required use and location.

(e) differential movement

When considering differential movement in relation to setting out, levels and finishes, allowances should be made for:
- casting tolerances
- deflection under load
- foundation settlement
- creep and shrinkage
- storey height.

STAIRCASE WIDTH AND HEADROOM

6.6 - D4 **Staircase design shall ensure adequate provision for:**

(a) headroom

The minimum headroom above stairs should be measured vertically from the pitch line. The clear headroom over the entire length and width of a stairway, including landings, should be as follows:

Location	Headroom (h)
England and Wales	2.0m
Scotland	2.05m
Northern Ireland and the Isle of Man	2.0m

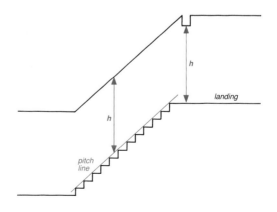

Performance Standards

Guidance

(b) **minimum unobstructed width**

Generally, stairs within dwellings (private stairs) should have a minimum width of 800mm; stairs serving more than one property (common or access stairs) should be at least 900mm wide.

The following ways of measuring staircase width should be used:

Staircases	Measurement
Private stairs	**b** or **c**
Access and escape stairs in Scotland	**a** (where **x** is not greater than 100mm)
Common stairs in England, Wales, Northern Ireland and the Isle of Man	**b** or **c**

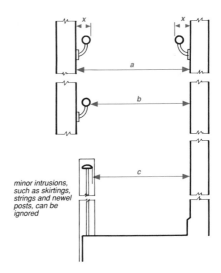

minor intrusions, such as skirtings, strings and newel posts, can be ignored

6.6 Staircases

DESIGN OF STEPS

6.6 - D5 **The design of steps shall allow safe use of the staircase**

Items to be taken into account include:

(a) pitch

The maximum angle of pitch of a stairway should not exceed:
- 42° for private stairs
- 38° for common or access stairs.

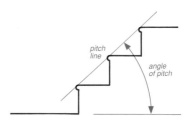

The dimensions for maximum rise and minimum going should be:

Type of stairs	Maximum rise [mm]	Minimum going [mm]
Private stairs	220	220
Common stairs (not Scotland)	190	240
Access stairs (Scotland)	not specified	250

The dimensions of the rise (R) and the going (G) should usually be related so that 2R+G is between 550mm and 700mm.

A design aid giving the relationship between rise and going is given in Appendix 6.6-B.

Further information on staircase design may be found in BS 5395 : Part 2.

Performance Standards	Guidance

(b) consistent rise and going

In each flight of stairs all the steps should have the same rise and going.

The thicknesses of screeds and floor finishes should be taken into account.

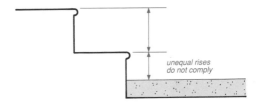

unequal rises do not comply

(c) tapered treads and winders

The rise of tapered treads should be the same as that of adjacent parallel treads. The going should be uniform and not less than the going of the associated straight flight. The going should be measured from the centre line of the straight flight (as shown below).

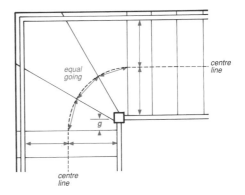

	Minimum going (**g**) [mm]
England and Wales	50
Scotland	75
Northern Ireland	50
Isle of Man	50

Performance Standards	Guidance

DESIGN OF STEPS (continued)

6.6 - D5 (d) safe foothold

All steps should have level treads.

Stairs with open risers should have treads that overlap 15mm minimum.

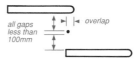

all gaps less than 100mm — overlap

Where stairs are open to the weather or may otherwise become wet, a non-slip finish or an insert to each tread should be specified.

LANDINGS

6.6 - D6 Landings shall be designed to allow safe use of the staircase

Landings should be provided at the top and bottom of every flight. The width and depth of landings should be at least the same as the width of the stair.

Landings should be properly framed to provide full support and secure fixings for flights, nosings, newels, etc.

Where pivot windows are being used, they should not obstruct the landing area or stair flight when in the open position.

Generally, door swings should not obstruct landings. However, a door may open across the bottom landing of a flight of private stairs if the swing is at least 400mm from the first tread and the dwelling is not over two storeys high.

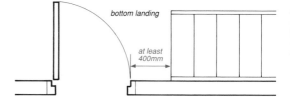

bottom landing

at least 400mm

Performance Standards　　　　　　　　**Guidance**

HANDRAILS

6.6 - D7　Handrails shall be designed to provide an uninterrupted, safe handhold

A continuous handrail is required to all flights of stairs that rise over 600mm.

Where winders are used, Building Regulations (Northern Ireland) and the Isle of Man Byelaws require a handrail to be fitted on the side where tapered treads have the greater going.

Handrails should be at a height between 840mm and 1000mm above the pitch line.

Design should ensure:
- a firm handhold
- that trapping or injuring the hand is prevented
- a minimum 25mm clearance at the back of the handrail
- secure fixing
- that handrail ends do not project to catch clothing, etc.

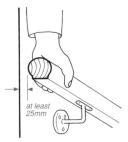

at least 25mm

GUARDING

6.6 - D8　Guarding shall be designed to prevent accidents by falling

Items to be taken into account include:

(a) resistance to loads

Guarding should be:
- capable of resisting a horizontal force of 0.36kN/m at its minimum required height
- a solid wall or balustrading.

Where guardrails or balustrades are long, the newel posts may not be sufficient to transfer horizontal forces to the structure and intermediate posts may be needed.

The method of fixing newels should be specified (eg through-bolted to joists).

Any glazing in the guarding should be toughened or laminated glass, or glass blocks. Wired glass is not regarded as safe for this purpose and should not be used.

Performance Standards

Guidance

GUARDING (continued)

6.6 - D8 **(b) dimensional requirements**

Guarding should be provided along the full length of the open sides of all stairs and landings when the drop is more than 600mm at any point.

Guarding is not needed when the rise is less than 600mm and when the stair or landing is not a means of escape.

Balustrading should be designed so that it is not easily climbed by children.

No opening in the balustrade should be large enough for a 100mm diameter sphere to pass through.

Type of stairs		Minimum guarding height [mm]	
		flights	landings
Private stairs		840	900
Common stairs	(Northern Ireland and		
	the Isle of Man)	900	1100
Common stairs	(England and Wales)	900	1000
Access stairs	(Scotland)	900	1100

FIRE PRECAUTIONS

6.6 - D9 **Staircases shall provide the necessary means of escape in case of fire**

Timber staircases are acceptable within a single family dwelling where there are no more than four storeys, excluding the basement.

Houses of three or more storeys and flats in buildings of three or more storeys should comply with the relevant Building Regulations listed in Appendix 6.6-A.

Ventilation of staircases serving flats in buildings of three or more storeys should comply with CP 3 : Chapter IV : Part 1.

LIGHTING

6.6 - D10 **Lighting shall be provided to ensure safe use of the staircase**

Artificial light sources should be provided to all staircases and landings. Within dwellings, lighting to stairs should be controlled by two way switching.

Where the Public Lighting Authority specify and maintain control of entrance lighting, their requirements should be met. Otherwise, landings and staircases in common areas to dwellings should be provided with adequate artificial lighting. Manual two way switching, controlled by people using these areas is acceptable. Automatic light sensitive controls may be used, provided lights can also be switched two way manually.

Performance Standards

Guidance

Reference should be made to Chapter 8.1 'Internal services' (Design) for further details on lighting.

Where staircases are lit by glazing, any glass below the minimum height of guarding (see Table to Clause D8(b)) should be:
- protected by a balustrade or railing, or
- glass (toughened or laminated), or
- constructed of glass blocks.

PROVISION OF INFORMATION

6.6 - D11 Designs and specifications shall be produced in a clearly understandable format and include all relevant information

Usually, staircase drawings and specifications should show:
- layout of stairs
- dimensions covering width, rise and going, handrail height, etc
- fixings of stairs, treads, risers, strings, balustrades, newel posts and handrails, as appropriate
- the length of time before formwork can be removed from in-situ concrete stairs
- whether precast concrete or steel staircases can be used immediately after erection or whether time should be allowed to cure grouted connections.

6.6 - D12 All relevant information shall be distributed to appropriate personnel

Ensure that design and specification information is issued to site supervisors and relevant specialist subcontractors and/or suppliers.

| Performance Standards | Guidance |

MATERIALS STANDARDS

6.6 - M1 All materials shall:
(a) meet the Technical Requirements
(b) take account of the design

Materials that comply with the design and the guidance below will be acceptable for staircases.

Materials for staircases should comply with all relevant standards, including those listed below. Where no standard exists, Technical Requirement R3 applies (see Chapter 1.1 'Introduction to the Standards and Technical Requirements').

References to British Standards and Codes of Practice include those made under the Construction Products Directive (89/106/EEC) and, in particular, appropriate European Technical Specifications approved by a European Committee for Standardisation (CEN).

STAIRCASE UNITS

6.6 - M2 Proprietary staircases and associated components shall comply with the design and Technical Requirements

Where proprietary staircases or associated components are proposed, they should meet the statutory and design requirements for stairs, as detailed in the drawings and/or specification.

Manufacturers of staircases and balustrading, etc should be sent all relevant drawings and other information to ensure their products meet the design requirements.

Allowance should be made for tolerances or actual site dimensions.

TIMBER AND WOOD-BASED PRODUCTS

6.6 - M3 Timber and wood-based materials shall be of sufficient quality and durability for use in staircases

Items to be taken into account include:
(a) timber

Timber for joinery should:
● comply with BS 1186 : Part 1
● be Class 3 or better, and
● be free of resinous knots, splits, shakes and wanes.

Fits of joints, construction of joints, moving parts, glueing, laminating, construction of finger joints and surface finish should be to BS 1186 : Part 2.

Timber which is to be exposed to the weather should be suitably durable or be pre-treated with preservative against fungal attack.

Performance Standards	Guidance

TIMBER AND WOOD-BASED PRODUCTS (continued)

6.6 - M3 **(b) plywood**

Plywood should be used only for risers and should comply with BS 6566.

(c) chipboard

Chipboard should comply with Types C3 or C4 of BS 5669.

(d) medium density fibreboard

Fibre building boards should comply with BS 1142 : Part 2.

(e) laminated timber

Glued laminated timber structural members should comply with BS 4169.

IN-SITU AND PRECAST CONCRETE

6.6 - M4 **Concrete shall be of the mix proportions to achieve adequate strength as required by the design**

Reference should be made to Chapter 2.1 'Concrete and its reinforcement' (Design and Materials) for guidance on concrete, reinforcement and additives.

FIXINGS

6.6 - M5 **Fixings shall be of adequate strength and durability and comply with the design**

Fixings should be checked for compliance with the design and whether they are provided by the supplier, especially for:
- timber and steel staircases
- newel posts
- handrails
- guarding and balustrading.

| Performance Standards | Guidance |

SITEWORK STANDARDS

6.6 - S1 **All sitework shall:**
    (a) meet the Technical Requirements
    (b) take account of the design
    (c) follow established good practice and workmanship

Construction that follows the design and the guidance below will be acceptable for staircases.

LOCATION AND FIXING

6.6 - S2 **Staircases shall be correctly located and fixed**

Items to be taken into account include:
    (a) headroom

The overall floor opening should be checked for size to accept the stairs and to allow sufficient headroom.

The minimum headroom above stairs should be measured vertically from the pitch line. The clear headroom should be over the entire length and width of a stairway, including landings.

Location	Headroom (h) [m]
England and Wales	2.0
Scotland	2.05
Northern Ireland and the Isle of Man	2.0

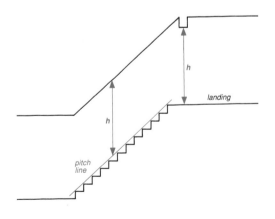

Performance Standards	Guidance

LOCATION AND FIXING (continued)

6.6 - S2 **(b) overall vertical rise**

Staircases are normally manufactured off site so the floor-to-floor dimensions should be accurate. An allowance should be made for floor finishes to structural floors or staircase treads.

(c) pitch

Staircases should be accurately located and fixed with the string at the correct angle so all treads are horizontal.

(d) landings

Landings, where required, should be properly framed to provide full support to and secure fixings for flights, nosings, newels, apron linings, etc.

(e) floor finishes

Allowance should be made for stair and floor finishes to ensure that all risers are equal.

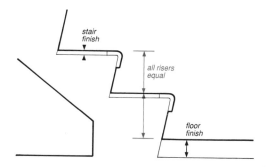

Performance Standards

Guidance

TIMBER STAIRCASES

6.6 - S3   Timber staircases shall:

(a) have secure component parts, including strings, treads and risers, newel posts, balusters and handrails

(b) be securely fixed to the supporting structure

Strings should be glued to newel posts and secured with dowels or screws. Particular attention should be given to winders; remedying problems, such as deflection and/or squeaking, can be difficult, especially if the soffit covering has been fixed.

Landings should be framed to provide full support and solid fixings for the tops of flights, nosings, newels, apron linings, etc.

Newel posts should be plumb and fixed securely.

The top nosing should be level with the floor decking and should be fixed firmly.

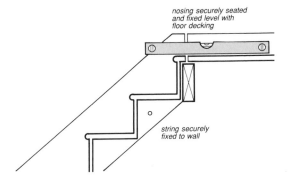

nosing securely seated and fixed level with floor decking

string securely fixed to wall

6.6 - S4   Finished joinery shall be free from unsightly blemishes

Finished joinery should be free from splits, knocks and other damage which would impair its structural performance or finish.

Handrails should have a smooth finish, free from rough edges. No handrail bracket or screw head should present a sharp edge.

Nails should be punched below the surface of the wood and stopped.

Performance Standards	Guidance

CONCRETE STAIRCASES

6.6 - S5 **The structure shall be set out and constructed to ensure that staircases are correctly located and levelled**

PRECAST CONSTRUCTION

When setting out levels, account should be taken of the thickness of finishes to the floor or landing, as well as any finish to be applied to the stair treads. Particular care is needed at the top and bottom of each flight.

Precast units should be accurately located and levelled.

IN-SITU CONSTRUCTION

Shuttering for in-situ concrete elements or connections should be accurately constructed to ensure a consistent rise and going.

FLOOR FINISHES

For both precast and in-situ staircases, allowance should be made for the thickness of finish at the top and bottom of flights.

6.6 - S6 **Concrete staircases shall be constructed to provide satisfactory final performance**

Items to be taken into account include:

(a) correct placing of reinforcement to give the required cover

Chairs or spacing blocks should be used to give the following minimum cover to reinforcement:

	Minimum cover [mm]
Internal staircases	25
Staircases open to the weather	50

(b) allowance for nosings and any cast-in finishes

Allowance should be made for pre-formed nosings or non-slip finishes, if specified (see also Clause S5).

(c) correct striking of formwork

Formwork should be struck in accordance with the design, normally:

● side formwork - after 24 hours

● soffit and support formwork - after 28 days.

6.6 - S7 **Appropriate measures shall be taken when concreting in cold weather**

Reference should be made to Chapter 1.4 'Cold weather working' when concrete, mortar, grout or other materials containing water are used.

Performance Standards

Guidance

STEEL STAIRCASES

6.6 - S8   **The supporting structure shall be accurately set out to receive steel staircases**

The supporting structure should be constructed within the tolerance limits set for the steel staircase. Treads should be checked for level. The correct fixings should be available.

6.6 - S9   **All work shall be carried out strictly in accordance with manufacturers' instructions**

Manufacturers' assembly and erection instructions should be available and followed.

HANDRAILS AND BALUSTRADES

6.6 - S10   **A handrail shall be correctly located and fixed to provide a safe handhold**

A handrail should be provided for any flight that rises 600mm or more. The handrail should be fixed between 840mm and 1000mm vertically above the pitch line.

The ends of the handrail should be shaped or returned to the wall to prevent clothes catching on projections.

Throughout its whole length the handrail should be:

● fixed securely
● continuous
● smooth and unobstructed
● at least 25mm from any surface.

Check that fixing and location are in accordance with the design.

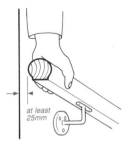

at least 25mm

Performance Standards   Guidance

HANDRAILS AND BALUSTRADES (continued)

6.6 - S11   **Balustrading shall be securely fixed and constructed to reduce the risk of it being climbed or fallen through**

Statutory regulations require that balustrading:
- is fixed securely
- cannot be easily climbed, and
- has no gaps which would allow a 100mm diameter sphere to pass through.

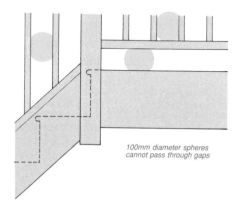

100mm diameter spheres cannot pass through gaps

In concrete staircases, balustrading may be:
- grouted into pre-formed holes or pockets
- bolted or screwed into pre-drilled holes
- bolted to brackets cast into the concrete.

Fixing methods for balustrading should allow a degree of tolerance. It may be preferable to take measurements from the completed staircase, whether of in-situ or precast construction, before manufacturing the balustrading. This will ensure that the fixings are positioned correctly and allow for variations in the surrounding structure.

Design details on the spacing of bolt fixings for balustrades or handrails should be followed.

Performance Standards

Guidance

Care should be taken when using expanding fixings near the edges of concrete (whether in-situ or precast).

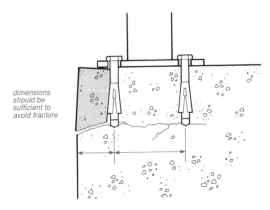

dimensions should be sufficient to avoid fracture

PROTECTION OF FINISHED WORK

6.6 - S12 On completion, staircases shall be undamaged, fixed properly and suitable for handover

When stored, staircases should be stacked on bearers. Wood staircases should be stored under cover and be fixed in place only once the building is weathertight.

Staircases, stair treads, nosings, balustrades and handrails may be protected with timber strips, plywood or building paper. Plastic sheeting should not be used to protect stairs because it gives a slippery surface which is not safe to walk on.

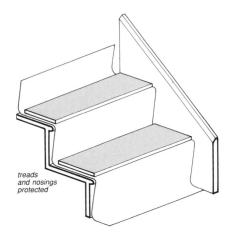

treads and nosings protected

Guidance

Statutory references

The following table lists references to building legislation and associated documents applicable at August 1990.

		Statute			
Clause	Subject	Building [1] Regulations	Building [2] Standards (Scotland)	Building [3] Regulations (N Ireland)	Isle of Man [4] Bye-laws
D9	Safety in use	K1	Part S	Part H	Part H
D9	Fire spread	B2/3/4	Part D Part E	Part E	Part E
		Associated documents			
D9	Safety in case of fire	BS CP 3 : Chapter IV : Part 1			

[1] Approved Documents to the Building Regulations 1985 for England and Wales (and 1990 edition).
[2] Building Standards (Scotland) Regulations 1981 and all published amendments.
[3] Building Regulations (Northern Ireland) 1990.
[4] Isle of Man Bye-laws 1976, amended 1980 and 1987.

Guidance

Design aid for rise and going

Rise and going which intersect within the relevant shaded areas meet the criteria 2R+G between 550mm and 700mm.

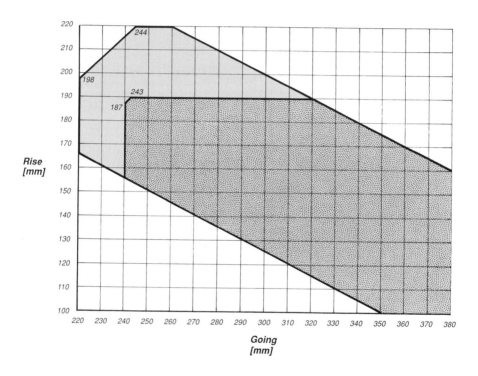

Key

Private stairs — whole of red shaded area
Common stairs — textured area only

Based on Figure 11 in BS 5395 : Part 1.

BUILDMARK

NHBC, Buildmark House, Chiltern Avenue, Amersham, Bucks HP6 5AP

NHBC, 5 Manor Place, Edinburgh, Scotland EH3 7DH

NHBC, Holyrood Court, 59 Malone Road, Belfast BT9 6SA

NHBC STANDARDS

Doors, windows and glazing

This Chapter gives the Technical Requirements and
recommendations for doors, windows and glazing.

LIST OF CHAPTERS

Volume 1

Volume 2

THE STANDARDS

The NHBC Standards give:
● Technical Requirements in red
● Performance Standards in dark blue
● Guidance in light blue
for the design and construction of dwellings acceptable to NHBC.

Diagrams may contain text in red. This is to highlight points but has no mandatory significance.

The Standards come into effect for every NHBC registered home whose foundations are concreted on or after the publication date shown on the cover of each Chapter and apply throughout the UK, unless otherwise stated.

COMPOSITION OF THE STANDARDS
The Standards are divided into 10 Parts, each containing one or more Chapters covering a particular aspect. The Parts follow the usual construction process.

In general, each Chapter is made up of sections dealing with Design, Materials and Sitework. In some cases one or more of these aspects may not be included.

TECHNICAL REQUIREMENTS
Each Chapter (except former Practice Notes) contains the five mandatory Technical Requirements which MUST be met by the Builder.

The Technical Requirements are printed in red. Chapter 1.1 'Introduction to the Standards and Technical Requirements' contains full details.

PERFORMANCE STANDARDS
Most Chapters consist of detailed Performance Standards printed in dark blue, normally in the left-hand column of each Design, Materials or Sitework page, subdivided into Clauses designated D, M or S, respectively.

Alternative standards of performance will be acceptable ONLY if, in the opinion of NHBC, the Technical Requirements are met and the standard achieved is not lower than the stated Performance Standard.

GUIDANCE
Guidance on how the Performance Standard may be met is normally shown, printed in light blue, in the right-hand column opposite the relevant Performance Standard. Some Chapters contain pages which are all Guidance.

Guidance is based on normal procedures and recommended practices shown by experience to be satisfactory and acceptable. NHBC will consider alternative methods to meet specific requirements, subject to prior consultation and evaluation.

SCOPE

This Chapter gives the Technical Requirements and recommendations for doors, windows and glazing.

NHBC Standards do not cover aspects of health and safety relating to building operations and to the handling and use of certain building materials. Such matters are covered by statutory requirements.

FINDING INFORMATION

To find information on a particular subject, the following procedure is recommended:

1 Identify the **Part** most appropriate for the subject.

2 Identify the **Chapter** which deals with the particular element of construction.

3 Decide whether the information required relates to the Design, Materials or Sitework **Section** of the Chapter.

4 Decide from the Contents list the **heading** under which the required information is most likely to be found.

5 Review the **clauses** listed against the heading to see which has the relevant Performance Standard.

6 Review the **items** under the Performance Standards and decide which is relevant.

7 Review the guidance in the right-hand column opposite the item most relevant to the subject. If a clause number is known, use the above procedure to find the clause.

For example: **6.7 - S3(b)** means:

6	Part 6	Superstructure (excluding roofs)
7	Chapter 7	Doors, windows and glazing
S	Section	SITEWORK
3	Clause 3	LOCATION AND FIXING
(b)	Item (b)	fixing.

CONTENTS
Clause

Technical Requirements	Performance Standards

R1 Statutory requirements

Work shall comply with all relevant Building Regulations and other statutory requirements

Chapter 1.1 gives the detailed Performance Standards which relate to these Technical Requirements.

R2 Design requirement

Design and specification shall provide satisfactory performance

R3 Materials requirement

All materials, products and building systems shall be suitable for their intended purpose

R4 Workmanship requirement

All work shall be carried out in a proper, neat and workmanlike manner

R5 Structural design requirement

Structural design shall be carried out by suitably qualified persons in accordance with British Standards and Codes of Practice

Performance Standards	Guidance

DESIGN STANDARD

6.7 - D1 **Design shall meet the Technical Requirements**

Design that follows the guidance below will be acceptable for doors, windows, and glazing.

STATUTORY REQUIREMENTS

6.7 - D2 **Design shall comply with all statutory requirements**

A list of statutory references applicable to this Chapter is given in Appendix 6.7-A.

ENVIRONMENTAL FACTORS

6.7 - D3 **Design and selection of doors, windows and glazing shall take account of location and planning requirements**

Items to be taken into account include:

(a) noise control

Where noise levels are very high, for example near airports or motorways, it may be advisable to install sound-insulating windows, usually of special design and construction.

(b) planning requirements

Local planning authorities may impose limitations on the shape, size and choice of materials for windows and doors, for example in conservation areas.

(c) climatic conditions

Climatic conditions, especially wind speed, together with the required level of window performance (eg in relation to air tightness), may govern the size of glass panes and opening lights in exposed locations.

DESIGN

Performance Standards	Guidance

SECURITY

6.7 - D4 **Door frames, windows and locks shall be designed and specified so as to improve their resistance to unauthorised entry**

General guidance on security is given in Chapter 1.3 'Improving security'.

Items to be taken into account include:

(a) fittings for main entrance doors

The main entrance doors of individual dwellings should be fitted with the following ironmongery:

● one (or more) securely-fixed lock and keep which has:
  - at least 1000 differs
  - key operation from the inside where the lock is used in locations which permit access to the lock from the outside by breaking glass or removing panels (this does not apply to individual flats)
  - a fixing which, if burst open, would not pull out without breaking the door or its frame
  - a hardened steel bolt or inserts to prevent sawing

● an opening limitation device fixed securely

● bolts securely fixed at both top and bottom of the door on the opening edge.

For reasons of access in an emergency, door bolts are not required in sheltered housing accommodation.

Door limitation devices should be of a type which is capable of being disengaged from the outside with a key.

Guidance on the type of lock suitable for entrance doors of individual flats and maisonettes is given in Chapter 1.3 'Improving security'. These entrance doors should not lock automatically.

(b) view outside of main entrance door

There should be a means of giving a wide angle view of the area immediately outside the main entrance door. Acceptable ways are:

● a through-door viewer

● clear glazing to either part of the door or an adjacent window.

Obscured glazing is not acceptable for this purpose.

Performance Standards

Guidance

(c) fittings for secondary external access doors

Secondary external access doors should have:
- a 5-lever lock fixed securely
- bolts fixed securely at both top and bottom of the door on the internal opening edge.

(d) fittings for windows

Ironmongery for windows should be supplied as follows:
- hinges and fastenings of opening lights of windows should be of a type which prevents them from being opened from the outside when in the closed position
- opening lights on all ground floor windows and others which can be easily reached from the outside should be fitted with lockable devices which cannot be released without a key.

IN SERVICE PERFORMANCE

6.7 - D5   Doors, windows and glazing shall be designed and specified to ensure adequate performance in service

Items to be taken into account include:

(a) weather resistance

Windows and external doors exposed to wind-driven rain may need particular protection to ensure they remain weathertight.

BS 6375 contains recommendations for the classification of window components according to their resistance (under test) to air and water penetration, and wind pressure. A similar classification is used by BBA for certification of windows.

Water penetration may occur not only between frame and opening leaf or light, but also between the frame and the surrounding structure. Vertical and horizontal dpcs should be provided around the frame in accordance with Chapter 6.1 'External masonry walls' (Design and Sitework).

In Scotland, Northern Ireland and other locations of severe exposure, rebated reveal construction should be sealed with an appropriate mastic.

BS 6375 : Part 1 identifies 6 categories of exposure related to the 'local spell index' of driving rain, as described in BS Draft for Development 93. Reference should also be made to Chapter 6.1 'External Masonry Walls' and Appendix 6.1-B and Chapter 3.1 'Siting of dwellings'.

Performance Standards | **Guidance**

IN SERVICE PERFORMANCE (continued)

6.7 - D5(a) (continued)

In all locations where weathertightness is likely to be a problem, additional precautions may be needed, such as:

- setting the frame back from the facade
- fixing the frame behind a rebate in the structural opening (sometimes known as a 'check' reveal)
- weatherstripping opening joints
- fixing weather boards and water bars to external doors
- building a projecting porch
- rain check grooves to inward opening external door frames
- a combination of the above.

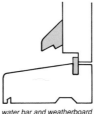
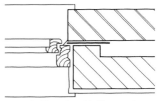

water bar and weatherboard provided for external doors

'check' reveal provided in areas of Severe or Very severe exposure

(b) thermal break

Where metal windows are to be used, designs which incorporate a thermal break should be considered.

(c) ventilation control

In timber frame dwellings, windows should be provided with controllable trickle ventilators, or other background ventilation.

It is beneficial to provide trickle ventilators in all dwellings. Trickle ventilators do not have to be located in window frames.

Mechanical ventilation is covered in Chapter 8.1 'Internal services' (Design).

Performance Standards   **Guidance**

(d) fire safety

Fire resisting doors should be fitted with a positive self-closing device. Rising butts are not acceptable.

Any door between a dwelling and an attached or integral garage should be:
● a half-hour fire-check door
● fitted in a suitable frame.

The design should take account of current requirements for means of escape (see Appendix 6.7-A).

(e) strength

Door frames and windows and their fittings should be adequate to withstand operational loads. Structural loads should be carried on lintels, beams or some other structural element. If frames are required to carry structural loads, they should be designed accordingly.

(f) resistance to movement, shrinkage and the effects of moisture

Doors and windows should be designed and selected to avoid significant distortion, such as twisting and bowing during use. Timber shrinkage should be allowed for.

To reduce twisting, doors should be hung on hinges as follows:

Type of door	Hinges
External	1½ pairs x 100mm
Fire door	1½ pairs x 100mm
Airing or cylinder cupboard	1½ pairs x 75mm
Other internal	1 pair x 75mm

Window boards may be wetted by condensation. Materials other than natural timber should be moisture-resistant.

(g) emergency access

Where doors to rooms containing a bath or WC have a securing device, it should be of a type capable of being opened from the outside in an emergency.

In sheltered accommodation, additional special provisions may be needed for all door locks, limiters and other fasteners, to enable wardens to gain access to dwellings when necessary.

DESIGN

Performance Standards	Guidance

RESISTANCE TO DECAY

6.7 - D6 Joinery for external doors and windows shall be adequately protected against decay

The following elements of timber doors and windows should be of naturally durable timber or timber pre-treated against fungal decay:

● external door frames

● windows

● timber surrounds to metal windows

● external doors, other than flush doors.

For detailed information, reference should be made to Chapter 2.3 'Timber preservation (natural solid timber)' (each section).

GLAZING

6.7 - D7 Glass and the method of glazing shall be selected to:

(a) resist wind loads

The quality and thickness of normal window glass should be specified to suit the design wind load for the location, in accordance with BS 6262 and relevant data sheets issued by the Glass and Glazing Federation.

(b) minimise risk of injury

Where there is a high risk of accidental breakage, the glazing should be designed and selected to comply with the safety recommendations for risk areas specified in BS 6262. Where there is a particular risk, such as at door side panels, 'low level' glazing and where fully glazed panels can be mistaken for doors, toughened or laminated glass, or other materials, such as acrylic or polycarbonate, may be needed.

Details of acceptable safety glazing in doors and side panels are given in Appendix 6.7-B.

PROVISION OF INFORMATION

6.7 - D8 All relevant information shall be distributed to appropriate personnel

Ensure that design and specification information is issued to site supervisors and relevant specialist subcontractors and/or suppliers.

Performance Standards	Guidance

MATERIALS STANDARDS

6.7 - M1 All materials shall:
(a) meet the Technical Requirements
(b) take account of the design

Materials that comply with the design and the guidance below will be acceptable for doors, windows and glazing.

Materials for doors, windows and glazing should comply with all relevant standards, including those listed below. Where no standard exists, Technical Requirement R3 applies (see Chapter 1.1 'Introduction to the Standards and Technical Requirements').

References to British Standards and Codes of Practice include those made under the Construction Products Directive (89/106/EEC) and, in particular, appropriate European Technical Specifications approved by a European Committee for Standardisation (CEN).

TIMBER DOORS AND WINDOWS

6.7 - M2 Timber and wood-based materials shall be of the quality and dimensions required by the design

Items to be taken into account include:

(a) classification and use

All timber and wood-based materials should comply with the relevant requirements of BS 1186 : Part 1 as follows:
- glazing beads   - Class 1
- window casements/sashes - Class 2 or better
- all other elements   - Class 3 or better.

In England, Wales, Northern Ireland and the Isle of Man, planted stops are not permitted on frames to external doors.

Storey-height frames should be of a section appropriate to their height and function.

External doors should be not less than 42.5mm (44mm nominal) in thickness.

Performance Standards | Guidance

TIMBER DOORS AND WINDOWS (continued)

6.7 - M2   (b) drying shrinkage

To minimise drying shrinkage, the moisture content of joinery, when fixed, should not exceed the following:

Joinery items	Moisture content [%]*
Windows and frames	17
Internal joinery in:	
- intermittent heating	15
- continuous heating	12
- close proximity to a heat source	9

* on delivery, the moisture content should be within 2% either side of the values specified.

(c) workmanship

All prefabricated items should be constructed to a good standard of workmanship, including:

● fit and construction of joints
● construction of finger joints
● glueing and laminating
● construction of moving parts
● surface finishes.

Prefabricated components should comply with the relevant parts of BS 1186 : Part 2.

(d) surface finish

Any surface finishing defects should be such that they would not be apparent with a matt paint finish, whether the surface is to be stained or painted, gloss or matt.

6.7 - M3   Timber for doors and windows shall be of a naturally durable timber species or preservative treated and primed

Items to be taken into account include:

(a) timber species

Non-durable timbers should be treated, see Chapter 2.3 'Timber preservation (natural solid timber)' (each section) for details.

Performance Standards	Guidance

(b) preservation

Preservative treatment is required for the following:
- external door frames
- windows
- timber surrounds to metal windows
- external doors, other than flush doors.

(c) priming

Material to be painted should be primed before fixing.

For further guidance on preparing elements for painting, see Chapter 8.5 'Painting and decorating' (each section).

(d) staining

Material to be stained should have the first coat applied before delivery to site.

6.7 - M4 Glazing compounds and timber stains shall be compatible

Compatibility of glazing, sealants and finishes should be checked.

Linseed-oil based putty should not be used where windows are to have a stained finish.

Timber windows to be finished with exterior stain should be glazed with beads and sealants.

Where manufacturers issue specific glazing instructions, these should be followed.

NON-TIMBER DOORS AND WINDOWS

6.7 - M5 Doors and windows of materials other than timber shall be in accordance with appropriate standards

Relevant standards include the following:

BS 4873 Specification for aluminium alloy windows

BS 6510 Specification for steel windows, window boards and doors.

Windows and doors made of materials for which no British Standard exists should have been assessed in accordance with Technical Requirement R3.

At the present time, there is no British Standard for uPVC windows. When an appropriate British Standard for uPVC windows is published, third party certification will also be required. Windows which are 'Kite marked' will meet with this requirement.

MATERIALS

Performance Standards	Guidance

IRONMONGERY

6.7 - M6   **Ironmongery shall be of the type and material required by the design**

Items to be taken into account include:

(a) relevant standards

Ironmongery should be provided in accordance with the design and specification. For critical functions, materials should comply with appropriate standards, including the following:

BS 1227 Part 1A : Specification for hinges : Hinges for general building purposes

BS 3621 Specification for thief-resistant locks

BS 4951 Specification for builders' hardware: lock and latch furniture (doors)

BS 5872 Specification for locks and latches for doors in buildings

BS 6459 Door closers.

(b) door hinges

To reduce twisting, doors should be hung on hinges as follows:

Type of door	Hinges
External	1½ pairs x 100mm
Fire door	1½ pairs x 100mm
Airing or cylinder cupboard	1½ pairs x 75mm
Other internal	1 pair x 75mm

(c) fittings for main entrance doors

The main entrance doors of individual dwellings should be fitted with the following ironmongery:

● one (or more) securely-fixed lock and keep which has:
  - at least 1000 differs
  - key operation from the inside where the lock is used in locations which permit access to the lock from the outside by breaking glass or removing panels (this does not apply to individual flats)
  - a fixing which, if burst open, would not pull out without breaking the door or its frame
  - a hardened steel bolt or inserts to prevent sawing

● an opening limitation device fixed securely

● bolts securely fixed at both top and bottom of the door on the opening edge.

For reasons of access in an emergency, door bolts are not required in sheltered housing accommodation.

Door limitation devices should be of a type which is capable of being disengaged from the outside with a key.

Performance Standards	Guidance

(d) through door viewers

Guidance on the type of lock suitable for entrance doors of individual flats and maisonettes is given in Chapter 1.3 'Improving security'. These entrance doors should not lock automatically.

If there is no clear glazing to provide a wide angle view of the area immediately outside the main entrance door, a through-door viewer should be provided.

(e) fittings for secondary external access doors

Secondary external access doors should have:
- a 5-lever lock fixed securely
- bolts securely fixed at both top and bottom of the door on the internal opening edge.

(f) fittings for windows

Ironmongery for windows should be supplied as follows:
- hinges and fastenings of opening lights of windows should be of a type which prevents them from being opened from the outside when in closed position
- opening lights of all ground floor windows and others which can easily be reached from the outside should be fitted with lockable devices which cannot be released without a key.

GLAZING

6.7 - M7   Glazing shall be as required by the design

Glass and glazing materials should comply with appropriate British Standards, including the following:

BS 5516 Code of Practice for patent glazing

BS 5713 Specification for hermetically sealed flat double glazed units

BS 6262 Code of Practice for glazing for buildings.

Other materials used should have been assessed in accordance with Technical Requirement R3.

Glazing materials should be compatible with the required levels of safety and security. Glazing to be used where there is a high risk of accidental breakage should comply with the safety requirements of BS 6262 and the Glass and Glazing Federation Glazing Manual.

Glazing components should be compatible with the frame finishes.

Linseed-oil based putty should not be used for laminated glass or sealed double glazed units.

Glazing systems, and associated materials, should comply with manufacturers' requirements.

Performance Standards

Guidance

SITEWORK STANDARDS

6.7 - S1 **All sitework shall:**

(a) **meet the Technical Requirements**

(b) **take account of the design**

(c) **follow established good practice and workmanship**

Sitework that complies with the design and the guidance below will be acceptable for doors, windows and glazing.

PROTECTION AGAINST DAMP

6.7 - S2 **Door and window components shall, where necessary, be adequately protected against damp**

Items to be taken into account include:

(a) **priming**

Material to be painted should be primed before fixing. Material to be stained should have the first coat applied before delivery to site. Any material delivered untreated should be treated promptly.

Neither primer nor the first coat prevent joinery from taking in moisture.

(b) **storage**

When joinery is stored on site, precautions should include:

● avoiding wetting during unloading

● stacking external joinery on bearers off the ground and covering with waterproof material

● storing internal joinery in a weather-protected condition.

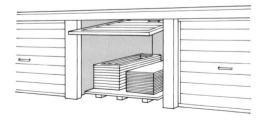

Joinery which is not properly stored or protected may not meet Technical Requirement R3.

Performance Standards	Guidance

LOCATION AND FIXING

6.7 - S3 **Doors and windows shall be correctly located and securely fixed**

Items to be taken into account include:

(a) weathertightness

Doors and windows should be installed correctly so they perform satisfactorily in use.

Dpcs should be correctly installed.

The dpc should extend approximately 25mm into the cavity. If a thick block is used to close the cavity and form the reveal, a wider dpc will be required.

Vertical dpcs should extend to the full height of the frame.

In Scotland, Northern Ireland and areas of severe exposure in England, Wales and the Isle of Man, 'check' reveals should be used. Additionally, an appropriate sealant is required between doors and windows and masonry.

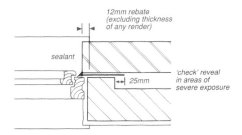

12mm rebate (excluding thickness of any render)

sealant

25mm

'check' reveal in areas of severe exposure

(b) fixing

Window frames and linings should be fixed solidly, level and plumb and should be either:

● secured by door/window cramps, or

● plugged and screwed.

Fixings should be not more than 600mm apart and not more than 150mm from top or bottom. Alternative locations and fixings are acceptable as long as they provide the same structural stability.

When driving wedges or other fixings, frames or other components should not be distorted.

Frames and linings should fit tightly into openings and be blocked or packed out at fixing points, where necessary.

Performance Standards

Guidance

Frames for external elements should be located in openings so that the head of the frame is protected by the lintel, and throatings in sill members are not obstructed by the wall face.

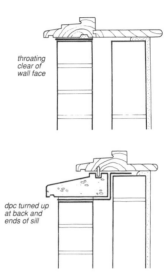

throating clear of wall face

dpc turned up at back and ends of sill

In Scotland, Northern Ireland and areas of severe exposure in England, Wales and the Isle of Man, it is not acceptable to fix window frames in the outer leaf of external walls.

(c) bay windows

To prevent sagging and bowing, bay and bow type windows should be adequately supported and secured to the structure to prevent casements becoming twisted.

Bay windows should be properly linked to dpcs at reveals.

bay windows adequately supported

Performance Standards | Guidance

LOCATION AND FIXING (continued)

6.7 - S3   **(d) cut ends**

Where pre-treated joinery is cut or adjusted on site, the affected surfaces should be pre-treated with two flood brush coats of appropriate preservative.

(e) window boards

The top surface of window boards should be flat and level. Boards should be fixed close to the frame and adequately secured against twist and other movement, particularly any back slope towards the frame.

Medium-density fibreboard should be either:

● moisture resistant grade, or

● completely sealed (including any cut ends on site) with sealer recommended by the manufacturer.

In Scotland, Northern Ireland and the Isle of Man, only moisture-resistant grades are acceptable.

(f) hanging doors and opening lights

Opening lights and door leaves should hang square within the frame or lining and fit neatly with minimum gaps, subject to the requirements of effective weatherstripping. Doors to bathrooms and WCs with mechanical ventilation should be hung with a gap at the bottom or be fitted with a ventilation grill.

Where a standard flush door is reduced in height, the bottom rail should be replaced if necessary. The leading edges of doors should be protected with timber lipping, where necessary.

(g) ironmongery generally

Where required, hinges and other ironmongery should be housed neatly flush with the surface.

(h) door hinges

To reduce twisting, doors should be hung on hinges as follows:

Type of door	Hinges
External	1½ pairs x 100mm
Fire door	1½ pairs x 100mm
Airing or cylinder cupboard	1½ pairs x 75mm
Other internal	1 pair x 75mm

Performance Standards	Guidance

(i) fittings for main entrance doors

The main entrance doors of individual dwellings should be fitted with the following ironmongery:

- one (or more) securely-fixed lock and keep which has:
  - at least 1000 differs
  - key operation from the inside where the lock is used in locations which permit access to the lock from the outside by breaking glass or removing panels (this does not apply to individual flats)
  - a fixing which, if burst open, would not pull out without breaking the door or its frame
  - a hardened steel bolt or inserts to prevent sawing
- an opening limitation device fixed securely
- bolts securely fixed at both top and bottom of the door on the opening edge.

For reasons of access in an emergency, door bolts are not required in sheltered housing accommodation.

Door limitation devices should be of a type which is capable of being disengaged from the outside with a key.

Guidance on the type of lock suitable for entrance doors of individual flats and maisonettes is given in Chapter 1.3 'Improving security'. These entrance doors should not lock automatically.

(j) fittings for secondary external access doors

Secondary external access doors should have:

- a 5-lever lock fixed securely
- bolts securely fixed at both top and bottom of the door on the internal opening edge.

(k) fittings for windows

Ironmongery for windows should be supplied as follows:

- hinges and fastenings of opening lights of windows should be of a type which prevents them from being opened from the outside when in closed position
- opening lights of all ground floor windows and others which can easily be reached from the outside should be fitted with lockable devices which cannot be released without a key.

The full complement of matching screws should be provided and properly screwed home.

Locks should not be fitted in mortices too tightly and keyholes should be aligned and locks should turn easily. The clearance between a door handle and a door stop should be at least 25mm.

Performance Standards	Guidance

LOCATION AND FIXING (continued)

6.7 - S3 **(l) through door viewers**

If there is no clear glazing to provide a wide angle view of the area immediately outside the main entrance door, a through-door viewer should be provided.

(m) workmanship

Internal door frames and linings should be of the correct widths to match the wall or partition thickness, including finish.

Frames and linings should be blocked off walls, wherever possible, to allow for full architraves.

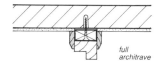

full architrave

All timber trim should be:
● sufficiently wide to mask joints, and
● fixed so as to minimise movement and shrinkage.

Architraves should be:
● parallel to frame and lining arrises
● accurately mitred or scribed to fit tightly and neatly
● fixed with an equal margin to each frame member
● fixed securely together with linings to prevent curling.

Nails should be punched below the surface of the timber and holes stopped. Nails should not be driven home with the hammer head. Damage should be avoided where easing is necessary. Any damage should be made good.

(n) finish upon completion of work

Work should be left in a clean state and brought to an appropriate level of finish for other trades.

Finishing trades should not be relied upon to correct untidy work.

Performance Standards	Guidance

GLAZING

6.7 - S4 **Glass and glazing shall be installed upon delivery or shall be adequately stored and protected until required**

Glass should be inspected for significant defects which are not acceptable.

Glass should be stored, where necessary in a sheltered, dry area out of the sun.

Often, defects are caused by:
● water accumulating between sheets, which may cause surfaces to become marked, and
● edge damage or scratching.

6.7 - S5 **Glazing shall be carried out in accordance with relevant standards**

Items to be taken into account include:

(a) cutting sheets

When cutting glass or plastics for timber windows, an allowance should be made for thermal movement of the pane, taking into account:
● the material being used, and
● the size of the pane.

This allowance is especially important when window rebates are shallow, allowing limited tolerance for expansion of the glazing.

(b) rebates

Before glazing, rebates should:
● have been primed,
● be rigid and true, and
● of the correct size for the glazing.

Setting and locating blocks should be of a suitable resilient material.

(c) bead glazing

Beads and linings should be used in:
● all internal glazing
● other locations where shock absorption properties are required.

Beads should be used:
● where doors or windows are to be finished with water-borne stains.

In external situations the bottom bead should project slightly over the rebate edge.

Performance Standards

Guidance

GLAZING (continued)

6.7 - S5 **(d) glazing compounds**

Linseed-oil based putty should not be used for laminated glass because it may allow water to reach the edge of the laminated glass. If this happens, delamination can occur.

When bedding is carried out in compound, sprigs or clips should be used and the compound neatly struck off. Beads should be fixed at not more than 150mm centres.

Beads should be bedded in compound against the glass only.

(e) sealed units

Sealed units should be installed so that:

● setting blocks and distance pieces are correctly located to avoid stress points or distortion of the frame and glazing, and

● any drainholes or ventilation channels are not accidentally blocked.

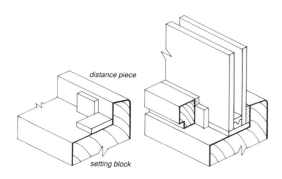

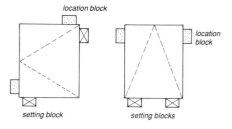

Performance Standards	Guidance

(f) doors and windows of materials other than wood

Where doors and windows of materials other than timber are delivered to the site unglazed, the glazing should be carried out in strict accordance with the manufacturer's instructions.

Appropriate fixing and sealing systems should include:
- distance pieces
- setting blocks
- beads
- compounds
- gaskets and sealants.

PROTECTION

6.7 - S6 Completed work shall be free from damage

Keep internal doors covered with polyethylene or original wrapping.

Door frames and linings should be protected with timber strips or plywood to at least 1m above skirting level. Thresholds and window sills should be covered. Scaffolding and walkways should be kept away from frames.

Joinery should be protected from paint splashes and other damage.

All temporary coverings should be removed after all other work has been completed, before handover.

Guidance

Statutory references

The following table lists references to building legislation and associated documents applicable at August 1990.

		Statute			
Clause	Subject	Building [1] Regulations	Building [2] Standards (Scotland)	Building [3] Regulations (N Ireland)	Isle of Man [4] Bye-laws
D2	Control of fire spread	B2/3/4	Part D	Part E	Part E
D2	Escape in case of fire	A5	Part E	Part EE	Part E
D2	Ventilation	F1	Part K	Part K	Part K
D2	Heat loss	L2/3	Part J	Part F	Part F
D2	Cleaning upper storey windows	-	Part P	-	-
D2	Fire	**Associated documents** "Mandatory rules for means of escape in the case of fire"			

[1] Approved Documents to the Building Regulations 1985 for England and Wales (and 1990 edition).
[2] Building Standards (Scotland) Regulations 1981 and all published amendments.
[3] Building Regulations (Northern Ireland) 1990.
[4] Isle of Man Bye-laws 1976, amended 1980 and 1987.

Guidance

Safety glazing in doors and side panels

Glazed Doors and Side Panels which can be mistaken for doors

The code recommends that fully glazed doors, e.g. patio doors and ordinary doors where the glazing takes up most of the door, should use a safety glazing material to B.S. 6206 and of the appropriate class.

Doors with more than one pane or where a single pane does not take up most of the door can be glazed in 6mm or thicker annealed (normal) glass.

Where a door side panel could be mistaken for a door these recommendations also apply.

The sketches of various door types show where safety glazing should be used and where 6mm or thicker annealed glass may be used.

N.B. Bent glass and glass bullions are excluded from the code.

Doors and Door Side Panels.

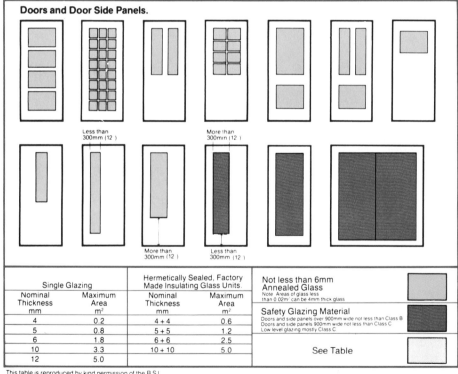

Single Glazing		Hermetically Sealed, Factory Made Insulating Glass Units.		Not less than 6mm Annealed Glass
Nominal Thickness mm	Maximum Area m²	Nominal Thickness mm	Maximum Area m²	Note. Areas of glass less than 0.02m² can be 4mm thick glass
4	0.2	4 + 4	0.6	**Safety Glazing Material**
5	0.8	5 + 5	1.2	Doors and side panels over 900mm wide not less than Class B Doors and side panels 900mm wide not less than Class C Low level glazing mostly Class C
6	1.8	6 + 6	2.5	
10	3.3	10 + 10	5.0	See Table
12	5.0			

This table is reproduced by kind permission of the B.S.I.

'Low Level' Glazing

Other than doors or side panels.
For balustrades see separate Code BS 6130.

The code recommends that in places where many people, especially children, are moving about, e.g. corridors, landings, bottom of stairs, glazing that comes lower than 800mm (31") from the floor should be safety glazing. When glazing is protected by a barrier rail, annealed glass within the limits set by the table (reproduced here) may be used.

In more usual situations where few people are likely to be moving about, annealed glass within the limits set by the table may be used. The sketches show typical examples of these recommendations.

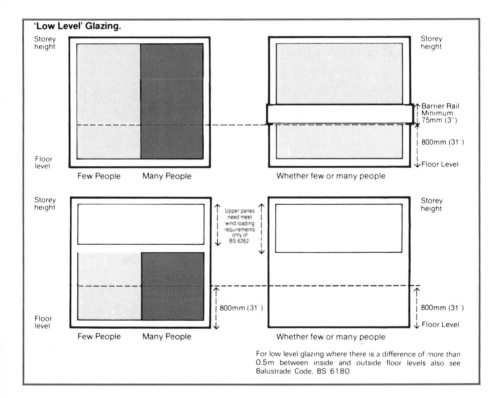

'Low Level' Glazing.

Storey height — Floor level

Few People   Many People   Whether few or many people

Barrier Rail Minimum 75mm (3")
800mm (31")
Floor Level

Storey height — Floor level

Upper panes need meet wind loading requirements only of BS 6262

800mm (31")

Few People   Many People   Whether few or many people

800mm (31")
Floor Level

For low level glazing where there is a difference of more than 0.5m between inside and outside floor levels also see Balustrade Code, BS 6180.

BUILDMARK™

NHBC, Buildmark House, Chiltern Avenue, Amersham, Bucks HP6 5AP

NHBC, 5 Manor Place, Edinburgh, Scotland EH3 7DH

NHBC, Holyrood Court, 59 Malone Road, Belfast BT9 6SA

Part 7 ROOFS

Part 7 ROOFS

informing the industry

| CI/SfB | 81 | (27) | |
| CAWS | G20 | J21 | J41 |

Operative from January 1992

Chapter **7.1**

NHBC STANDARDS

Flat roofs and balconies

This Chapter gives the Technical Requirements and
recommendations for flat roofs and balconies,
and pitched roofs with a fully supported continuous
weatherproofing membrane.

LIST OF CHAPTERS

THE STANDARDS

The NHBC Standards give:
● Technical Requirements in red
● Performance Standards in dark blue
● Guidance in light blue
for the design and construction of dwellings acceptable to NHBC.

Diagrams may contain text in red. This is to highlight points but has no mandatory significance.

The Standards come into effect for every NHBC registered home whose foundations are concreted on or after the publication date shown on the cover of each Chapter and apply throughout the UK, unless otherwise stated.

COMPOSITION OF THE STANDARDS

The Standards are divided into 10 Parts, each containing one or more Chapters covering a particular aspect. The Parts follow the usual construction process.

In general, each Chapter is made up of sections dealing with Design, Materials and Sitework. In some cases one or more of these aspects may not be included.

TECHNICAL REQUIREMENTS

Each Chapter (except former Practice Notes) contains the five mandatory Technical Requirements which MUST be met by the Builder.

The Technical Requirements are printed in red. Chapter 1.1 'Introduction to the Standards and Technical Requirements' contains full details.

PERFORMANCE STANDARDS

Most Chapters consist of detailed Performance Standards printed in dark blue, normally in the left-hand column of each Design, Materials or Sitework page, subdivided into Clauses designated D, M or S, respectively.

Alternative standards of performance will be acceptable ONLY if, in the opinion of NHBC, the Technical Requirements are met and the standard achieved is not lower than the stated Performance Standard.

GUIDANCE

Guidance on how the Performance Standard may be met is normally shown, printed in light blue, in the right-hand column opposite the relevant Performance Standard. Some Chapters contain pages which are all Guidance.

Guidance is based on normal procedures and recommended practices shown by experience to be satisfactory and acceptable. NHBC will consider alternative methods to meet specific requirements, subject to prior consultation and evaluation.

SCOPE

This Chapter gives the Technical Requirements and recommendations for flat roofs and balconies, and pitched roofs with a fully supported continuous weatherproofing membrane.

NHBC Standards do not cover aspects of health and safety relating to building operations and to the handling and use of certain building materials. Such matters are covered by statutory requirements.

FINDING INFORMATION

To find information on a particular subject, the following procedure is recommended:

1 Identify the **Part** most appropriate for the subject.

2 Identify the **Chapter** which deals with the particular element of construction.

3 Decide whether the information required relates to the Design, Materials or Sitework **Section** of the Chapter.

4 Decide from the Contents list the **heading** under which the required information is most likely to be found.

5 Review the **clauses** listed against the heading to see which has the relevant Performance Standard.

6 Review the **items** under the Performance Standards and decide which is relevant.

7 Review the guidance in the right-hand column opposite the item most relevant to the subject. If a clause number is known, use the above procedure to find the clause.

For example: **7.1 - S4(c)** means:

7	Part 7	Roofs
1	Chapter 1	Flat roofs and balconies
S	Section	SITEWORK
4	Clause 4	TIMBER STRUCTURE
(c)	Item (c)	strutting.

CONTENTS   Clause

7.1 | Flat roofs and balconies

Technical Requirements	Performance Standards

R1 Statutory requirements

Work shall comply with all relevant Building Regulations and other statutory requirements

Chapter 1.1 gives the detailed Performance Standards which relate to these Technical Requirements.

R2 Design requirement

Design and specification shall provide satisfactory performance

R3 Materials requirement

All materials, products and building systems shall be suitable for their intended purpose

R4 Workmanship requirement

All work shall be carried out in a proper, neat and workmanlike manner

R5 Structural design requirement

Structural design shall be carried out by suitably qualified persons in accordance with British Standards and Codes of Practice

Performance Standards	Guidance

DESIGN STANDARD

7.1 - D1 Design shall meet the Technical Requirements

Design that follows the guidance below will be acceptable for both flat roofs and balconies.

For the purposes of this Chapter, a flat roof should be regarded as having a maximum slope of 10° from the horizontal.

STATUTORY REQUIREMENTS

7.1 - D2 Design shall comply with all relevant statutory requirements

A list of statutory references applicable to this Chapter is given in Appendix 7.1-A.

STRUCTURAL DESIGN

7.1 - D3 Flat roofs shall be designed to resist the applied loading

Structural design shall be undertaken in accordance with a recognised standard.

Items to be taken into account include:

(a) dead and imposed loads

Dead and imposed loads should be calculated in accordance with BS 6399.

ROOF GARDENS/CAR PARKS

Appropriate provision should be made where a flat roof is to act as a roof garden or car parking area.

(b) wind loads

Wind loads appropriate to the site should be calculated in accordance with CP 3 : Chapter V : Part 2. The design should resist uplift from wind forces either by anchorage to the main structure or by being of sufficient weight to prevent lifting.

In Scotland, Northern Ireland, the Isle of Man and other areas where the basic wind speed is 48m/s and over (see Appendix 7.1-F for wind speed map), all roofs of timber or lightweight construction should be anchored to the supporting structure to prevent lifting. Holding down straps should be provided at 1.2m centres (see Materials clause 7.1 - M1, Sitework clause 7.1 - S4(d) and BS 8103 : Part 1).

DESIGN

Performance Standards	Guidance

STRUCTURAL DESIGN (continued)

7.1 - D4 **Structural design shall be undertaken to a recognised standard to ensure that loads are transmitted to the supporting structure without undue movement**

Items to be taken into account include:

(a) timber construction

Structural design should be in accordance with one of the following:

- BS 5268 : Part 2
- appropriate load/span tables in conjunction with Building Regulations and associated documents
- load/span tables in Appendix 7.1-E
- tables produced to a recognised standard.

Note

Reference should be made to Materials clause 7.1 - M1 and Chapter 2.3 'Timber preservation (natural solid timber)' (Design) for timbers requiring preservative treatment.

(b) in-situ reinforced concrete construction

In-situ reinforced concrete construction should be designed in accordance with BS 8110 and, where appropriate, Chapter 2.1 'Concrete and its reinforcement'. A concrete mix with low shrinkage characteristics should be specified.

(c) precast concrete construction

Precast concrete construction should be designed in accordance with BS 8110. Provision should be made for the following:

- continuity or anti-crack reinforcement
- allowance for movement at about 15m intervals and at abutments.

(d) structural steelwork

Structural steelwork should be designed in accordance with BS 5950 and Technical Requirement R5.

(e) differential movement

Allowance should be made for movement in larger roofs (eg roofs to blocks of flats), particularly where the span of the roof deck changes, eg in L-shaped buildings. The expansion joint should be continuous through the vertical upstands, walls and edges of the building. Details are shown in Appendix 7.1-D.

(f) lateral restraint

Where walls require lateral restraint, this may be provided by flat roof joists and concrete roofs. The bearings of both should be at least 90mm.

Where joists or concrete beams are parallel to walls, restraint straps at 2m centres (maximum) should be provided in accordance with BS 8103 : Part 1.

Performance Standards	Guidance

PRINCIPLES OF DESIGN

7.1 - D5   Flat roofs shall be to a recognised design

Appendix 7.1-B shows the three flat roof constructions acceptable to NHBC with variations for timber and concrete structural support.

They are:
1 warm deck   -   timber
              -   concrete
2 warm deck   -   inverted timber
              -   inverted concrete
3 cold deck   -   timber.

Note
Cold deck roofs are not acceptable in Scotland.

Cold deck roofs may be used only in the rest of the UK where:
● the required level of ventilation can be achieved
● ventilation paths are not blocked by structural or other members
● a ventilation space of 50mm can be maintained.

DECKING

7.1 - D6   Decking shall be of adequate strength and moisture resistance

Decking materials suitable for the different types of roof design are given in Appendix 7.1-B. Other materials are subject to prior acceptance by NHBC.

THERMAL INSULATION

7.1 - D7   Flat roofs (and balconies functioning as roofs) shall have adequate thermal insulation

Thermal insulation materials suitable for the different types of roof design are given in Appendix 7.1-B together with materials for vapour checks and their position in the structure.

WEATHERPROOFING AND SURFACE FINISHES

7.1 - D8   Flat roofs and balconies shall resist adequately the passage of moisture to the inside of the building

The roof coverings and surface finishes suitable for different types of roof design are given in Appendices 7.1-B and 7.1-C.

Appendix 7.1-B includes typical details of the following:
● built-up roofing felt
● mastic asphalt finish
● details at abutments and where projections pass through the waterproofing
● surface finishes.

DESIGN

Performance Standards	Guidance

RAINWATER DRAINAGE

**7.1 - D9 Flat roofs and balconies
shall have adequate
rainwater disposal to
a suitable outfall**

Items to be taken into account
include:

(a) falls

All flat roofs should be designed with a fall of not less than
1 : 40.

Allowance should be made in the structural design where falls
are achieved by screeds, particularly on large roofs.

On flat dormer roofs, the fall should be away from the
intersection with the pitched roof.

Falls to balconies should be away from or be parallel to the
dwelling.

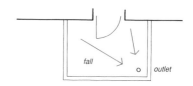

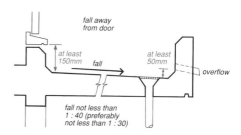

(b) outlets

Outlets should have a recessed mouth to allow the free flow
of water. Rainwater drainage design is covered in Chapter 7.2
'Pitched roofs'. Reference should be made to Chapter 5.3
'Drainage below ground', where necessary.

(c) prevention of flooding

Where a flat roof or balcony has an upstand on all sides,
an overflow outlet should be provided through parapet walls or
perimeter upstands to prevent a build-up of water in the event
of other outlets becoming blocked. The size of the overflow
should not be less than the size of the outlet (or outlets if there
are several outlets).

Performance Standards

Guidance

GUARDING TO BALCONIES

7.1 - D10 **Balconies and flat roofs to which persons have regular access shall be guarded adequately**

Items to be taken into account include:

(a) provision of guarding

Guarding should be provided to the perimeter of all flat roofs and balconies to which persons have regular access, unless the drop is 600mm or less. The minimum height of guarding should be 1100mm.

Guarding should be designed as follows:

● the balustrading should not be easily climbed

● no opening in the balustrading should be large enough for a 100mm diameter sphere to pass through

● any glazing in the balustrading should be toughened or laminated glass or glass blocks. Wired glass is not safety glass and should not be used

● balustrading should not be fixed through the weatherproofing unless special precautions are taken.

(b) stability of guarding

Parapet walls and balustrading should be designed to resist horizontal pressure as required by the relevant Building Regulations or BS 6399 : Part 1. Particular care is needed when the design incorporates balustrading fixed to parapet walls to ensure stability and prevent overturning. End fixings or returns may be needed to ensure stability.

horizontal force can overturn balustrade and coping

slip plane at dpc

In balcony walls (especially long balconies) check the structural stability as the dpc at the base of the wall can create a slip plane that can seriously limit the ability of the wall to resist horizontal forces. In such cases, it may be necessary to incorporate a ring beam or other support to ensure stability.

In the design of parapet walls, movement should be allowed for.

DESIGN

Performance Standards	Guidance

ACCESS FOR MAINTENANCE

7.1 - D11 Adequate access shall be provided to flat roofs for the purpose of maintenance

Where the flat roof is 3 or more storeys above the ground, access should be provided from within the dwelling. In blocks of flats, access should be obtained from the common areas.

PROVISION OF INFORMATION

7.1 - D12 Designs and specifications shall be produced in a clearly understandable format and include all relevant information

Clear and fully detailed drawings should be available on site to enable work to be carried out in accordance with the design. The drawings should show:

- amount and direction of falls and position of outlets
- sections through the construction indicating how the falls are formed, means of ventilation, if required, and size, specification and position of all the roof components
- details of construction at critical junctions
- details of balustrading and method of fixing
- details of fixings for insulation and surfacing.

7.1 - D13 All relevant information shall be distributed to appropriate personnel

Ensure that design and specification information is issued to site supervisors and relevant specialist subcontractors and/or suppliers.

Performance Standards | Guidance

MATERIALS STANDARDS

7.1 - M1 All materials shall:
(a) meet the Technical Requirements
(b) take account of the design

Materials that comply with the design and the guidance below will be acceptable for flat roofs and balconies.

Materials for flat roofs and balconies should comply with all relevant standards, including those listed below. Where no standard exists, Technical Requirement R3 applies (see Chapter 1.1 'Introduction to the Standards and Technical Requirements').

References to British Standards and Codes of Practice include those made under the Construction Products Directive (89/106/EEC) and, in particular, appropriate European Technical Specifications approved by a European Committee for Standardisation (CEN).

Appendix 7.1-B lists the materials suitable for:
● weatherproofing, including flashings
● structure and decking
● thermal insulation
● vapour barriers
● preservative treatment.

Roofing felts to BS 747 : 1977 (1986) are colour coded for identification. The codes are as follows:
● felt Type 2 - green
● felt Type 3 - red
● felt Type 5 - blue.

Appendix 7.1-C gives suitable surface treatments to the weatherproofing.

Appendix 7.1-E gives suitable sizes of structural timbers for given spans.

Joists and carcassing timber should have a maximum moisture content of 21%.

Joist hangers should be the correct size for the timber joists being supported and meet with BS 6178.

Pre-drilled vertical holding down straps should be:
● at least one metre long, and
● 30mm x 5mm in cross section.

Restraint straps should have a minimum cross section of 30mm x 5mm.

All mild steel straps and fixings should be protected against corrosion in accordance with Tables 1 and 14 of BS 5628 : Part 3.

MATERIALS

Performance Standards	Guidance

MATERIALS STANDARDS (continued)

7.1 - M1 (continued)

SHEET METAL ROOF

Lead sheet roof should be in accordance with BS 6915. Other types of sheet roofing should be in accordance with the relevant parts of CP 143.

PROPRIETARY ROOFING SYSTEMS

Proprietary roofing systems which do not meet with the specifications in Appendix 7.1-B should be assessed in accordance with Technical Requirement R3.

Performance Standards	Guidance

SITEWORK STANDARDS

7.1 - S1 **All sitework shall:**
(a) **meet the Technical Requirements**
(b) **take account of the design**
(c) **follow established good practice and workmanship**

Construction that complies with the design and the guidance below will be acceptable for flat roofs and balconies.

IN-SITU REINFORCED CONCRETE

7.1 - S2 **In-situ reinforced concrete shall be constructed to ensure it achieves the required design strength and durability**

Items to be taken into account include:
(a) **accuracy of formwork**

The formwork should be constructed accurately.

Items to take into consideration are:
● accurate location of holes
● adequate support
● proper allowance for placing of steelwork
● cast-in features, such as drips and weatherchecks
● surface finishes.

(b) **concrete grade**

Reference should be made to Chapter 2.1 'Concrete and its reinforcement' for guidance on concreting. The design should have specified a concrete mix with low shrinkage characteristics.

PRECAST CONCRETE

7.1 - S3 **Precast concrete decking units shall be set out accurately and installed properly**

The supporting structure should:
● be even and true
● have a minimum 75mm bearing for the pre-cast units (90mm bearing where the structure provides lateral restraint).

Precast units should be:
● installed to provide an even surface
● grouted, where required by the design.

Performance Standards	Guidance

TIMBER STRUCTURE

7.1 - S4 Timber joists shall be suitable for the span and loads

Items to be taken into account include:

(a) grades and sizes of joists

Materials delivered to site should be checked for conformity with the design and specification.

(b) the spacing and bearing required to achieve reasonably level support for firrings and decking

Timber joists should be:
- level - where necessary, hard packing should be used, eg tiles or slates bedded in mortar. Loose or soft packing, including timber, should not be used
- spaced at the centres specified on the drawing (not more than 600mm centres).

The use of regularised timber joists will help to achieve a level ceiling.

(c) strutting

Strutting should be one of the following:
- herringbone type (timber 38mm x 38mm)
- solid blocking (38mm thick timber x ¾ depth of joist)
- proprietary steel strutting.

Strutting should be located as follows:

Joist span [m]	Rows of strutting
Up to 2.5	none needed
2.5 to 4.5	1 (at centre of span)
Over 4.5	maximum 2.5m centres, spaced equally along the span

In cold deck roofs, the strutting should not prevent free cross ventilation.

Performance Standards

Guidance

(d) holding down metal strapping

If the design specifies holding down straps, they should be at a maximum of 1.2m centres to prevent the roof being lifted off the supporting structure.

Where straps are fixed to masonry, hardened nails 8SWG x 75mm long or wood screws into plugs No 12 x 50mm long should be used.

The number of fixings should be in accordance with design requirements and the lowest fixing should be within 150mm of the bottom of the vertical strap.

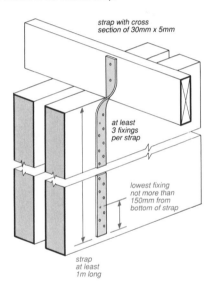

strap with cross section of 30mm x 5mm

at least 3 fixings per strap

lowest fixing not more than 150mm from bottom of strap

strap at least 1m long

(e) timber quality

Timber should be rejected if it:
- is excessively bowed, twisted or cambered
- is excessively wet
- has large edge knots or shakes
- has a waney edge more than half the thickness
- has fissures
- has any sign of rot.

Where treated timber has been cut on site, re-treat cut edges with a coloured preservative.

SITEWORK

7.1 | Flat roofs and balconies

Performance Standards	Guidance

JOIST HANGERS

7.1 - S5 Hangers shall be of the correct size and built-in properly

The joist hanger should be the correct size for the timber joist or trimmer and nailed in accordance with the design.

The masonry course to carry the joist hangers should be level and at the correct height. Do not cut into the walling.

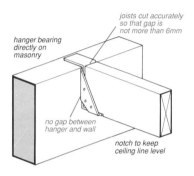

joists cut accurately so that gap is not more than 6mm

hanger bearing directly on masonry

no gap between hanger and wall

notch to keep ceiling line level

FALLS

7.1 - S6 Falls shall ensure effective drainage

Falls and gutters should be constructed in accordance with the design. Falls should be at least 1 : 40.

Items to be taken into account include:

(a) falls on concrete roofs

CEMENT/SAND SCREEDS
Cement sand screeds should be 1 : 4, cement : sand. Minimum screed thicknesses should be as follows:

Location of screed	Minimum thickness [mm]
Bonded monolithically to in-situ concrete	25
Laid on in-situ concrete	40
Laid on precast concrete	50
Laid on woodwool	13 (sealing screed)

Reference should be made to Chapter 8.3 'Floor finishes' for further guidance on laying screeds.

Performance Standards

Guidance

LIGHTWEIGHT SCREEDS
Lightweight screeds should be laid only by specialist contractors. Lightweight concrete screeds should have a topping of 1 : 6, cement : sand, 13mm thick.

SCREED FINISH
Screeds should be free from ridges and indentations. They should be finished with a wooden float to provide a smooth, even surface for the vapour barrier and waterproof finish.

PROTECTION AGAINST TRAPPED MOISTURE
When laying wet screeds, allowance should be made for draining away excess moisture.

(b) falls on timber roofs

Firring pieces should be used to form falls, unless the design shows sloping joists and ceiling. Where laid across the joists, firrings should be not less than the following sizes:

Joist centres [mm]	Minimum firring dimensions [mm]	
	width	depth
400 or 450	38	38
600	38	50

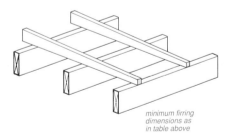

minimum firring dimensions as in table above

Performance Standards	Guidance

DECKING

7.1 - S7 **Decking shall be installed to form a satisfactory surface for the weatherproofing system**

Items to be taken into account include:

(a) fixing of softwood boarding

Softwood tongued and grooved boarding should be closely clamped together. Each board should be nailed with two ring shank nails to each joist or firring. Nail heads should be punched below the timber surface.

End joints should be staggered. Boards should be no greater than 100mm wide.

(b) fixing of plywood and chipboard

Tongued and grooved boards laid either with the long edge at right angles to the joists or parallel to the joists should have the short edge supported on a joist or nogging.

With any profile board, perimeter edges which do not coincide with joists should be supported on noggings.

In accordance with manufacturers' recommendations, gaps should be left around boards for movement.

The table below shows recommended fixing centres and allowances for movement between boards:

	Chipboard [mm]	Plywood [mm]
Fixing centres:		
- at board perimeters	200 to 300	150
- elsewhere	400 to 500	300
Movement gaps:		
- between boards	3	2
- at abutments	10	5

Designs may require fixing centres closer than those shown above, particularly in areas where high wind speeds are experienced. Where this occurs, the design centre dimensions should be used.

Performance Standards

Guidance

Chipboard should be fixed with ring shank nails (length at least 2 ½ x board thickness, 10 gauge) not less than 9mm from the edge of the board.

Plywood should be fixed with ring shank nails (length at least 2 ½ x board thickness, 10 gauge).

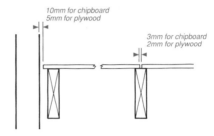

10mm for chipboard
5mm for plywood

3mm for chipboard
2mm for plywood

(c) protection of decking

The decking should be installed in dry conditions and be protected from wetting until the roof is complete. The joints in sheet materials which are pre-felted or coated should be sealed immediately after fixing.

The amount of decking installed in any working day should be no greater than can be quickly protected from wetting.

Damaged materials and materials that have been adversely affected by moisture should be discarded.

THERMAL INSULATION AND VAPOUR BARRIERS

7.1 - S8   Insulation and vapour barriers shall be installed in accordance with the design

Appendix 7.1-B gives details of suitable materials for insulation and vapour barriers for the different types of roof designs.

WARM DECKS

The design should indicate that the vapour barrier is below the insulation and that it is sealed to the weatherproofing at the perimeter and at all penetrations through the roof, eg pipes.

Insulation boards should be kept dry at all stages to prevent:

● lack of bonding

● entrapment of moisture.

Performance Standards	Guidance

THERMAL INSULATION AND VAPOUR BARRIERS (continued)

7.1 - S8 (continued)

The area of insulation laid at any time should be that which can quickly be covered by the weatherproofing or protected from wetting.

Insulation should be fixed in accordance with manufacturers' recommendations.

INVERTED ROOFS

The insulation material for inverted roofs should be suitable for external use and to withstand any traffic.

COLD DECKS

Ventilation should not be blocked by the thickness of the insulation. A minimum of 50mm clear air space should be maintained.

WEATHERPROOFING

7.1 - S9 **Weatherproofing shall prevent water entering the building**

Items to be taken into account include:

(a) preparation of surfaces

The structure and the surface to receive the weatherproofing should be checked and approved by the weatherproofing contractor. All nails should be well punched below the surface, which should be even and dry.

Manufacturers' recommendations should be followed on priming upstands, roof outlets, etc to achieve a satisfactory bond with the weatherproofing.

(b) construction sequence

Weatherproofing systems should be laid to the design and specification following the recommendations of the manufacturer. Some proprietary membranes should be laid only by specialist roofing contractors approved by the manufacturer.

It is preferable that the vapour barrier and insulation (if both are required), the weatherproofing and surface finish are laid in one operation by the same contractor.

Performance Standards	Guidance

(c) weather conditions

Sheet membranes should not be laid or handled when the air temperature is:
- 0°C or below, for lighter types
- less than 5°C, for heavier types.

Manufacturers' recommendations for 'conditioning', unrolling in advance of laying, etc should be followed.

Membranes should not be laid on damp or frosted surfaces or when any rain, sleet or snow is falling.

(d) correct detailing

Appendix 7.1-B gives, for the different roof types, typical details of:
- abutments
- parapets
- edge details
- fixing of guarding
- projections through the waterproofing
- roof lights.

GUARDING TO BALCONIES

7.1 - S10   Guarding to balconies shall be of adequate strength to prevent people falling and be fixed securely

Items to be taken into account include:

(a) strength and movement of masonry balcony walls

Masonry balcony walls should be built in accordance with Chapter 6.1 'External masonry walls'. In particular, ensure that:
- walls incorporate strengthening as required by the design
- movement joints are provided in accordance with the design
- copings are firmly bedded.

SITEWORK

Performance Standards	Guidance

GUARDING TO BALCONIES (continued)

7.1 - S10 (b) fixing of balustrading and guard rails

Balustrading and guard rails should be fixed in accordance with the design details. Reference should also be made to Appendix 7.1-D.

Checks should be made that there are no gaps in the guarding that a 100mm sphere can pass through.

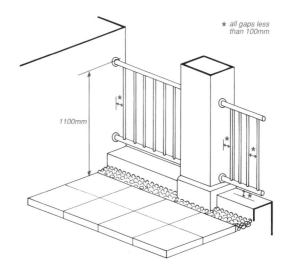

★ all gaps less than 100mm

1100mm

PROTECTION OF MATERIALS FROM WEATHER

7.1 - S11 Moisture sensitive materials shall be protected from wetting

Timber-based roof decking and insulation materials should be stored under cover to prevent wetting.

Timber-based roof decks that have been fixed in position should be temporarily covered to prevent wetting, unless the weatherproofing is to be laid immediately.

Guidance

Statutory references

The following table lists references to building legislation and associated documents applicable at August 1990.

Clause	Subject	Statute			
		Building [1] Regulations	Building [2] Standards (Scotland)	Building [3] Regulations (N Ireland)	Isle of Man [4] Bye-laws
D2	Structural design	Part A	Part C	Part D	Part D
D7	Thermal insulation	Part F Part L	Part J	Part F	Part F
D9	Rainwater drainage	Part H	Part M	Part N	Part N
D10	Guarding	Part K	Part S	Part H	Part H
		Associated documents			

[1] Approved Documents to the Building Regulations 1985 for England and Wales (and 1990 edition).
[2] Building Standards (Scotland) Regulations 1981 and all published amendments.
[3] Building Regulations (Northern Ireland) 1990.
[4] Isle of Man Bye-laws 1976, amended 1980 and 1987.

Guidance

Commonly used flat roofs

Three types of flat roof are shown here to illustrate the principles of their design:

WARM DECK DESIGN (insulation on top of deck)	
timber deck	concrete deck

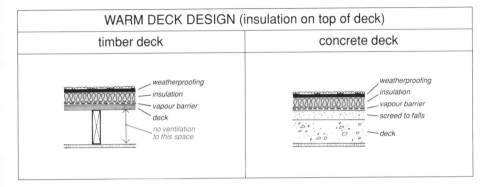

INVERTED ROOF DESIGN (insulation on top of weatherproofing)	
timber deck	concrete deck

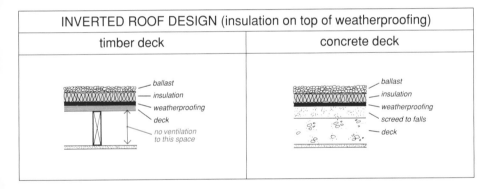

COLD DECK DESIGN (insulation at ceiling level)	
timber deck	concrete deck

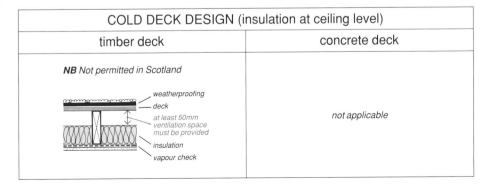

APPENDIX 7.1-B

Guidance

Commonly used flat roofs (continued)

WARM DECK (timber)

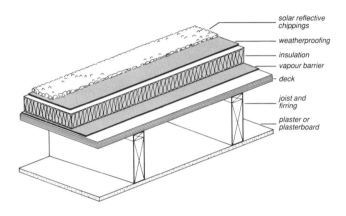

solar reflective chippings
weatherproofing
insulation
vapour barrier
deck
joist and firring
plaster or plasterboard

Reflective surface

Solar reflective treatment consisting of stone chippings or tiles of concrete or fibre cement (see Appendix 7.1-C for built-up felt and asphalt).

Weatherproofing

Weatherproofing should be one of the following:

● mastic asphalt (BS 988 or BS 6577), 20mm thick on the flat, laid on sheathing felt (Class 4 in BS 747)

● sheet metal roof complying with BS 6915 for lead or the relevant parts of CP 143 for other sheet materials

● bitumen roofing felt to BS 747 from the following table:

Type of roofing felt			Insulation material	Method of fixing first layer
First layer	Second layer	Cap sheet		
Type 3B	Type 5U	Type 3B or 3E	glass fibreboards rock fibreboards	full bond
Type 5U	-	Type 5B or 5E	corkboards	
Type 3G	Type 3B	Type 5B or 5E	polyurethane and polyisocyanurate boards	partial bond
Type 3G	Type 5U	Type 5B or 5E		

Cap sheets with a 'B' suffix require a separate stone chipping finish. Normally, a separate stone chipping finish is required for fire regulation purposes.

Guidance

Insulation
The following rigid insulation boards are suitable:

Rigid insulation materials	Minimum insulation thickness [mm] to satisfy U values of	
	0.35W/m²K	0.25W/m²K
Polyurethane and polyisocyanurate	60	90
Glass fibre or rock fibre	85	125
Corkboard	100	150

Vapour barrier
Vapour barrier must consist of at least one layer of bitumen roofing felt Type 2B or 3B partially bonded to the structural deck: all laps must be sealed with bitumen.

Preservative treatment
All roof timbers, joists, wall plates, blocking, strutting, battens, firrings and noggings to be preservative treated, unless naturally durable. Chapter 2.3 'Timber preservation (natural solid timber)' gives full details of preservative treatments.

Deck
Timber or timber-based decks should be one of the following:

Material	Minimum board thickness [mm] for joist centres of		
	400mm	450mm	600mm
Pre-treated timber boarding (tongued and grooved)	16	16	19
Pre-treated plywood, WBP grade	12	12	15
Marine plywood, WBP grade	12	12	15
Wood chipboard, Type C4	18	18	22
Woodwool slabs, Type SB	51	51	51

Reference should be made to Sitework clause 7.1 - S7 for fixing of the deck to joists.

Joists and firrings
For sizes and spacing, reference should be made to Appendix 7.1-E or to tables prepared to recognised standards.

Detailing
Typical details are shown in Appendix 7.1-D.

Guidance

Commonly used flat roofs (continued)
WARM DECK (concrete)

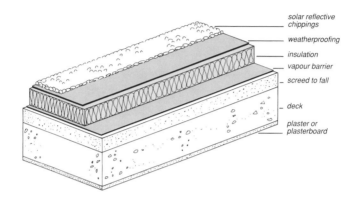

solar reflective chippings
weatherproofing
insulation
vapour barrier
screed to fall
deck
plaster or plasterboard

Reflective surface
Solar reflective treatment consisting of stone chippings or tiles of concrete or fibre cement (see Appendix 7.1-C for built-up felt and asphalt).

Weatherproofing
Weatherproofing should be one of the following:
● mastic asphalt (BS 988 or BS 6577), 20mm thick on the flat, laid on sheathing felt (Class 4 in BS 747)
● sheet metal roof complying with BS 6915 for lead or the relevant parts of CP 143 for other sheet materials
● bitumen roofing felt to BS 747 from the following table:

| Type of roofing felt | | | | |
First layer	Second layer	Cap sheet	**Insulation material**	**Method of fixing first layer**
Type 3B	Type 5U	Type 3B or 3E	glass fibreboards rock fibreboards corkboards	full bond
Type 5U	-	Type 5B or 5E		
Type 3G	Type 3B	Type 5B or 5E	polyurethane and polyisocyanurate boards	partial bond
Type 3G	Type 5U	Type 5B or 5E		

Cap sheets with a 'B' suffix require a separate stone chipping finish. Normally, a separate stone chipping finish is required for fire regulation purposes.

Guidance

Insulation
The following rigid insulation boards are suitable:

Rigid insulation materials	Minimum insulation thickness [mm] to satisfy U values of	
	0.35W/m²K	0.25W/m²K
Polyurethane and polyisocyanurate	60	90
Glass fibre or rock fibre	85	125
Corkboard	100	150

Vapour barrier
Vapour barrier must consist of at least one layer of bitumen roofing felt Type 2B or 3B partially bonded to the structural deck: all laps must be sealed with bitumen.

Concrete deck and screeds
Concrete roof deck, with dense screed topping to achieve the falls. The screed should be a minimum of 40mm in thickness.

Adequate time for drying out of the slab should be allowed prior to plastering/dry lining.

For in-situ construction, allowance should be made for draining away excess construction moisture.

Detailing
Typical details are shown in Appendix 7.1-D.

APPENDIX 7.1-B

Guidance

Commonly used flat roofs (continued)

INVERTED ROOF (timber)
(NOT suitable for slopes greater than 10°)

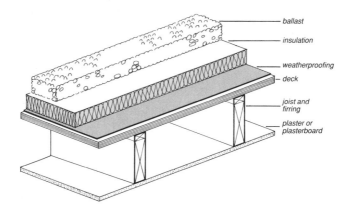

ballast

insulation

weatherproofing

deck

joist and
firring

plaster or
plasterboard

Ballast
Ballast may consist of paving slabs or a 50mm thickness of rounded pebbles of minimum diameter 19mm.

Insulation
Insulation must be of a type unaffected by exposure to the weather. The following materials are suitable:

Insulation materials	Minimum insulation thickness [mm] to achieve U values of	
	0.35W/m²K	0.25W/m²K
Extruded polystyrene	80	120
Extruded polystyrene with ballast surface	80	120
Compressed boards of glass fibre/rock fibre	100	150

Weatherproofing

Weatherproofing should be one of the following:
- mastic asphalt (BS 988 or BS 6577), 20mm thick on the flat, laid on sheathing felt (Class 4 in BS 747)
- bitumen roofing felt to BS 747 from the following table: Pre-felting of the deck material cannot be counted as part of the weatherproofing.

Type of roofing felt			Deck material	Method of fixing first layer
First layer	Second layer	Cap sheet		
Type 2B	Type 5U	Type 3B or 3E	timber boarding	nailing
Type 2B	Type 5U	Type 5B or 5E	cement screed	partial bond
Type 3G	Type 3B	Type 5B or 5E	pre-felted surfaces plywood	
Type 3G	Type 5U	Type 5B	chipboard	

Preservative treatment

All roof timbers, joists, wall plates, blocking, strutting, battens, firrings and noggings to be preservative treated, unless naturally durable. Chapter 2.3 'Timber preservation (natural solid timber)' gives full details of preservative treatments.

Deck

Timber or timber-based decks should be one of the following:

Material	Minimum board thickness [mm] for joist centres of		
	400mm	450mm	600mm
Pre-treated timber boarding (tongued and grooved)	16	16	19
Pre-treated plywood, WBP grade	12	12	15
Marine plywood, WBP grade	12	12	15
Wood chipboard, Type C4	18	18	22
Woodwool slabs, Type SB	51	51	51

Reference should be made to Sitework clause 7.1 - S7 for fixing of the deck to joists.

Joists and firrings

The use of ballast may affect the timber sizing: for correct sizes and spacing, reference should be made to Appendix 7.1-E or to tables prepared to recognised standards.

The weight of a 50mm thickness of pebbles is approximately 80kg/m². The highest dead load figure (0.75kN/m² to 1.00kN/m²) in Appendix 7.1-E should be used for joist sizing.

APPENDIX 7.1-B

Guidance

Commonly used flat roofs (continued)
INVERTED ROOF (concrete)
(NOT suitable for slopes greater than 10°)

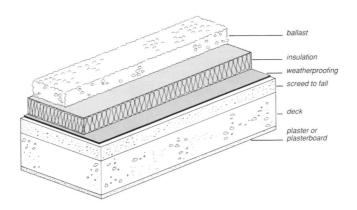

ballast
insulation
weatherproofing
screed to fall
deck
plaster or plasterboard

Ballast
Ballast may consist of paving slabs or a 50mm thickness of rounded pebbles of minimum diameter 19mm.

Insulation
Insulation must be of a type unaffected by exposure to the weather. The following materials are suitable:

Insulation materials	Minimum insulation thickness [mm] to achieve U values of	
	0.35W/m²K	0.25W/m²K
Extruded polystyrene	80	120
Extruded polystyrene with ballast surface	80	120
Compressed boards of glass fibre/rock fibre	100	150

Guidance

Weatherproofing

Weatherproofing should be one of the following:

- mastic asphalt (BS 988 or BS 6577), 20mm thick on the flat, laid on sheathing felt (Class 4 in BS 747)
- bitumen roofing felt to BS 747 from the following table: Pre-felting of the deck material cannot be counted as part of the weatherproofing.

Type of roofing felt			Deck material	Method of fixing first layer
First layer	Second layer	Cap sheet		
Type 3G	Type 3B	Type 5B or 5E	concrete	partial bond
Type 3G	Type 5U	Type 5B	concrete screed	

Concrete deck and screeds

Concrete roof deck, with dense screed topping to achieve the falls. The screed should be a minimum of 40mm in thickness.

Adequate time for drying out of the slab should be allowed prior to plastering/dry lining.

For in-situ construction, allowance should be made for draining away excess construction moisture.

Detailing

Typical details are shown in Appendix 7.1-D.

APPENDIX 7.1-B

Guidance

Commonly used flat roofs (continued)
COLD DECK
(NOT permitted in Scotland - NOT recommended in the rest of the UK)

Cold deck roofs may be used in the UK (excluding Scotland) only where:
- the required level of ventilation can be achieved
- ventilation paths are not blocked by structural or other members
- a ventilation space of 50mm can be maintained.

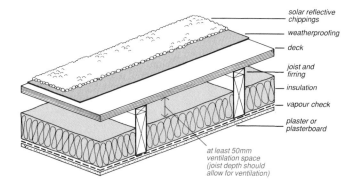

solar reflective chippings
weatherproofing
deck
joist and firring
insulation
vapour check
plaster or plasterboard

at least 50mm ventilation space (joist depth should allow for ventilation)

Reflective surface
Solar reflective treatment consisting of stone chippings or tiles of concrete or fibre cement (see Appendix 7.1-C for built-up felt and asphalt).

Weatherproofing
Weatherproofing should be one of the following:
- mastic asphalt (BS 988 or BS 6577), 20mm thick on the flat, laid on sheathing felt (Class 4 in BS 747)
- sheet metal roof complying with BS 6915 for lead or the relevant parts of CP 143 for other sheet materials
- bitumen roofing felt to BS 747 from the following table:

Type of roofing felt			Deck material	Method of fixing first layer
First layer	Second layer	Cap sheet		
Type 2B	Type 5U	Type 3B or 3E	timber boarding	nailing
Type 2B	Type 5U	Type 5B or 5E		
Type 3G	Type 3B	Type 5B or 5E	cement screed	partial bond
Type 3G	Type 5U	Type 5B or 5E	pre-felted surfaces plywood or chipboard	

Cap sheets with a 'B' suffix require a separate stone chipping finish. Normally, a separate stone chipping finish is required for fire regulation purposes. In areas of high wind exposure, a first layer of Type 5U should be used in place of Type 2B. Pre-felting of the deck material cannot be counted as part of the weatherproofing.

Guidance

Preservative treatment
All roof timbers, joists, wall plates, blocking, strutting, battens, firrings and noggings to be preservative treated, unless naturally durable. Chapter 2.3 'Timber Preservation (natural solid timber)' gives full details of preservative treatments.

Deck
Timber or timber-based decks should be one of the following:

	Minimum board thickness [mm] for joist centres of		
Material	400mm	450mm	600mm
Pre-treated timber boarding (tongued and grooved)	16	16	19
Pre-treated plywood, WBP grade	12	12	15
Marine plywood, WBP grade	12	12	15
Wood chipboard, Type C4	18	18	22

Reference should be made to Sitework clause 7.1 - S7 for fixing of the deck to joists.

Joists and firrings
For sizes and spacing, reference should be made to Appendix 7.1-E or to tables prepared to recognised standards.

Ventilation
Ventilate every void with a totally unobstructed air flow to two opposite sides of the roof. The area of ventilation openings should be at least equal to continuous ventilation running the full length of the eaves and 25mm wide. A ventilation space of at least 50mm should be left between the insulation and the decking. Strutting should not obstruct ventilation.

For roof forms other than a single rectangle or roofs with a span exceeding 10m, the eaves ventilation should be increased to 0.6% of the roof plan area. The actual width of ventilation openings will depend on the length of eaves and the shape of the roof.

Insulation
Insulation of rock fibre or glass fibre, directly above the ceiling. The thickness should satisfy the Building Regulations current at the time; 100mm thickness will achieve a U value of $0.35W/m^2K$, 150mm thickness will achieve $0.25W/m^2K$. Joist depths should allow for at least a 50mm air space above the insulation.

Vapour check
Vapour check of foil-backed or moisture-resistant plasterboard with board joints fixed over joists, or taped; alternatively polyethylene sheeting, minimum 250g with 150mm laps.

Detailing
Typical details are shown in Appendix 7.1-D.

APPENDIX 7.1-C

Flat roofs and balconies

Guidance

Surface treatments acceptable to NHBC

The following surface treatments are suitable. They apply to cold and warm decks only.

	Maintenance only for roofs up to 10°	Access roof, walkway or terrace deck	Further information may be obtained from
Built-up felt	reflective stone chippings* in dressing compound or ballast laid loose or mineral surfaced capsheets (such as Type 3E or Type 5E)	precast concrete paving slabs or proprietary paving slabs	British Flat Roofing Council
Mastic asphalt	solar reflective paint as permitted by MACEF or reflective stone chipping* bedded in a bitumen-based compound	concrete or GRC tiles bedded in bitumen or cement/sand screed**	Mastic Asphalt Council and Employers' Federation

* Prevent loose surface finishes being removed by weather and discharged into gutters and drain pipes. Choose chippings of size and shape which will not penetrate the roof covering under maintenance foot traffic.

** Cement/sand screed should be laid on a waterproof building paper or 1000 gauge polyethylene separating membrane. The pavings must be kept back 75mm at perimeters and a 25mm movement gap incorporated for every 9m² of pavings laid.

Construction details of flat roofs and balconies

This Appendix contains the most common details in flat roofs and balconies. The details are typical and variations for different roofs are indicated beneath each sketch.

CONCRETE DECK

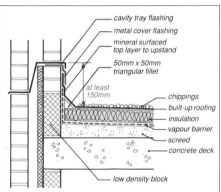

- cavity tray flashing
- metal cover flashing
- mineral surfaced top layer to upstand
- 50mm x 50mm triangular fillet
- at least 150mm
- chippings
- built-up roofing
- insulation
- vapour barrier
- screed
- concrete deck
- low density block

Upstand - concrete deck

- upstand may be fixed to wall
- upstand to be at least 150mm high above chippings
- similar details apply to inverted roofs with concrete decks.

TIMBER DECK

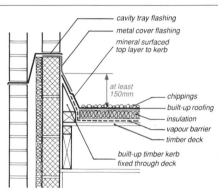

- cavity tray flashing
- metal cover flashing
- mineral surfaced top layer to kerb
- at least 150mm
- chippings
- built-up roofing
- insulation
- vapour barrier
- timber deck
- built-up timber kerb fixed through deck

Independent skirting detail - timber deck

- keep upstands separate from wall - allow for movement
- upstand to be at least 150mm high above chippings
- similar details apply to cold deck timber roofs.

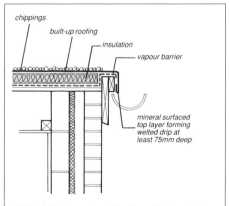

- chippings
- built-up roofing
- insulation
- vapour barrier
- mineral surfaced top layer forming welted drip at least 75mm deep

Welted drip to external gutter - timber deck

- similar details apply to cold deck timber roofs
- inverted timber decks need special consideration to avoid insulation being lifted off by wind suction. Use an alternative detail.

APPENDIX 7.1-D

Guidance

Construction details of flat roofs and balconies (continued)

CONCRETE DECK

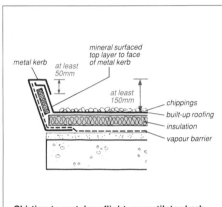

Skirting to metal rooflight or ventilator kerb - concrete deck

● similar details apply to inverted roofs. Allow for thickness of ballast to achieve upstand dimension.

TIMBER DECK

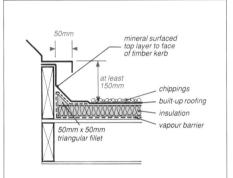

Upstand to ventilator or rooflight kerb - timber deck

● similar details apply to cold and inverted roofs. Allow for thickness of ballast in inverted roofs to achieve upstand dimension.

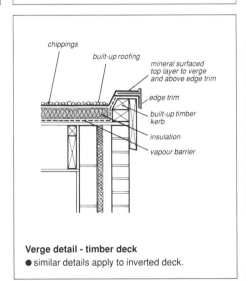

Verge detail - timber deck

● similar details apply to inverted deck.

CONCRETE DECK

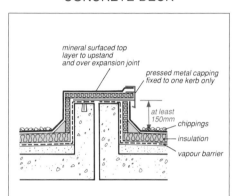

Twin-kerb expansion joint - concrete roof
- expansion joint is similar for both warm and inverted concrete roofs.

TIMBER DECK

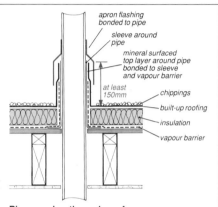

Pipe passing through roof
- ensure vapour barrier is bonded to weatherproofing
- detailing of upstand and flashing is similar for all roofs.

Handrail fixing
- form an upstand in concrete roofs
- grout or rag bolt ends of standards into pockets
- do not penetrate timber roofs.
  Use alternative methods of fixing.

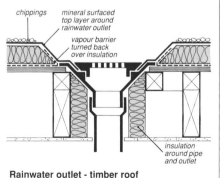

Rainwater outlet - timber roof
- properly trim the opening
- ensure outlet is at lowest point in roof
- similar details apply to concrete roof
- ensure outlet is fixed securely to decking to prevent displacement by thermal expansion of rainwater pipe.

Guidance

Structural timber sizes for flat roofs

This table is not to be used for balcony design. The figures in columns relating to dead loads of not more than $0.5kN/m^2$ and between $0.5kN/m^2$ and $0.75kN/m^2$ should not be used for joist calculations for inverted roof systems.

Table **B21** **Joists** for flat roofs with access only for the purposes of maintenance or repair

Timber of strength class **SC3** *(see Table B1)*†

Size of joist [mm × mm]	Not more than 0.50			More than 0.50 but not more than 0.75			More than 0.75 but not more than 1.00		
	Spacing of joists [mm]								
	400	450	600	400	450	600	400	450	600
	Maximum clear span of joist [m]								
38 × 75	1.22	1.20	1.18	1.18	1.16	1.12	1.14	1.12	1.08
38 × 89*	1.54	1.53	1.49	1.49	1.47	1.41	1.43	1.41	1.35
38 × 100	1.81	1.79	1.74	1.74	1.71	1.64	1.67	1.64	1.57
38 × 125	2.45	2.41	2.32	2.32	2.28	2.18	2.22	2.18	2.07
38 × 140*	2.84	2.80	2.68	2.68	2.63	2.51	2.56	2.51	2.37
38 × 150	3.10	3.05	2.93	2.93	2.87	2.73	2.79	2.73	2.57
38 × 175	3.77	3.70	3.47	3.54	3.46	3.27	3.36	3.28	3.09
38 × 184*	4.01	3.94	3.64	3.76	3.68	3.43	3.56	3.48	3.26
38 × 200	4.44	4.34	3.96	4.15	4.06	3.73	3.93	3.83	3.54
38 × 225	5.06	4.87	4.44	4.77	4.60	4.18	4.50	4.37	3.97
47 × 75	1.35	1.34	1.30	1.30	1.28	1.24	1.26	1.24	1.19
47 × 100	2.00	1.98	1.91	1.91	1.88	1.80	1.84	1.80	1.72
47 × 125	2.69	2.65	2.55	2.55	2.50	2.38	2.43	2.38	2.26
47 × 150	3.39	3.34	3.19	3.19	3.13	2.97	3.04	2.97	2.80
47 × 175	4.10	4.03	3.72	3.85	3.77	3.50	3.65	3.56	3.33
47 × 200	4.82	4.65	4.24	4.50	4.38	4.00	4.26	4.16	3.80
47 × 225	5.40	5.21	4.76	5.10	4.92	4.48	4.86	4.68	4.26
50 × 75	1.39	1.38	1.34	1.34	1.32	1.28	1.30	1.28	1.23
50 × 100	2.06	2.03	1.96	1.96	1.93	1.85	1.89	1.85	1.77
50 × 125	2.76	2.72	2.61	2.61	2.57	2.45	2.50	2.45	2.32
50 × 150	3.48	3.42	3.26	3.28	3.21	3.05	3.12	3.05	2.87
50 × 175	4.21	4.13	3.79	3.94	3.86	3.58	3.74	3.65	3.40
50 × 200	4.91	4.74	4.32	4.61	4.47	4.08	4.36	4.26	3.88
50 × 225	5.50	5.31	4.85	5.20	5.02	4.58	4.96	4.78	4.35
63 × 100	2.28	2.25	2.17	2.17	2.14	2.05	2.08	2.05	1.95
63 × 125	3.04	3.00	2.88	2.88	2.82	2.69	2.74	2.69	2.54
63 × 150	3.82	3.75	3.51	3.59	3.52	3.31	3.41	3.34	3.14
63 × 175	4.60	4.47	4.09	4.31	4.21	3.85	4.08	3.98	3.67
63 × 200	5.27	5.09	4.65	4.99	4.81	4.39	4.75	4.58	4.18
63 × 225	5.90	5.70	5.22	5.59	5.39	4.93	5.33	5.14	4.69
75 × 125	3.27	3.22	3.09	3.09	3.03	2.88	2.94	2.88	2.72
75 × 150	4.08	4.02	3.71	3.84	3.76	3.51	3.65	3.56	3.34
75 × 175	4.88	4.71	4.32	4.59	4.46	4.08	4.35	4.25	3.88
75 × 200	5.55	5.36	4.91	5.26	5.07	4.64	5.02	4.84	4.42
75 × 225	6.21	6.00	5.50	5.89	5.68	5.20	5.62	5.42	4.96

Notes

* North American surfaced size

† Dead load is the load supported by the joist, excluding the mass of the joist

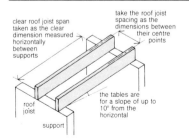

clear roof joist span taken as the clear dimension measured horizontally between supports

take the roof joist spacing as the dimensions between their centre points

the tables are for a slope of up to 10° from the horizontal

roof joist

support

Notes

Tables B21 to B24 inclusive give sizes, spacings and spans for flat roof joists. Tables B21 and B22 are designed for access only for maintenance. Full access has been allowed for in Tables B23 and B24. The member sizes, spacings and spans will support the dead loads given in the tables and the maximum imposed loads shown below.

Access only for maintenance
$0.75kN/m^2$ or a concentrated load of 0.9kN

Full access allowed
$1.50kN/m^2$ or a concentrated load of 1.8kN

Reproduced from Approved Document A1/2 by permission of HMSO.

Guidance

This table is not to be used for balcony design. The figures in columns relating to dead loads of not more than 0.5kN/m² and between 0.5kN/m² and 0.75kN/m² should not be used for joist calculations for inverted roof systems.

Table **B22** **Joists** for flat roofs with access only for the purposes of maintenance or repair

Timber of strength class **SC4** *(see Table B1)*

Size of joist [mm × mm]	Not more than 0.50			More than 0.50 but not more than 0.75			More than 0.75 but not more than 1.00		
	400	450	600	400	450	600	400	450	600
	Maximum clear span of joist [m]								
38 × 75	1.29	1.28	1.24	1.24	1.23	1.19	1.21	1.19	1.14
38 × 89*	1.63	1.62	1.57	1.57	1.55	1.49	1.51	1.49	1.43
38 × 100	1.92	1.89	1.83	1.83	1.80	1.73	1.76	1.73	1.65
38 × 125	2.58	2.54	2.45	2.45	2.40	2.29	2.34	2.29	2.17
38 × 140*	2.99	2.94	2.82	2.82	2.77	2.63	2.69	2.63	2.49
38 × 150	3.26	3.21	3.07	3.07	3.01	2.86	2.93	2.86	2.70
38 × 175	3.96	3.89	3.61	3.71	3.63	3.40	3.52	3.44	3.23
38 × 184*	4.21	4.13	3.79	3.94	3.86	3.57	3.73	3.64	3.39
38 × 200	4.65	4.51	4.11	4.35	4.25	3.87	4.11	4.01	3.68
38 × 225	5.25	5.06	4.62	4.96	4.78	4.35	4.71	4.54	4.13
47 × 75	1.43	1.41	1.37	1.37	1.36	1.31	1.33	1.31	1.26
47 × 100	2.11	2.08	2.01	2.01	1.98	1.90	1.93	1.90	1.81
47 × 125	2.83	2.79	2.68	2.68	2.63	2.50	2.56	2.50	2.37
47 × 150	3.56	3.50	3.32	3.35	3.29	3.12	3.19	3.12	2.94
47 × 175	4.30	4.23	3.87	4.03	3.95	3.64	3.82	3.73	3.46
47 × 200	5.00	4.82	4.40	4.71	4.56	4.15	4.46	4.34	3.95
47 × 225	5.60	5.41	4.94	5.30	5.11	4.66	5.05	4.87	4.43
50 × 75	1.47	1.45	1.41	1.41	1.40	1.35	1.37	1.35	1.29
50 × 100	2.17	2.14	2.07	2.07	2.04	1.95	1.99	1.95	1.86
50 × 125	2.90	2.86	2.75	2.75	2.70	2.57	2.62	2.57	2.43
50 × 150	3.65	3.59	3.39	3.44	3.37	3.19	3.27	3.19	3.01
50 × 175	4.41	4.32	3.94	4.13	4.04	3.72	3.91	3.82	3.53
50 × 200	5.10	4.92	4.49	4.82	4.64	4.24	4.56	4.42	4.03
50 × 225	5.71	5.51	5.04	5.40	5.21	4.76	5.15	4.96	4.52
63 × 100	2.40	2.37	2.29	2.29	2.25	2.15	2.19	2.15	2.04
63 × 125	3.20	3.15	3.02	3.02	2.96	2.82	2.88	2.82	2.66
63 × 150	4.00	3.93	3.65	3.76	3.68	3.44	3.57	3.49	3.28
63 × 175	4.81	4.64	4.24	4.50	4.39	4.01	4.27	4.16	3.81
63 × 200	5.46	5.28	4.83	5.17	4.99	4.56	4.94	4.76	4.34
63 × 225	6.11	5.91	5.41	5.79	5.59	5.12	5.53	5.33	4.87
75 × 125	3.43	3.37	3.23	3.24	3.17	3.02	3.08	3.02	2.85
75 × 150	4.27	4.20	3.86	4.02	3.93	3.64	3.81	3.73	3.47
75 × 175	5.06	4.89	4.48	4.79	4.63	4.23	4.54	4.41	4.03
75 × 200	5.75	5.56	5.10	5.45	5.26	4.82	5.21	5.02	4.59
75 × 225	6.43	6.22	5.71	6.10	5.89	5.40	5.83	5.63	5.15

Notes

* North American surfaced size
† Dead load is the load supported by the joist, excluding the mass of the joist

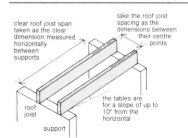

clear roof joist span taken as the clear dimension measured horizontally between supports

take the roof joist spacing as the dimensions between their centre points

the tables are for a slope of up to 10° from the horizontal

roof joist

support

Notes

Tables B21 to B24 inclusive give sizes, spacings and spans for flat roof joists. Tables B21 and B22 are designed for access only for maintenance. Full access has been allowed for in Tables B23 and B24. The member sizes, spacings and spans will support the dead loads given in the tables and the maximum imposed loads shown below.

Access only for maintenance
0.75kN/m² or a concentrated load of 0.9kN

Full access allowed
1.50kN/m² or a concentrated load of 1.8kN

Reproduced from Approved Document A1/2 by permission of HMSO.

Guidance

Structural timber sizes for flat roofs (continued)

The figures in columns relating to dead loads of not more than 0.5kN/m² and between 0.5kN/m² and 0.75kN/m² should not be used for joist calculations for inverted roof systems.

Table **B23**   **Joists** for flat roofs with access not limited to the purposes of maintenance or repair

Timber of strength class **SC3** *(see Table B1)*

Size of joist [mm × mm]	Dead load† [kN/m²]								
	Not more than 0.50			More than 0.50 but not more than 0.75			More than 0.75 but not more than 1.00		
	Spacing of joists [mm]								
	400	450	600	400	450	600	400	450	600
	Maximum clear span of joist [m]								
38 × 75	0.76	0.76	0.75	0.75	0.74	0.73	0.74	0.73	0.71
38 × 89*	1.04	1.03	1.01	1.01	1.01	0.98	0.99	0.98	0.95
38 × 100	1.28	1.27	1.24	1.24	1.23	1.19	1.21	1.19	1.15
38 × 125	1.86	1.85	1.81	1.81	1.78	1.72	1.74	1.72	1.64
38 × 140*	2.19	2.18	2.13	2.13	2.10	2.04	2.07	2.04	1.94
38 × 150	2.42	2.40	2.34	2.34	2.31	2.24	2.27	2.24	2.16
38 × 175	3.00	2.97	2.88	2.88	2.85	2.75	2.79	2.75	2.63
38 × 184*	3.21	3.18	3.08	3.08	3.04	2.93	2.98	2.93	2.81
38 × 200	3.59	3.55	3.38	3.44	3.40	3.25	3.32	3.26	3.12
38 × 225	4.20	4.15	3.80	4.02	3.95	3.65	3.86	3.79	3.51
47 × 75	0.94	0.93	0.92	0.92	0.91	0.89	0.90	0 89	0.86
47 × 100	1.50	1.49	1.47	1.47	1.46	1.42	1.44	1.42	1.38
47 × 125	2.07	2.06	2.01	2.01	1.99	1.94	1.96	1.94	1.87
47 × 150	2.68	2.65	2.59	2.59	2.55	2.47	2.51	2.47	2.38
47 × 175	3.31	3.27	3.18	3.18	3.13	3.02	3.07	3.02	2.89
47 × 200	3.95	3.91	3.63	3.78	3.73	3.49	3.64	3.58	3.37
47 × 225	4.61	4.48	4.08	4.40	4.32	3.92	4.22	4.14	3.79
50 × 75	0.99	0.99	0.97	0.97	0.96	0.94	0.95	0.94	0.91
50 × 100	1.55	1.54	1.52	1.52	1.50	1.47	1.48	1.47	1.43
50 × 125	2.14	2.12	2.07	2.07	2.05	1.99	2.02	1.99	1.93
50 × 150	2.76	2.73	2.66	2.66	2.63	2.54	2.58	2.54	2.44
50 × 175	3.40	3.36	3.25	3.27	3.22	3.10	3.15	3.10	2.97
50 × 200	4.06	4.01	3.71	3.89	3.83	3.57	3.74	3.67	3.44
50 × 225	4.73	4.58	4.16	4.51	4.40	4.00	4.33	4.25	3.87
63 × 100	1.74	1.73	1.70	1.70	1.68	1.64	1.66	1.64	1.59
63 × 125	2.39	2.37	2.31	2.31	2.29	2.22	2.25	2.22	2.14
63 × 150	3.07	3.04	2.95	2.95	2.92	2.82	2.86	2.82	2.70
63 × 175	3.77	3.73	3.51	3.61	3.56	3.38	3.48	3.43	3.26
63 × 200	4.48	4.39	4.00	4.28	4.22	3.85	4 12	4.04	3.72
63 × 225	5.11	4.93	4.49	4.93	4.75	4.32	4.75	4.59	4.18
75 × 125	2.59	2.57	2.51	2.51	2.48	2.40	2.43	2.40	2.31
75 × 150	3.31	3.28	3.19	3.19	3.15	3.04	3.08	3.04	2.91
75 × 175	4.06	4.01	3.72	3.89	3.83	3.58	3.75	3.68	3.45
75 × 200	4.82	4.64	4.24	4.60	4.47	4.08	4.42	4.32	3.94
75 × 225	5.40	5.20	4.75	5.20	5.02	4.58	5.04	4.85	4.42

Notes
* North American surfaced size
† Dead load is the load supported by the joist, excluding the mass of the joist

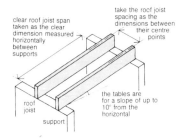

clear roof joist span taken as the clear dimension measured horizontally between supports

take the roof joist spacing as the dimensions between their centre points

roof joist

support

the tables are for a slope of up to 10° from the horizontal

Notes
Tables B21 to B24 inclusive give sizes, spacings and spans for flat roof joists. Tables B21 and B22 are designed for access only for maintenance. Full access has been allowed for in Tables B23 and B24. The member sizes, spacings and spans will support the dead loads given in the tables and the maximum imposed loads shown below.

Access only for maintenance
0.75kN/m² or a concentrated load of 0.9kN

Full access allowed
1.50kN/m² or a concentrated load of 1.8kN

Reproduced from Approved Document A1/2 by permission of HMSO.

Guidance

The figures in columns relating to dead loads of not more than $0.5kN/m^2$ and between $0.5kN/m^2$ and $0.75kN/m^2$ should not be used for joist calculations for inverted roof systems.

Table **B24** **Joists** for flat roofs with access not limited to the purposes of maintenance or repair

Timber of strength class **SC4** *(see Table B1)*

Size of joist [mm × mm]	Dead load† [kN/m²]								
	Not more than 0.50			More than 0.50 but not more than 0.75			More than 0.75 but not more than 1.00		
	Spacing of joists [mm]								
	400	450	600	400	450	600	400	450	600
	Maximum clear span of joist [m]								
38 × 75	0.93	0.93	0.92	0.92	0.91	0.90	0.90	0.90	0.88
38 × 89*	1.21	1.20	1.18	1.18	1.17	1.15	1.16	1.15	1.12
38 × 100	1.43	1.42	1.40	1.40	1.39	1.36	1.37	1.36	1.32
38 × 125	1.98	1.96	1.92	1.92	1.90	1.85	1.87	1.85	1.79
38 × 140*	2.32	2.30	2.25	2.25	2.23	2.16	2.19	2.16	2.08
38 × 150	2.56	2.54	2.47	2.47	2.45	2.37	2.40	2.37	2.28
38 × 175	3.17	3.13	3.05	3.05	3.01	2.90	2.94	2.90	2.77
38 × 184*	3.39	3.35	3.24	3.26	3.21	3.09	3.14	3.09	2.96
38 × 200	3.79	3.75	3.52	3.63	3.58	3.38	3.50	3.44	3.26
38 × 225	4.43	4.35	3.95	4.23	4.16	3.80	4.06	3.98	3.67
47 × 75	1.05	1.04	1.03	1.03	1.02	1.00	1.01	1.00	0.98
47 × 100	1.60	1.59	1.56	1.56	1.55	1.51	1.52	1.51	1.46
47 × 125	2.20	2.18	2.13	2.13	2.11	2.05	2.07	2.05	1.98
47 × 150	2.83	2.80	2.73	2.73	2.70	2.61	2.65	2.61	2.50
47 × 175	3.49	3.45	3.31	3.35	3.30	3.18	3.23	3.18	3.04
47 × 200	4.16	4.12	3.78	3.98	3.92	3.63	3.83	3.76	3.51
47 × 225	4.84	4.66	4.24	4.62	4.49	4.08	4.43	4.33	3.94
50 × 75	1.08	1.08	1.06	1.06	1.05	1.04	1.04	1.04	1.01
50 × 100	1.65	1.64	1.61	1.61	1.59	1.55	1.57	1.55	1.51
50 × 125	2.26	2.24	2.19	2.19	2.17	2.11	2.13	2.11	2.03
50 × 150	2.91	2.88	2.81	2.81	2.77	2.68	2.72	2.68	2.57
50 × 175	3.59	3.55	3.38	3.44	3.39	3.25	3.32	3.27	3.12
50 × 200	4.28	4.23	3.86	4.09	4.03	3.71	3.93	3.86	3.58
50 × 225	4.94	4.76	4.33	4.74	4.58	4.17	4.55	4.42	4.02
63 × 100	1.85	1.83	1.80	1.80	1.78	1.74	1.76	1.74	1.68
63 × 125	2.52	2.50	2.44	2.44	2.41	2.34	2.37	2.34	2.25
63 × 150	3.23	3.20	3.11	3.11	3.07	2.96	3.01	2.96	2.84
63 × 175	3.97	3.92	3.65	3.80	3.75	3.51	3.66	3.60	3.39
63 × 200	4.71	4.56	4.16	4.50	4.39	4.00	4.32	4.24	3.87
63 × 225	5.31	5.12	4.67	5.12	4.93	4.49	4.95	4.77	4.34
75 × 125	2.73	2.71	2.64	2.64	2.61	2.53	2.56	2.53	2.43
75 × 150	3.49	3.46	3.32	3.36	3.31	3.19	3.24	3.19	3.06
75 × 175	4.27	4.22	3.86	4.09	4.03	3.72	3.93	3.87	3.59
75 × 200	5.00	4.82	4.40	4.82	4.64	4.24	4.63	4.49	4.10
75 × 225	5.60	5.40	4.94	5.40	5.21	4.76	5.23	5.04	4.60

Notes
* North American surfaced size
† Dead load is the load supported by the joist, excluding the mass of the joist

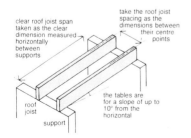

clear roof joist span taken as the clear dimension measured horizontally between supports

take the roof joist spacing as the dimensions between their centre points

the tables are for a slope of up to 10° from the horizontal

roof joist

support

Notes
Tables B21 to B24 inclusive give sizes, spacings and spans for flat roof joists. Tables B21 and B22 are designed for access only for maintenance. Full access has been allowed for in Tables B23 and B24. The member sizes, spacings and spans will support the dead loads given in the tables and the maximum imposed loads shown below.

Access only for maintenance
0.75kN/m² or a concentrated load of 0.9kN

Full access allowed
1.50kN/m² or a concentrated load of 1.8kN

Reproduced from Approved Document A1/2 by permission of HMSO.

APPENDIX 7.1-F

Guidance

Map of basic wind speeds for the UK

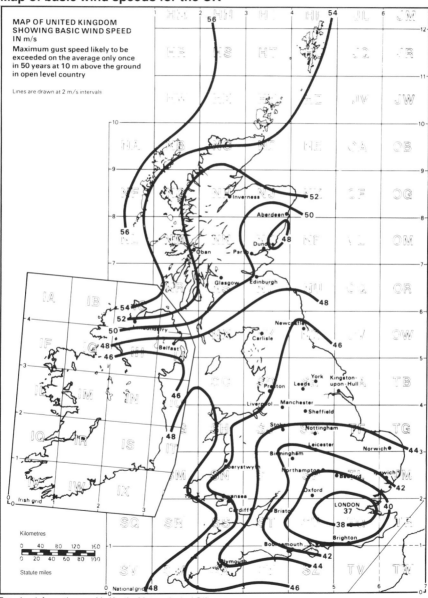

MAP OF UNITED KINGDOM
SHOWING BASIC WIND SPEED
IN m/s

Maximum gust speed likely to be
exceeded on the average only once
in 50 years at 10 m above the ground
in open level country

Lines are drawn at 2 m/s intervals

Based on information provided by the Meteorological Office.

Reproduced from CP 3 : Chapter V : Part 2 by permission of BSI

BUILDMARK™

NHBC, Buildmark House, Chiltern Avenue, Amersham, Bucks HP6 5AP

NHBC, 5 Manor Place, Edinburgh, Scotland EH3 7DH

NHBC, Holyrood Court, 59 Malone Road, Belfast BT9 6SA

informing the industry

CI/SfB	81	(27.2)		
CAWS	G20	H6		

Operative from January 1992

Chapter **7.2**

NHBC STANDARDS

Pitched roofs

This Chapter gives the Technical Requirements and recommendations for pitched roofs, including trussed rafter and traditional cut roofs, vertical tiling, weatherproofing and insulation.

LIST OF CHAPTERS

THE STANDARDS

The NHBC Standards give:
● Technical Requirements in red
● Performance Standards in dark blue
● Guidance in light blue
for the design and construction of dwellings acceptable to NHBC.

Diagrams may contain text in red. This is to highlight points but has no mandatory significance.

The Standards come into effect for every NHBC registered home whose foundations are concreted on or after the publication date shown on the cover of each Chapter and apply throughout the UK, unless otherwise stated.

COMPOSITION OF THE STANDARDS
The Standards are divided into 10 Parts, each containing one or more Chapters covering a particular aspect. The Parts follow the usual construction process.

In general, each Chapter is made up of sections dealing with Design, Materials and Sitework. In some cases one or more of these aspects may not be included.

TECHNICAL REQUIREMENTS
Each Chapter (except former Practice Notes) contains the five mandatory Technical Requirements which MUST be met by the Builder.

The Technical Requirements are printed in red. Chapter 1.1 'Introduction to the Standards and Technical Requirements' contains full details.

PERFORMANCE STANDARDS
Most Chapters consist of detailed Performance Standards printed in dark blue, normally in the left-hand column of each Design, Materials or Sitework page, subdivided into Clauses designated D, M or S, respectively.

Alternative standards of performance will be acceptable ONLY if, in the opinion of NHBC, the Technical Requirements are met and the standard achieved is not lower than the stated Performance Standard.

GUIDANCE
Guidance on how the Performance Standard may be met is normally shown, printed in light blue, in the right-hand column opposite the relevant Performance Standard. Some Chapters contain pages which are all Guidance.

Guidance is based on normal procedures and recommended practices shown by experience to be satisfactory and acceptable. NHBC will consider alternative methods to meet specific requirements, subject to prior consultation and evaluation.

SCOPE

This Chapter gives the Technical Requirements and recommendations for pitched roofs, including trussed rafter and traditional cut roofs, vertical tiling, weatherproofing and insulation.

NHBC Standards do not cover aspects of health and safety relating to building operations and to the handling and use of certain building materials. Such matters are covered by statutory requirements.

FINDING INFORMATION

To find information on a particular subject, the following procedure is recommended:

1 Identify the **Part** most appropriate for the subject.

2 Identify the **Chapter** which deals with the particular element of construction.

3 Decide whether the information required relates to the Design, Materials or Sitework **Section** of the Chapter.

4 Decide from the Contents list the **heading** under which the required information is most likely to be found.

5 Review the **clauses** listed against the heading to see which has the relevant Performance Standard.

6 Review the **items** under the Performance Standards and decide which is relevant.

7 Review the guidance in the right-hand column opposite the item most relevant to the subject. If a clause number is known, use the above procedure to find the clause.

For example: **7.2 - S12(c)** means:

7	Part 7	Roofs
2	Chapter 2	Pitched roofs
S	Section	SITEWORK
12	Clause 12	FLASHINGS AND WEATHERINGS
(c)	Item (c)	ridges and hips.

CONTENTS

TECHNICAL REQUIREMENTS

Technical Requirements	Performance Standards

R1 Statutory requirements
Work shall comply with all relevant Building Regulations and other statutory requirements

Chapter 1.1 gives the detailed Performance Standards which relate to these Technical Requirements.

R2 Design requirement
Design and specification shall provide satisfactory performance

R3 Materials requirement
All materials, products and building systems shall be suitable for their intended purpose

R4 Workmanship requirement
All work shall be carried out in a proper, neat and workmanlike manner

R5 Structural design requirement
Structural design shall be carried out by suitably qualified persons in accordance with British Standards and Codes of Practice

Performance Standards	Guidance

DESIGN STANDARD

7.2 - D1 Design shall meet the Technical Requirements

Design that follows the guidance below will be acceptable for pitched roofs.

STATUTORY REQUIREMENTS

7.2 - D2 Design shall comply with all relevant statutory requirements

A list of statutory references applicable to this Chapter is given in Appendix 7.2-A.

LOADBEARING STRUCTURE

7.2 - D3 All pitched roof structures shall be designed to support applied loads and self weight without undue movement

Items to be taken into account include:

(a) dead and imposed loads

Dead and imposed loads should be calculated in accordance with BS 6399 : Part 3. Dead loads include the self weight of the roof structure and the roof covering. Imposed loads include snow loadings and the weight of water tanks, insulation, etc.

Stuctural timber should be specified according to the strength classes in BS 5268 : Part 2. Timber specifications when using the BS 4978 grading rules (eg GS, M50) should also include the timber species. The strength class can then be determined from Table B1 in Approved Document A1/2 to the Building Regulations or Table 3 in BS 5268 : Part 2.

(b) wind loads

Wind loads appropriate to the site location should be calculated in accordance with CP 3 : Chapter V : Part 2. The roof should be designed to resist wind uplift. This resistance is often provided by the weight of the roof itself but holding down straps should be provided where the self weight of the roof is insufficient.

(c) holding down straps

Holding down straps are required in Scotland, Northern Ireland and other areas of severe exposure. Some roof covering manufacturers provide detailed guidance.

Where holding down straps are necessary, they should have a minimum cross section of 30mm x 5mm and be fixed at maximum 1.2m centres. Steel straps with a galvanized finish are normally acceptable. The design should detail how straps are to be fixed and what materials are to be used. The durability of fixings should be compatible with the straps.

Performance Standards	Guidance

LOADBEARING STRUCTURE (continued)

7.2 - D3 **(d) sizing and spacing of members**

Sizing and spacing of rafters and ceiling joists should be as:
- Clause D5 for trussed rafter roofs
- Clause D6 for traditional cut roofs.

Generally, the spacing of rafters and ceiling joists should be not more than 600mm. The spacing of ceiling joists should suit the thickness and size of the plasterboard sheets or other ceiling finish. Plasterboard sheets may be fixed at the following joist centres:

- 9.5mm sheets - up to 450mm spacing
- 12.5mm sheets - up to 600mm spacing.

Proprietary roof systems should be designed by an Engineer in accordance with Technical Requirement R5.

(e) size and spacing of tile battens

The size of tile battens should be in accordance with the roof covering manufacturer's recommendations, but not less than shown in the following table:

	Rafter centres			
	Up to 450mm		450mm to 600mm	
Type of roof covering	width [mm]	depth [mm]	width [mm]	depth [mm]
Plain tile	32	19	32	25
Single-lap tile	38	22	38	25
Slate (natural* or manufactured)	38	19	38	25
Vertical tile	38	19	38	25

* In Scotland it is acceptable to fix natural slates direct to rigid timber sarking.

Nails for fixing battens should be 3.35mm (10 gauge) x 65mm long. Galvanized smooth round nails are acceptable, except where the maximum basic wind speed is over 48m/s (from CP 3 : Chapter V : Part 2), when ring shank nails should be specified.

7.2 - D4 **All pitched roof structures shall be designed so as to transmit loads and give restraint to the supporting structure without undue movement**

Items to be taken into account include:

(a) wall plates

Normally, trussed rafter roofs and traditional cut roofs should be supported on timber wall plates.

Performance Standards

Guidance

Wall plates should be as detailed in Clause D6(b) with regard to the table concerning minimum sizes.

Fixings to connect the roof structure to the wall plate should be specified having regard to the roof construction and the exposure conditions of the site. For trussed rafter roofs not subject to uplift, the minimum fixing should be two 4.5mm x 100mm long galvanized round wire nails, skew nailed, one from each side of the trussed rafter. Alternatively, truss clips can be used, fixed in accordance with manufacturers' instructions.

In Scotland, nails should be appropriate to wall plate dimensions.

(b) holding down straps

In situations where the roof is required to resist uplift, skew nailing is unlikely to provide sufficient strength. Appropriate metal straps should be used.

(c) lateral restraint straps

For dwellings of masonry construction, restraint should be provided at rafter level for gable and separating walls. Larger gable or separating walls may also require restraint at ceiling level.

Guidance in assessing when ceiling restraint is needed can be found in the statutory references listed in Appendix 7.2-A.

Lateral restraint straps should have a minimum cross section of 30mm x 5mm and a minimum anchorage down-turn of 100mm. The level of galvanizing for straps and their fixings should be in accordance with BS 5628 : Part 3 (reference should be made to Appendix 7.2-B). Sheradizing is not acceptable in Northern Ireland and the Isle of Man. Straps should be of sufficient length to be fixed to two trusses and should be fixed with solid blocking.

In framed roofs, as an alternative, purlins and pole plates can also provide restraint if the timber abuts a gable construction. Where purlins are used to provide restraint they should not be spaced at more than 2 metre centres, unless the design shows they are adequate at greater spacing.

In trussed rafter roofs, an alternative is to provide restraint through gable ladder detailing.

(d) timber frame construction

For dwellings of timber frame construction, the designer should ensure stability in accordance with BS 5268.

DESIGN

Performance Standards	Guidance

TRUSSED RAFTER ROOFS

7.2 - D5   **Trussed rafters shall be designed to support applied loads and self weight without undue movement**

Items to be taken into account include:

(a) recognised design standards

Trussed rafters should be designed in accordance with BS 5268 : Part 3. Truss manufacturers may have their own computer programs for calculating truss designs in accordance with the British Standard.

(b) design information

To ensure that trussed rafters are correctly designed and fabricated, and are suitable for their intended purpose, an accurate specification is necessary.

BS 5268 : Part 3 gives a list of information to be supplied to the truss manufacturer, including the:

● height and location of building with reference to unusual wind conditions

● profile of the trussed rafter, including camber, if required

● span of the trussed rafter

● pitch or pitches of the roof

● method of support and position of supports

● type and weights of roof tiles or covering, including sarking, insulation and ceiling materials

● size and approximate position of any water tanks or other equipment to be supported on the trussed rafters

● overhang of rafters at eaves and other eaves details

● positions and dimensions of hatches, chimneys and other openings

● use of the building with reference to any unusual environmental conditions

● type of preservative treatment, where required

● spacing of trussed rafters and special timber sizes, where these are required to match existing construction.

The building designer should ensure that the design of the roof as a whole is satisfactory in achieving the overall stability of the complete structure. This includes its connection to, and compatibility with, the supporting structure and adjacent elements of the building.

Performance Standards

Guidance

(c) bracing

The building designer should specify all bracing. Trussed rafter roofs should be braced in accordance with Table 1 in Appendix 7.2-E, unless the roof is designed and braced in accordance with BS 5268 : Part 3.

All timber bracing to trussed rafters should be at least 100mm x 25mm in section and twice nailed to each trussed rafter. Nailing should be 3.35mm (10 gauge) x 65mm long galvanized round wire nails.

(d) spacing

Trussed rafters should not be spaced at centres greater than 600mm. Where this cannot be achieved, eg to accommodate hatch openings or chimneys, the spacing of trussed rafters may be increased as shown below provided that the spacing between centres of trimming trussed rafters does not exceed 2 times the design spacing of trussed rafters and that **b** is smaller than or equal to **2a - c**, where:

a = design spacing of trussed rafters

b = distance between centres of trimming trussed rafter and adjacent trussed rafter

c = nominal width of required opening

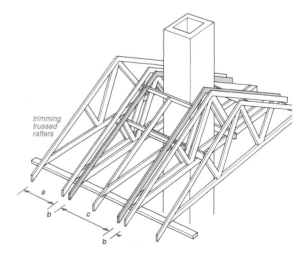

trimming trussed rafters

Performance Standards	Guidance

TRUSSED RAFTER ROOFS (continued)

7.2 - D5   **(e) mono-pitch trusses and girder trusses**

Hipped roofs constructed with trussed rafters will generally require a series of diminishing mono-pitched trusses supported by a girder truss.

The bearing of mono-pitched trusses into shoes should be as follows:

Span	Minimum bearing length	Minimum thickness of truss member
Less than 4m	50mm	35mm
4m or more	75mm	35mm

Alternative bearings should be designed by an Engineer in accordance with Technical Requirement R5.

(f) water tank support

Where water tanks are supported by roof trusses, their load should be transferred to the node points of the trussed rafter and spread over at least three trussed rafters in accordance with BS 5268 : Part 3.

A correct method of water tank support is shown in Appendix 7.2-F.

Proprietary tank support systems should be assessed in accordance with Technical Requirement R3.

(g) multiple trussed rafters

All multiple and reinforcing timbers to simple or multiple trussed rafters should be designed to be permanently fastened together. The timber members should be either fixed together during manufacture or, alternatively, fully detailed drawings and specifications showing the fixing method should be supplied to the site to enable the components to be assembled correctly.

(h) roofs incorporating valleys or other special features

Roofs with hips, valleys or other special features should be designed by an Engineer in accordance with Technical Requirement R5. Standard designs supplied by manufacturers which incorporate these features may usually be acceptable.

(i) combined trussed rafter and cut roofs

Particular care is needed where trussed rafters and a cut roof are combined in a roof design. The designer should provide details of the complete roof. Trussed rafters supporting traditional cut roof members should be designed by an Engineer in accordance with Technical Requirement R5.

Performance Standards

Guidance

TRADITIONAL CUT ROOFS

7.2 - D6 **Cut roofs shall be designed to support applied loads and self weight without undue movement**

Items to be taken into account include:

(a) recognised design standards

Sizes of certain roof members for basic pitched roofs are given in Appendix 7.2-C.

Where spans, sizes, spacing or strength classes of timber are outside the scope of the tables in the statutory regulations or where the form of roof is other than a basic pitched roof, the roof should be designed by an Engineer in accordance with Technical Requirement R5. Calculations should be based on BS 5268 : Part 2.

(b) member sizes

Unless the roof is designed by an Engineer in accordance with Technical Requirement R5, traditionally, nominal sizes of members would be as follows:

Member	Minimum size [mm]
Struts and braces	100 x 50
Wall plates (Scotland)	100 x 25
Wall plates (Northern Ireland & the Isle of Man)	100 x 38
Wall plates (other)	75 x 50
Hips	rafter cut + 25
Valleys	32 thick
Ridges	rafter cut + 25

(c) triangulation

In the design of a cut roof, timber members should be triangulated or otherwise arranged to form a coherent structure. All forces inherent in the design should be resolved. The method of fixing or jointing members should be specified.

Particular care should be taken to ensure adequate triangulation when designs incorporate hips and valleys, and when cut roofs are used in conjunction with trussed rafters.

Details of all structural members should be provided.

DESIGN

Performance Standards

Guidance

TIMBER TREATMENT

7.2 - D7 **Measures shall be taken to ensure durability of timber**

Items to be taken into account include:

(a) treatment against House Longhorn Beetle

In some areas of the UK, treatment against House Longhorn Beetle is required. Reference should be made to Appendix 7.2-A for relevant statutory requirements. Reference should also be made to Chapter 2.3 'Timber preservation (natural solid timber)' (Design).

(b) timber requiring treatment

The following timber members should be either naturally durable or suitably treated:

● fascias
● bargeboards
● soffits
● other trim.

For full protection, these timber members should also be painted or stained in accordance with the recommendations in Chapter 8.5 'Painting and decorating' (each section).

In pitched roofs with a fully supported weatherproofing membrane, the following timber members should be either naturally durable or suitably treated:

● rafters
● purlins
● ceiling joists
● bracing
● sarking
● tiling battens
● wall plates
● battens for fixing vertical cladding.

The level of durability of all the above members can be achieved by natural durability or treatment with preservative. Reference should be made to Chapter 2.3 'Timber preservation (natural solid timber)' (each section) for guidance.

Performance Standards

Guidance

WEATHERTIGHTNESS

7.2 - D8 **Roofs shall be designed to satisfactorily resist the passage of rain and snow to the inside of the building**

Items to be taken into account include:

(a) weathertightness of roof coverings

Roofs with a tile or slate covering should be designed in accordance with BS 5534 : Parts 1 and 2.

(b) tiles

For tiled roofs, the pitch, gauge and lap should be within the limits given in Table 1 in Appendix 7.2-D, unless the manufacturer specifies otherwise.

Fixings for single and double lap tiles should be as given in Tables 2 and 3 of Appendix 7.2-D, unless designed in accordance with BS 5534, in which Part 1 explains how to calculate wind loads and Part 2 has design charts and tables for typical situations. Manufacturers may have computer programs based on the British Standards and their recommendations should be followed.

(c) slates

Natural slates should be fixed in accordance with BS 5534. This may require double nailing in exposed areas.

(d) roof coverings other than tiles or slates

Lead sheet roofing should be in accordance with BS 6915.

Other types of sheet roofing should be in accordance with the relevant parts of CP 143.

Roofs with the following traditional coverings should be designed in accordance with satisfactory custom and practice:
- natural stone
- shingles
- thatch.

Thatching should be as recommended by the Thatch Advisory Service or other appropriate authority in accordance with Technical Requirement R3.

Proprietary roof coverings should be assessed in accordance with Technical Requirement R3.

Performance Standards	Guidance

WEATHERTIGHTNESS (continued)

7.2 - D8   **(e) roof underlays**

An underlay should be provided for all tiled roofs.

The underlay may be felt to BS 747 or a proprietary sarking membrane complying with Technical Requirement R3. Some proprietary roofing underlays have a higher vapour resistance than bitumen felt and may need additional roof ventilation. Manufacturers' recommendations should be followed.

The commonly used type IF felt has been known to disintegrate after a few years where it is exposed at the eaves and it is recommended that a better quality felt is used in this position.

To prevent the underlay sagging at the eaves and forming a water trap behind the fascia, it is recommended that the underlay is supported by a continuous fillet. Where the pitch is below 30°, a continuous support fillet should be provided.

(f) rigid sarking

In areas of *severe* exposure, a rigid sarking with underlay is recommended as is normal practice in Scotland.

The choice of rigid sarking should take account of the type and fixing of the roof covering. The following materials are acceptable:

● tongued and grooved or square edged boarding to BS 1297
● bitumen impregnated insulating board to BS 1142 : Part 3 (sarking and sheathing grade)
● WBP or CBR plywood to BS 6566, durability Class G
● Type C4 chipboard to BS 5669
● proprietary products which have been assessed in accordance with Technical Requirement R3.

To avoid damage from condensation, proprietary insulation boards should be used strictly in accordance with the recommendations given in the independent assessment.

Where an underlay is fully supported and has a low vapour resistance (less than 5.7MNs/g), it should be used with counter battens, battens and roof covering.

Where underlay with a high vapour resistance is used (over 5.7MNs/g), the counter battens should be located between the sarking and the underlay. This is to allow ventilation below the underlay.

Performance Standards

Guidance

(g) flashings and other weathering details where a pitched roof abuts a vertical surface

Where a roof abuts a vertical surface, cover flashings, stepped cover flashings, soakers and back or parapet gutters should be provided as necessary. Where the roof is over an enclosed area the wall construction should include cavity trays linked to the flashings. Reference should be made to Sitework clause 7.2 - S12(f) for details.

Cover flashings should be tucked 25mm into a brick joint or chase not less than 150mm above the intersection with the roof.

Flashings and soakers should be of non-ferrous metal and of the same material to avoid electrolytic action.

Where lead is used, soakers should be at least Code 3 and flashings, gutters, saddles, etc should be Code 4 or better.

In the case of gutters behind parapet walls, provision should be made for an overflow in case the outlet becomes blocked.

(h) weathering details where a pitched roof intersects with a continuous waterproof membrane

For information on intersections with flat roofs, gutters or valleys, reference should be made to Sitework clause 7.2 - S12(e).

(i) pipes

Where soil pipes, vent pipes or other pipes penetrate roof tiling, a lead slate flashing, or a purpose-made accessory supplied by the roof covering manufacturer to form a weathertight joint, should be used.

If lead slates are used, they should be supported (eg using marine plywood) to prevent the lead sagging.

(j) chimneys

Flashings should connect with the chimney dpcs. The normal flashing components are shown in Sitework clause 7.2 - S12(g). Components will vary depending on whether the chimney intersects the roof at eaves or ridge level and the type of roof covering. Reference should be made to roof covering manufacturers' information sheets.

For information on the construction and weatherproofing of chimneys, reference should be made to Chapters 6.1 'External masonry walls' (Design and Sitework) and 6.3 'Internal walls' (Design and Sitework).

DESIGN

Performance Standards	Guidance

WEATHERTIGHTNESS (continued)

7.2 - D8   (k) ridges and hips

Ridge and hip tiles may be bedded on mortar or mechanically fixed. It is recommended that ridge tiles at gable ends and over separating walls are always mechanically fixed.

In areas of high exposure or where complex ridge features are involved, it may be necessary to mechanically fix all ridge tiles. The tile manufacturers' recommendations should be followed.

(l) valleys

A valley may be formed of purpose-made valley tiles or as an open valley lined with lead or other material acceptable under Technical Requirement R3.

Where slates or plain tiles are used, a laced valley, swept valley or mitred tiles with soakers may also be used.

Care should be taken to ensure that the true pitch of the valley is not less than the minimum allowance pitch.

(m) verges

Tiling at verges should project 40mm to 50mm beyond the gable wall or bargeboard.

Unless a proprietary dry verge system or cloaked verge is used, tiles should be bedded into mortar on an undercloak of plain tile, slate or cement-based board. Plain tiles should not be used as an undercloak below 30° pitch or on a bargeboard.

Purpose-made tile-and-a-half, or half-tiles, should be used at verges. Cut tiles are not acceptable.

Consider using an overhanging verge (by means of a gable ladder) to provide better weather protection to the gable wall, especially in exposed positions or where cavity insulation is used.

(n) proprietary roof coverings

Roof coverings not covered by a British Standard should comply with Technical Requirement R3.

Performance Standards

Guidance

7.2 - D9 **Vertical tiling and slating shall adequately resist the passage of rain and snow to the inside of the building**

Items to be taken into account include:

(a) moisture barrier

A moisture barrier should be provided behind all vertical tiling and slating.

Moisture barriers should be:
- underfelt or equivalent where the wall structure is brickwork or blockwork
- a breather membrane where the supporting structure is of timber construction.

For detailed information on the use of moisture barriers in association with timber frame construction, reference should be made to Chapter 6.2 'External timber framed walls and wall panels'.

(b) batten size

Batten sizes should comply with Clause D3(e).

(c) fixing

Every tile or slate should be nailed twice and comply with the general requirements of BS 5534.

(d) weathering details

Bottom edges should be finished with an under-course tile. At dormer cheeks, the tiles or slates should be specified to be cut close to the slope of the roof, over a flashing fixed to the side of the dormer.

At internal or external angles, purpose made corner tiles or soakers should be used to form a weathertight joint.

Where pitched roofs abut masonry walls, a stepped flashing should be specified, turned behind the tiles. Details are shown in Sitework clause 7.2 - S12.

For information regarding vertical tiling or slating on walls, reference should be made to Chapter 6.1 'External masonry walls' (Design and Sitework) or Chapter 6.2 'External timber framed walls and wall panels'.

Performance Standards | Guidance

INSULATION AND CONTROL OF CONDENSATION

7.2 - D10 Roofs directly above habitable rooms shall be adequately insulated

Insulation should be of sufficient thickness to meet the requirements of Building Regulations.

To reduce the risk of freezing, and condensation on pipework, the guidance in Sitework clause 7.2 - S14 should be followed.

7.2 - D11 Measures shall be taken to control condensation

Items to be taken into account include:

(a) ventilation of main roof spaces

Pitched roofs with insulation at ceiling level should always be ventilated to the outside air to minimise the risk of condensation.

Some proprietary underlays are highly impervious and special precautions are necessary to limit condensation, particularly during the drying out period.

Eaves ventilation should be provided on opposite sides of the roof to permit cross ventilation. Reference should be made to Sitework clause 7.2 - S11(a) for illustrations showing where ventilation should be provided.

Where the roof pitch is 15° or more, cross ventilation should be provided to the roof void equivalent to a 10mm slot running the full length of the eaves.

Where the ceiling follows the slope of a 'cold roof' regardless of pitch or where a cold roof has a pitch less than 15°, cross ventilation should be provided to the roof void equivalent to a 25mm slot running the full length of the eaves. At least 50mm clearance should be maintained between the insulation and the roof deck.

When the roof pitch is 35° or greater and when the span exceeds 10m, it is recommended that high level ventilation, equivalent to a continuous 5mm opening, be used in addition to eaves ventilation.

The means of providing cross ventilation to mono-pitched roofs should be specified. BS 5250 indicates eaves ventilation together with the equivalent of a continuous 5mm slot at high level.

Performance Standards	Guidance

(b) position of vapour checks

Vapour checks should be used in roof constructions where the ceiling board is fixed to the rafters and insulation is placed between the rafters.

In normal pitched roofs where insulation is placed at ceiling level and the void above is ventilated, a vapour check is not recommended. Moisture from the dwelling will be diffused through the ceiling and removed by roof space ventilation.

Vapour checks, where required, should be placed on the warm side of insulation.

(c) ventilation of dormers

Pitched dormers should be ventilated from eaves to eaves or, where necessary, from eaves to ridge.

Flat roofed dormers of cold deck construction should be ventilated. The ventilation path should not be blocked by the timber structure, strutting, etc (reference should be made to Chapter 7.1 'Flat roofs and balconies' (Design and Sitework)).

(d) methods of ensuring unobstructed ventilation

Ventilation openings where the least dimension exceeds 10mm should be protected to prevent the entry of birds, etc.

Acceptable protection of openings can be provided by using materials complying with Materials clause 7.2 - M5(j).

A spacer in the eaves should be used so that ceiling insulation can be installed over and beyond the wall plate. This minimises the cold bridge without blocking the ventilation.

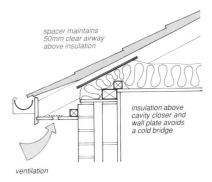

spacer maintains 50mm clear airway above insulation

insulation above cavity closer and wall plate avoids a cold bridge

ventilation

(e) other methods of reducing condensation

Methods of reducing condensation, such as draughtstripping loft hatches and sealing holes for services, are given in Sitework clause 7.2 - S14.

DESIGN

Performance Standards	Guidance

FIRE SPREAD

7.2 - D12 Roofs shall adequately resist fire spread

Items to be taken into account include:

(a) roof coverings

Slates and concrete or clay tiles are designated AA when tested to BS 476 : Part 3 and therefore can be used without limitation on any pitched roof. The use of some other materials is restricted by statutory requirements, particularly in relation to their distance from site boundaries (reference should be made to Appendix 7.2-A). These include:

● bitumen felt slates

● wood shingles

● thatch.

(b) chimneys and flue pipes

Combustible material, such as roof timbers and sarking felt, should be kept away from heat sources as described in Chapter 8.1 'Internal services' (Sitework).

7.2 - D13 Junctions between roofs and compartment or separating walls shall adequately resist fire spread

The junction between a separating or compartment wall and a roof should be firestopped. If there are gaps, fire, smoke and flame can spread from one compartment to the next across the wall.

Mineral wool firestopping should be used to allow for movement in the roof timber, and avoid 'hogging' of the roof which is often associated with mortar firestopping.

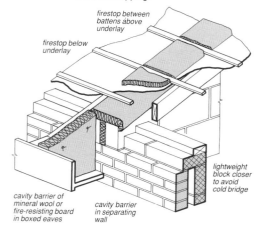

firestop between battens above underlay

firestop below underlay

lightweight block closer to avoid cold bridge

cavity barrier of mineral wool or fire-resisting board in boxed eaves

cavity barrier in separating wall

Where a wall separates an integral garage from the rest of a dwelling, other arrangements are possible provided the principle of half-hour fire separation is maintained.

Performance Standards	Guidance

ACCESS

7.2 - D14 Roof voids shall be provided with suitable access

Access should be provided to:
- the main roof space, and
- all roof voids that contain water services.

SIZE OF OPENINGS
Access openings should be not less than 520mm in any direction. They should *not* be located directly over stairs or in other hazardous locations.

PROVISION OF WALKWAYS
Boarded walkways should be provided for maintenance purposes:
- between the access opening and any cistern located in the roof space
- around each cistern (at least 1m²).

Boarding should be securely fixed without compressing the loft insulation.

ROOF DRAINAGE

7.2 - D15 Roof drainage shall adequately carry rainwater to an outfall

Items to be taken into account include:

(a) provision of gutters and downpipes

Roofs greater than 6m² in area should be provided with rainwater gutters and downpipes. Consideration should also be given to the provision of rainwater drainage to roof areas less than 6m², for example dormer and porch roofs.

(b) sizes

Gutters and downpipes should be of sufficient size to accommodate normal rainfall.

Care is needed in sizing gutters where dormer roofs interrupt the run-off from a pitched roof. The gutter should be sized to cope with the concentrated flows.

(c) discharge from one roof to another

Where water from a large roof surface discharges onto another surface, precautions should be taken to prevent erosion of the lower surface.

(d) discharge into drainage system

Unless designed otherwise, shoes should be provided to rainwater downpipes.

DESIGN

Performance Standards · Guidance

PROVISION OF INFORMATION

7.2 - D16 Designs and specifications shall be produced in a clearly understandable format and include all relevant information

Full details of trussed rafter roofs should be available on site, including the following:

- layout drawing of trusses and associated items
- bracing requirements
- trimming around chimneys, access hatches, etc
- mono-pitch and lean-to roofs
- girder trusses, multiple trusses and diminishing trusses and how they are fixed together and supported on truss shoes, layboards or similar
- roof intersections (ie hips and valleys).

Assembly drawings are also important where there are complicated roof shapes or where trussed rafter and framed roofs are used in combination.

The drawings should show:

- means of providing eaves ventilation
- firestopping at separating wall and boxed eaves
- flashing details at abutments, chimneys, etc
- supports for water cisterns in the roof space
- restraint strapping
- position, thickness and limits of insulation.

7.2 - D17 All relevant information shall be distributed to appropriate personnel

Ensure that design and specification information is issued to site supervisors and relevant specialist subcontractors and/or suppliers.

Performance Standards

Guidance

MATERIALS STANDARDS

7.2 - M1 All materials shall:
(a) meet the Technical Requirements
(b) take account of the design

Materials that comply with the design and the guidance below will be acceptable for pitched roofs.

Materials for pitched roofs shall comply with all relevant standards, including those listed below. Where no standard exists, Technical Requirement R3 applies (see Chapter 1.1 'Introduction to the Standards and Technical Requirements').

References to British Standards and Codes of Practice include those made under the Construction Products Directive (89/106/EEC) and, in particular, appropriate European Technical Specifications approved by a European Committee for Standardisation (CEN).

STRUCTURAL TIMBER

7.2 - M2 Structural timber shall be of the appropriate grades and sizes to support the imposed loads

Structural timber should be specified according to the strength classes in BS 5268 : Part 2. Roof members are usually SC3 or SC4.

Timber specifications when using the BS 4978 grading rules (eg GS, M50) should also include the timber species. The strength class can then be determined from Table B1 in Approved Document A1/2 to the Building Regulations or Table 3 in BS 5268 : Part 2.

A list of statutory references is given in Appendix 7.2-A.

7.2 - M3 Structural timber shall be of suitable durability

Structural timber should be pre-treated with preservative where specified by the designer. Chapter 2.3 'Timber preservation (natural solid timber)' (each section) recommends methods of preservative treatment.

Use of reclaimed materials is covered in Clause M6.

RESTRAINT STRAPS AND HOLDING DOWN STRAPS

7.2 - M4 Strapping shall be of adequate strength and durability

Lateral restraint straps should have minimum cross section dimensions of 30mm x 5mm. Vertical holding down straps should have minimum cross section dimensions of 30mm x 5mm.

Mild steel straps and fixings should be protected against corrosion in accordance with Tables 1 and 14 of BS 5628 : Part 3 (see Appendix 7.2-B). Fixings and straps should be compatible. Sheradizing is not acceptable in Northern Ireland and the Isle of Man.

Straps should be ordered to the correct length and with the correct number of bends and/or twists required by the design.

MATERIALS

Performance Standards	Guidance

ROOFING MATERIALS

7.2 - M5 **Roofing materials shall be of the quality, type and dimensions required by the design**

Items to be taken into account include:

(a) roof coverings

The following roof coverings are acceptable:

- clay tiles and fittings to BS 402
- concrete tiles and fittings to BS 473 and BS 550
- natural slates to BS 680. Check particularly that imported slates comply fully with this British Standard
- shingles should be of Western Red Cedar and pre-treated with CCA preservative to BS 4072 and be Grade 1 to the Canadian Standards Association. Care is needed in the selection of flashing materials and nail fixings to avoid corrosion. Follow the recommendations of the supplier.

Natural stone should be used in accordance with established custom and practice.

Thatch should be as recommended by the Thatch Advisory Service or other appropriate authority in accordance with Technical Requirement R3.

Use of reclaimed materials is covered in Clause M6.

Proprietary coverings should be assessed in accordance with Technical Requirement R3.

(b) fixings

Clout or slate nails for fixing slates and tiles should be one of the following and at least 38mm long:

- aluminium to BS 1202 : Part 3
- copper to BS 1202 : Part 2
- silicon bronze.

Galvanized steel nails are not suitable for fixing slates and tiles because of the risk of damaging the galvanizing but may be used to fix battens and underlay. Nails for fixing battens should be at least 30mm longer than the batten thickness. Ring shank nails should be used when specified by the designer.

Tile clips should be of aluminium or stainless steel.

Performance Standards	Guidance

(c) flashings

The following are acceptable:

- milled lead sheet to BS 1178. Flashings, gutter linings, etc should be at least Code 4, soakers may be Code 3
- aluminium and aluminium alloys to BS 1470 (0.6mm to 0.9mm thick) and protected from contact with mortar by a coating of bituminous paint
- zinc alloy to BS 6561 and 0.6mm thick
- copper to BS 2870, 0.7mm thick is suitable for gutters, 0.55mm thick fully annealed is suitable for flashing, soakers and saddles.

To prevent electrolytic action where metal items may be in contact, eg flashings and soakers, these should not be of different metals.

Proprietary flashings should be assessed in accordance with Technical Requirement R3.

(d) underlays

The commonly used type IF felt has been known to disintegrate after a few years where it is exposed at the eaves and it is recommended that a better quality felt be used in this position.

Some proprietary roofing underlays have a higher vapour resistance than bitumen felt and may need additional roof ventilation.

To minimise the risk of condensation in the case of a fully supported underlay above rigid sarking, underlays should have a low vapour resistance, preferably less than 5.7MNs/g. Underlays with a higher vapour resistance may need increased ventilation to the roof space and between the underlay and sarking. Manufacturer's recommendations should be followed.

Proprietary underlays should have been assessed in accordance with Technical Requirement R3. Manufacturers' recommendations should be followed.

(e) rigid sarking

The following materials are acceptable:

- tongued and grooved or square edged boarding to BS 1297
- bitumen impregnated insulating board to BS 1142 : Part 3 (sarking and sheathing grade)
- WBP or CBR plywood to BS 6566, durability Class G
- Type C4 chipboard to BS 5669
- proprietary products which have been assessed in accordance with Technical Requirement R3.

MATERIALS

Performance Standards	Guidance

ROOFING MATERIALS (continued)

7.2 - M5 **(f) battens and counter battens**

Battens and counter battens should be to the sizes specified in the design. Timber used for battens and counter battens should be as listed in BS 5534 : Part 1.

Preservative treatment is required for battens to vertical tiling and slating. Preservative treatment is recommended for roof battens in *severe* exposure areas. Reference should be made to Chapter 2.3 'Timber preservation (natural solid timber)' (Materials) for guidance on preservative treatments.

(g) insulation

Thermal insulation should be to the design specification.

The following materials are acceptable:
● mineral fibre mats   to BS 5803 : Part 1
● blown mineral fibre   to BS 5803 : Part 2
● blown cellulose fibre to BS 5803 : Part 3
● proprietary materials assessed in accordance with Technical Requirement R3.

Insulation of water pipes should be in accordance with Chapter 8.1 'Internal services' (Materials).

(h) fascias, bargeboards and soffits

Timber used for fascias, bargeboards, soffits, etc should be pre-treated with preservative. Reference should be made to Chapter 2.3 'Timber preservation (natural solid timber)' (Materials) for guidance on preservative treatments.

The following materials are also acceptable:
● WPB plywood to BS 6566, durability Class M or better
● high density fibre reinforced calcium silicate board that meets the performance requirements of BS 3536
● glass fibre reinforced cement (GRC) board that meets the performance requirements of BS 3536
● proprietary products which have been assessed in accordance with Technical Requirement R3.

(i) firestopping and cavity barriers

Cavity barriers in boxed eaves should be wire reinforced mineral wool blanket, at least 50mm thick. Ordinary mineral wool quilt is acceptable as firestopping above separating walls.

Performance Standards	Guidance

(j) protection to ventilation openings

Ventilation openings where the least dimension exceeds 10mm should be protected to prevent the entry of birds, etc.

Acceptable protection of openings can be be provided by:
- rigid fabrications with width of opening greater than 3mm and less than 10mm (no restriction on length)
- rigid fabrications with round holes greater than 3mm and less than 10mm in diameter
- square or rectangular mesh where the clear opening size is greater than 3mm and less than 10mm.

RECLAIMED MATERIALS

7.2 - M6   Reclaimed materials shall be:

(a) of the type, size and quality required in the design

(b) suitable for re-use

Materials recovered from older buildings, such as timber, slate or tile, may be re-used only with the prior agreement of the NHBC. Independent certification of suitability may be required.

Performance Standards	Guidance

SITEWORK STANDARDS

7.2 - S1 All sitework shall:
(a) **meet with the Technical Requirements**
(b) **take account of the design**
(c) **follow established good practice and workmanship**

Sitework that complies with the design and the guidance below will be acceptable for pitched roofs.

WALL PLATES

7.2 - S2 Wall plates shall be bedded to distribute roof loads and fixed to prevent wind uplift

Roof construction details should be available on site, particularly for combination and specialist roofs.

Wall plates should be bedded to line and level using nails or straps to hold them down in accordance with the design requirements.

Wall plates should be in lengths not less than 3 metres long and joined using half-lapped joints at corners and in running lengths. In Scotland, 100mm x 25mm wall plates should be used, in long lengths, butt jointed.

Where required, holding down straps should be fixed to the wall plate at maximum 1.2m centres. If the strap is not turned into a bed joint, it should be fixed to the wall with at least three screw fixings.

STRAPPING

7.2 - S3 Straps shall be used, where necessary, to restrain gable and separating walls and hold down the roof against wind uplift

RESTRAINT STRAPS
Restraint straps, or a restraining form of gable ladder, are required to provide stability to walls. They should be installed as shown in the design.

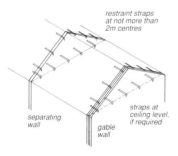

restraint straps at not more than 2m centres

straps at ceiling level, if required

separating wall

gable wall

SITEWORK

Performance Standards

Guidance

STRAPPING (continued)

7.2 - S3 (continued)

Restraint straps should be fixed to at least two trusses with two steel screws or two 75mm x 4mm (8SWG) round nails to each timber member.

Straps should be supported using noggings between rafters and packing provided between the wall and the rafter.

Rafters should not be notched to make the straps flush with the rafter. Straps should go under rafters and over ceiling joists. The turn-down should be on a substantial piece of blockwork, preferably the centre of an uncut block.

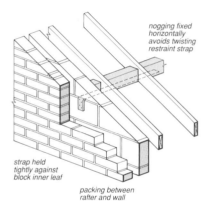

nogging fixed horizontally avoids twisting restraint strap

strap held tightly against block inner leaf

packing between rafter and wall

HOLDING DOWN STRAPS

Holding down straps should be used when detailed in the design.

Holding down straps may be required where the:
- roof is of lightweight construction
- site is exposed.

If in doubt, check with the designer.

Straps should be at least one metre long and either screwed to the face of masonry or have a tail built into a masonry bed joint. If screws are used, a minimum of three screws are necessary, at least one of which should be located within 150mm of the bottom end of the strap. Nailing is not acceptable.

Performance Standards

Guidance

TRUSSED RAFTERS

7.2 - S4 **Trussed rafters shall be protected from damage before and during construction**

Items to be taken into account include:

(a) storage

To avoid distortion and prevent damage, trussed rafters should be stored clear of the ground, either flat on level bearers placed under joints (for short term storage) or vertically and propped (for long term storage).

Trusses should be protected against weather to prevent corrosion of truss plates and deterioration of the timber. Ventilation should be provided.

support at wall plate position

ventilation

rafters clear of ground

Any damaged trussed rafters or trussed rafters with loose plates should be rejected, not repaired.

(b) handling

To prevent distortion during construction, trussed rafters should be carried upright (if carried flat, bending can loosen the fasteners).

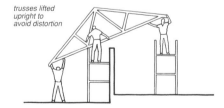

trusses lifted upright to avoid distortion

7.2 - S5 **Trussed rafters shall be erected in accordance with fabricators' instructions**

Detailed guidance on the use and handling of trussed rafters is given in the International Truss Plate Association Technical Handbook available from trussed rafter suppliers.

SITEWORK

Performance Standards

Guidance

TRUSSED RAFTERS (continued)

7.2 - S5 (continued)

Detailed drawings should be available on site to show the layout of the trussed rafters, especially at hips, valleys and trimmings to chimneys, etc.

Trussed rafters should be supported normally only at the junction between the ceiling tie and rafter, unless specifically designed otherwise, eg as a cantilever.

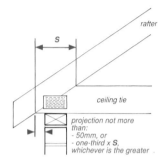

rafter

S

ceiling tie

projection not more than:
- 50mm, or
*- one-third x **S**,*
whichever is the greater .

Trussed rafters should be evenly spaced and vertical. Temporary bracing should be provided to control the spacing and keep trusses vertical.

Trussed rafters should be fixed to the wall plates either:
● in accordance with the design, or
● using double skew nailing or truss clips.

Avoid damaging the metal truss plates, trussed rafters or wall plates.

The spacing or structure of trusses should not be altered without the designer's approval.

Where the width of gable ladders exceeds that of the trussed rafter centres, noggings should be provided to reduce the span of the roofing tile battens.

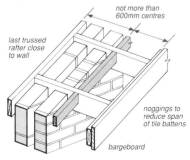

not more than 600mm centres

last trussed rafter close to wall

noggings to reduce span of tile battens

bargeboard

Performance Standards	Guidance

The gable ladder can be used to provide restraint to the external wall if:

- there is blocking between the last trussed rafter and the inner leaf (at a maximum of 2m spacing), *and*
- the soffit board is cut carefully and then fixed securely so as to restrain the outer leaf.

7.2 - S6   Trussed rafters shall be braced to prevent distortion

The roof should be braced using at least 100mm x 25mm timber. All bracing should be twice nailed with 3.35mm (10 gauge) x 65mm long galvanized round wire nails to every trussed rafter it crosses.

The minimum bracing requirements are shown in Appendix 7.2-E. Additional bracing may be needed in exposed areas. Check the design drawings for special requirements.

All bracing should be completed before starting to lay the roof covering.

Longitudinal binders should butt solidly against the wall at each end. This is most easily achieved by fixing the binder in two lap-jointed lengths.

Braces and binders, where not continuous, should have lapped joints and be nailed to at least two trusses.

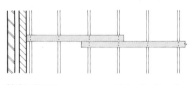

binders abutted
tightly against
gable and
separating walls

binders fixed to ceiling
ties of trussed rafters,
if necessary using
two lap-jointed lengths

TRADITIONAL CUT ROOFS

7.2 - S7   Roof timbers shall be of the grades and sizes shown on the drawings

Structural timber should be marked to show its strength class (normally SC3 or SC4). Alternatively, evidence of species and grade should be available to determine the equivalent strength class.

The correct size of timber should be used for each member, as shown on the design drawings.

Performance Standards   Guidance

TRADITIONAL CUT ROOFS (continued)

7.2 - S8   Construction of traditional cut roofs shall ensure adequate structural stability

Items to be taken into account include:

(a) location of members   All members should be accurately located. Purlins and binders should be built in, where necessary.

In a typical traditional roof, the basic timber members are:
- RAFTER: carries the weight of the roof finish, eg tiles, tile battens and underfelt
- CEILING JOIST or TIE: triangulates the rafters, stopping the walls and roof spreading outwards; supports the ceiling finish and any walkways, etc
- RIDGE: provides fixing and spacing for the tops of rafters
- PURLIN: supports long span rafters to prevent deflection and increase stiffness
- STRUTS: give support to purlins to prevent deflection and transmit roof loading to loadbearing structure below.

The following are extra members which may be used on large roofs:
- COLLAR: ties the roof together at purlin level
- CEILING BINDERS and HANGERS: support long span ceiling joists
- POLE PLATES: similar to purlins but used where ceiling joists are above wall plate level.

Positions of standard structural members are shown in the diagrammatic representation below:

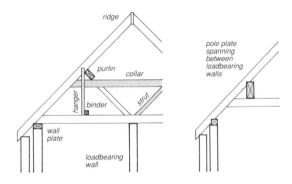

Performance Standards

Guidance

(b) prevention of distortion and overloading

The design details for sizes of timber members should be followed.

All framing should be completed before roof coverings are laid.

If a roof is not a simple triangle, all members should be fully supported and tied together. If necessary, temporary support to long span members should be used until the framing is complete.

(c) valley and hip construction

Particular care is needed in the construction of valleys and hips:

● VALLEY RAFTERS carry load from both sections of the roof. Valley rafters will need to be larger than ordinary rafters to take the extra load and to provide full bearing for the splay cut of JACK RAFTERS. (Long valley rafters may need intermediate support.)

● HIP RAFTERS provide spacing and fixing for jack rafters. They need to be a deeper section than other rafters to take the top cut of the JACK RAFTERS. Purlins should be mitred at hips, and lip cut to accept the bottom of the hip rafter.

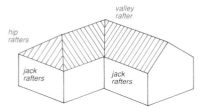

(d) dormer construction

On most dormers, the DORMER CHEEK STUDS should be supported either by a double rafter or by a double floor joist.

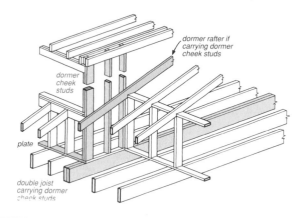

Performance Standards   **Guidance**

TRADITIONAL CUT ROOFS (continued)

7.2 - S8(d) (continued)

Where cheek framing does not extend to floor level, a double rafter will give necessary support to the cheek. The two rafters must be fixed together.

Trimming members around dormers should be large enough to take the extra load from the cut main roof members and dormer framing and cladding, as detailed in the design.

Dormers should be framed up so they are independent of the window frame, using a suitable lintel over the opening.

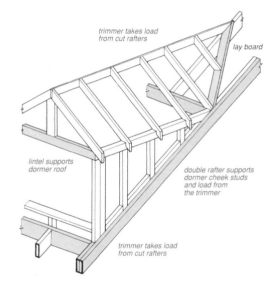

trimmer takes load from cut rafters

lay board

lintel supports dormer roof

double rafter supports dormer cheek studs and load from the trimmer

trimmer takes load from cut rafters

(e) jointing of members

All joints should be cut accurately to fit tightly. When they are nailed, care should be taken not to split members.

The following should be used at main connections:
- RAFTERS to ceiling joists: nailed lapped joint. The rafter should be birdsmouthed over and skew nailed to the wall plate

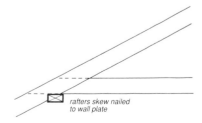

rafters skew nailed to wall plate

Performance Standards

Guidance

● RAFTERS to purlin: a birdsmouth joint should be used if the purlin is fixed vertically

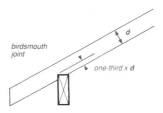

birdsmouth
joint

d

one-third x d

● PURLIN connections: support should be provided directly under joint or use a scarf joint. Any scarf joint should be made near a strut so that the joint supports the longer span.

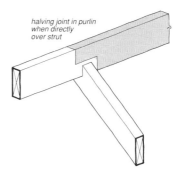

*halving joint in purlin
when directly
over strut*

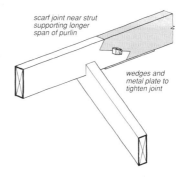

*scarf joint near strut
supporting longer
span of purlin*

*wedges and
metal plate to
tighten joint*

Performance Standards | **Guidance**

TRADITIONAL CUT ROOFS (continued)

7.2 - S8(e) (continued)

Angle ties should be used on hipped roof corners to prevent the wall plates spreading. For heavily loaded hip rafters, eg where they are carrying purlins, dragon ties or similar bracing should be used to prevent hip rafter spread.

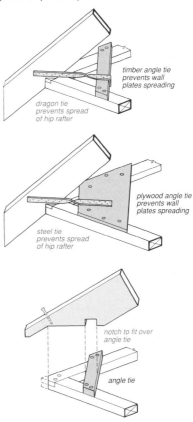

timber angle tie
prevents wall
plates spreading

dragon tie
prevents spread
of hip rafter

plywood angle tie
prevents wall
plates spreading

steel tie
prevents spread
of hip rafter

notch to fit over
angle tie

angle tie

WATER TANK SUPPORTS

7.2 - S9   Loads from water cisterns
shall be transferred to:

(a) the node points of
trussed rafters

In trussed rafter roofs, tank stands should be supported at the node points of the trussed rafters and the load spread over at least three trusses.

Correct supports are illustrated in Appendix 7.2-F.

(b) suitable bearers in
traditional cut roofs

In traditional cut roofs, tank stands should be supported as shown in the design.

Performance Standards	Guidance

FASCIAS, BARGEBOARDS AND SOFFITS

7.2 - S10 Fascias, bargeboards and soffits shall be selected, fixed and treated against decay in accordance with the design

Items to be taken into account include:

(a) timber quality

Timber for external feature work should be free from waney edges, large knots and resinous pockets, splits and other unsightly defects.

(b) fixing

All joints should be cut and fixed neatly. Mitred angles and splay joints should be used to prevent exposure of end-grain. Butt joints to fascias should be splayed.

(c) treatment against decay

Where preservative treated timber is cut or planed, a liberal brush coating of preservative should be applied.

All untreated timber that is to be painted should be knotted and primed all round before fixing. When timber requires a stained finish, one coat of stain should be applied before fixing.

ROOFING MATERIALS

7.2 - S11 Roofing materials shall be installed in accordance with the design

Items to be taken into account include:

(a) ventilation

All roof voids should be ventilated to prevent condensation problems.

Ventilation openings where the least dimension exceeds 10mm should be protected with mesh to prevent entry of birds, etc.

Where proprietary eaves ventilators are used, they should be fixed in accordance with the manufacturer's instructions.

Performance Standards   **Guidance**

ROOFING MATERIALS (continued)

7.2 - S11(a) (continued)

Ventilation should be provided on opposite sides of the roof space, equivalent to a continuous gap of the width shown in the following drawings:

ROOF PITCH OVER 15°

ROOF PITCH BELOW 15°

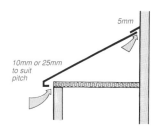

MONO-PITCHED ROOF

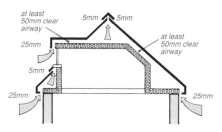

ROOM-IN-THE-ROOF (flat roof dormer)

Performance Standards

Guidance

Where the ceiling is partially or completely sloping and the ventilation path is blocked, the roof void should have additional ventilation openings immediately below and above the block.

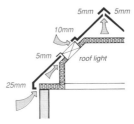

ROOM-IN-THE-ROOF (partially sloping ceiling)

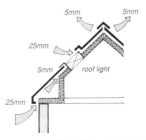

ROOM-IN-THE-ROOF (completely sloping ceiling)

PITCHED ROOF DORMER

Performance Standards

Guidance

ROOFING MATERIALS (continued)

7.2 - S11 (b) underlays

Horizontal laps should be as follows:

Pitch	Minimum horizontal lap (underlay not fully supported)
Less than 15°	225mm
15° to 34°	150mm
35° and above	100mm

Vertical laps in the underlay should occur only over rafters and be securely fixed. Where the pitch is below 30°, the underlay should be supported at eaves level by a tilting fillet. The underlay should be dressed into the gutter and pulled tight to ensure there are no troughs to retain water.

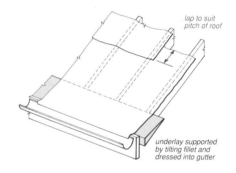

lap to suit pitch of roof

underlay supported by tilting fillet and dressed into gutter

The underlay should extend over the ridge.

A strip of underlay, at least 600mm wide, should be laid over hips and above the underlay to the main roof.

Performance Standards

Guidance

At valleys, a similar strip should be laid under the main roof underlay and held down by the valley battens, where used. The main roof underlay should be dressed over the valley battens.

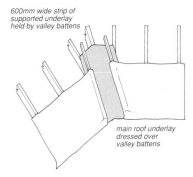

600mm wide strip of supported underlay held by valley battens

main roof underlay dressed over valley battens

The underlay should be turned up at least 100mm at all abutments to prevent rain and snow being blown into the roof space.

Where necessary to protect the heads of timber features, the underlay should extend 50mm beyond gable walls, bargeboards, etc.

Particular care is needed where pipes project through the underlay. Torn underlay around pipes can lead to the ceiling becoming wet and stained. Cut a small cross in the underlay and sleeve over the pipe so that the tongues turn up.

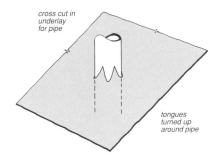

cross cut in underlay for pipe

tongues turned up around pipe

Performance Standards　　　　　　　　**Guidance**

ROOFING MATERIALS (continued)

7.2 - S11 (c) battens and counter battens

Battens should be set out in straight lines, parallel to the ridge and to the gauge required by the tile or slate. The lap should not be decreased because this would reduce weathertightness. The lowest batten should be fixed so that the tile projects halfway across the gutter.

Battens should be:
- at least 1.2m long
- supported by at least three rafters
- butt jointed on a rafter, *and*
- nailed to every rafter.

Batten ends should be cut square and nails skew driven on each side of the joint. Not more than one batten in four should be joined over any one truss or rafter.

Where underlay laps are not under a batten, an extra batten should be used to prevent the underlay lap opening due to wind uplift.

Battens on rigid sarking boards should be supported on counter battens to allow free drainage of any water that may reach the underlay. Counter battens should be fixed through to the rafters and not to the sarking boards alone. Battens should be fixed through counter battens to rafters.

Battens should be fixed with cut or wire nails. The nail shank can be smooth, annular ringed or helically threaded. Nails can be steel or aluminium. In coastal areas, steel nails should be hot dip galvanized.

(d) slates and tiles

Slates should be fully nailed over the whole roof. For clay and concrete tiles, Tables 2 and 3 in Appendix 7.2-D give the minimum nailing requirements. In areas of severe exposure, additional fixings may be required. This should be checked with the designer if not shown on drawings.

Careful setting out makes the actual tiling process faster and will influence the finished appearance on the roof. It helps to avoid problems such as unequal overhangs at verges and often makes it possible to avoid excessive tile cutting at abutments, chimneys and similar obstructions.

For plain tiles and slates, joints should be slightly open. This allows some flexibility in setting out. Interlocking tiles have a tolerance of about 3mm in the joint, giving sufficient latitude over the whole roof width to avoid tile cutting.

Performance Standards

Guidance

Bottom edges of slate and plain tile roofs should be finished with an under-eaves course.

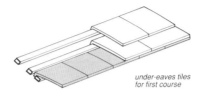

*under-eaves tiles
for first course*

Purpose-made tile-and-a-half, or half-tiles, should be used at verges. Cut tiles at verges are not acceptable.

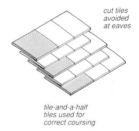

*cut tiles
avoided
at eaves*

*tile-and-a-half
tiles used for
correct coursing*

Tiles to be bedded on mortar should be wetted first. Allow the surface water to drain before fixing. Substantial thicknesses of mortar bedding may be needed, eg beneath a bold roll tile, to give it body. Mortar should normally be 1 : 3, cement : sharp sand.

(e) other roof coverings

When using the following materials, the detailing and workmanship should follow the design and recognised good building practice:
- sheet metal roofing including lead, copper and zinc
- thatch
- cedar shingles.

Thatching should be as recommended by the Thatch Advisory Service or other appropriate authority in accordance with Technical Requirement R3.

SITEWORK

Performance Standards	Guidance

FLASHINGS AND WEATHERINGS

7.2 - S12 Flashings and weatherings shall be constructed to prevent damp entering the dwelling

Items to be taken into account include:

(a) eaves

Tiles or slates should overhang to the centre of the gutter. For slates or plain tiles, an under-eaves course should be used.

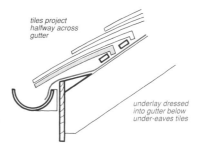

tiles project halfway across gutter

underlay dressed into gutter below under-eaves tiles

To prevent the underlay sagging at the eaves and forming a water trap behind the fascia, it is recommended that the underlay is supported by a continuous fillet. Where the pitch is below 30°, a continuous fillet should always be used. Plain tiles are unsuitable for pitches less than 35°.

(b) verges

All verge tiles and slates should be bedded on an undercloak. Alternatively, proprietary dry verge systems should be fixed in accordance with manufacturers' recommendations.

Where a bargeboard is used, the undercloak should be securely nailed to a true line, projecting 40mm to 50mm beyond the bargeboard. If laid directly on masonry, the undercloak should be bedded on mortar struck off flush with the external surface of the wall.

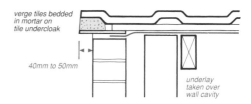

verge tiles bedded in mortar on tile undercloak

40mm to 50mm

underlay taken over wall cavity

The undercloak should lap the roof underlay but not tilt inwards. Verge slates or tiles should be bedded on the undercloak and the mortar struck off smoothly and cleanly. Interlocking single lap tiles should be secured with clips nailed in position at the tile lap, as well as bedded in mortar.

Performance Standards

Guidance

(c) ridges and hips

Ridge and hip tiles are normally bedded in mortar. Alternatively, ridge tiles can be mechanically fixed using a proprietary dry ridge fixing system following the manufacturer's instructions.

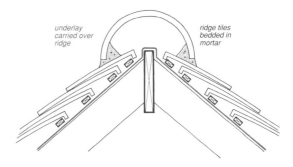

underlay carried over ridge

ridge tiles bedded in mortar

The following tiles should be nailed as well as bedded in mortar:
- bonnet hip tiles
- end ridge tiles
- ridge tiles over separating walls
- mono-pitch ridge tiles.

Where half-round tiles are used at hips, they should be supported at the base of the hip by a galvanized hip iron.

(d) valleys and hidden gutters

Construction should be adequate in relation to:
- depth
- width
- undercloaking
- pointing
- adequate support
- pitch.

SITEWORK

Performance Standards | Guidance

FLASHINGS AND WEATHERINGS (continued)

7.2 - S12(d) (continued)

Valleys should be formed using one of the following:
- valley coursing tiles (plain tiles)
- valley trough tiles (interlocking tiles)
- non-ferrous metal
- PVC
- semi-rigid asbestos bitumen.

Where roof coverings are of plain tiles or slates, laced and swept valleys may be used or, alternatively, a mitred valley with soakers.

The pitch of a valley is less than the pitch of the main roof. Where tiles are to be used for valleys, the valley pitch should be not less than the minimum permissible pitch given in Table 1 of Appendix 7.2-D.

VALLEY USING VALLEY TILES

In roofs with plain tiles, purpose-made valley coursing tiles should be used. Adjacent roof tiles should be cut neatly to form a smooth junction, preferably cutting from tile-and-a-half tiles.

For single lap interlocking tiles, purpose-made valley trough tiles should be supported by gutter boards. Roof tiles should be cut to the correct rake. Mechanical cutting gives a neater appearance than hand cutting. The tiles should be bedded in mortar, leaving a minimum 100mm wide channel (125mm minimum for pitches below 30°).

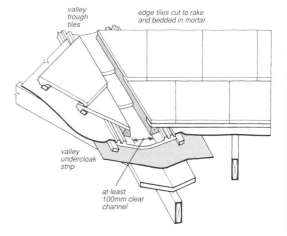

valley trough tiles

edge tiles cut to rake and bedded in mortar

valley undercloak strip

at least 100mm clear channel

Performance Standards

Guidance

LEAD-LINED VALLEY

Lead-lined valleys should be Code 4 (colour coded blue) or Code 5 (colour coded red) and supported on gutter boards of 6mm thick marine ply or as specified. Lead in valleys should be laid in lengths not exceeding 1.5m and be lapped 150mm at each length. Tiles should be cut and bedded as for valley trough tiles except that the mortar should be bedded on an undercloak (for example slate) to prevent direct contact between the lead and the mortar.

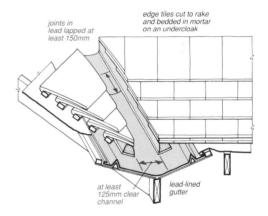

edge tiles cut to rake and bedded in mortar on an undercloak

joints in lead lapped at least 150mm

at least 125mm clear channel

lead-lined gutter

PROPRIETARY SYSTEMS

Proprietary gutter or valley systems should be fixed in accordance with the manufacturer's recommendations.

(e) flat roof intersection

Where a flat roof adjoins a pitched roof, or where valleys or gutters occur, the waterproof membrane should be carried up under the tiling to a height of 150mm above the flat roof, valley or gutter and lapped by the roofing underlay.

The lowest course of tiles/slates should not touch the roof membrane.

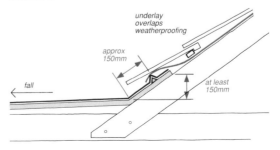

underlay overlaps weatherproofing

approx 150mm

fall

at least 150mm

Performance Standards	Guidance

FLASHINGS AND WEATHERINGS (continued)

7.2 - S12(e) (continued)

Note

Where the flat roof is over a dormer, it is recommended that the flat roof should be designed and constructed with a fall to the front or sides.

Flat roofs should comply with Chapter 7.1 'Flat roofs and balconies' (Sitework).

(f) abutments

All abutments should be weatherproofed using non-ferrous metal flashings. Lead flashings should be at least Code 4 (colour coded blue), while soakers are normally Code 3 (colour coded green). Normally, lead flashings should not exceed 1.8m in length, with laps of not less than 100mm.

Flashing should be tucked into a mortar joint or chase 25mm deep and at least 150mm above the tiling level and lead wedged in place. The joint should then be pointed in cement mortar of 1 : 3, cement : sharp sand.

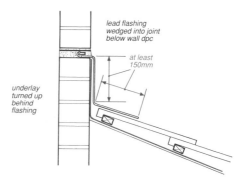

lead flashing
wedged into joint
below wall dpc

at least
150mm

underlay
turned up
behind
flashing

Cavity trays should be linked to the flashing to prevent water penetrating into an enclosed area below where a:
- flat or pitched roof over an enclosed area abuts a wall
- balcony abuts a wall.

Where a pitched roof abuts the wall at an angle, a stepped cavity tray linked to a stepped flashing should be used.

Performance Standards

Guidance

Stepped flashings should be cut from a strip at least 150mm wide.

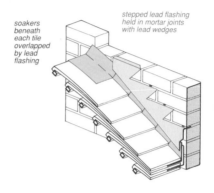

soakers beneath each tile overlapped by lead flashing

stepped lead flashing held in mortar joints with lead wedges

(g) projections through the roof

Chimney flashings should link with the chimney dpc.

DETAIL OF BACK GUTTER

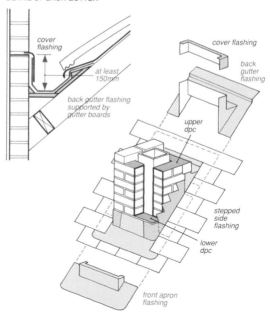

cover flashing

at least 150mm

back gutter flashing supported by gutter boards

cover flashing

back gutter flashing

upper dpc

stepped side flashing

lower dpc

front apron flashing

Performance Standards   Guidance

FLASHINGS AND WEATHERINGS (continued)

7.2 - S12(g) (continued)

A purpose-made one piece flashing and upstand should be used around pipes projecting through the tiling.

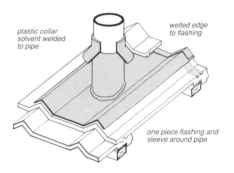

plastic collar
solvent welded
to pipe

welted edge
to flashing

one piece flashing and
sleeve around pipe

(h) changes in roof slope

Flashings or soakers should be used where there is a change in roof slope of 5° or more, eg at mansards and sprockets.

A saddle flashing should be used where a ridge meets the main roof.

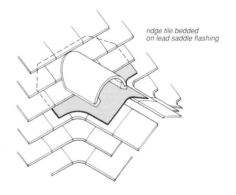

ridge tile bedded
on lead saddle flashing

Performance Standards

Guidance

FIRESTOPPING

7.2 - S13 Pitched roofs shall be constructed to offer adequate resistance to the spread of fire

Firestopping and cavity barriers should be provided:
● at junctions between cavities
● above separating walls
● within boxed eaves of separating walls.

The separating wall should stop about 25mm below the top of adjacent roof trusses.

A soft fire-resistant packing, such as mineral wool, should be used to allow for movement in roof timbers and prevent 'hogging' of the tiles.

A cavity barrier should be provided within boxed eaves. The cavity barrier should be wire reinforced mineral wool blanket, at least 50mm thick, nailed to the rafter and carefully cut to shape to fully seal the boxed eaves.

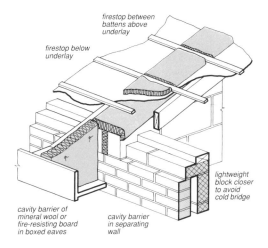

firestop between battens above underlay

firestop below underlay

lightweight block closer to avoid cold bridge

cavity barrier of mineral wool or fire-resisting board in boxed eaves

cavity barrier in separating wall

SITEWORK

Performance Standards | Guidance

THERMAL INSULATION

7.2 - S14 Thermal insulation and ventilation of roofs shall prevent the adverse effects of condensation

To avoid condensation forming in the roof space ensure that:
- cross ventilation of the roof is provided in accordance with the design
- insulation does not block the ventilation path at eaves level
- insulation is laid over the whole loft area, including the wall plate
- there are no gaps in the insulation.

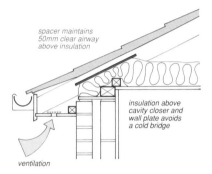

spacer maintains
50mm clear airway
above insulation

insulation above
cavity closer and
wall plate avoids
a cold bridge

ventilation

The amount of moist air entering the loft space from the dwelling should be controlled by:
- draughtstripping the loft hatch or using a proprietary loft hatch
- ensuring that the hatch is heavy enough (or suitably fixed) to compress the draught seal
- sealing gaps where services pass through the ceiling.

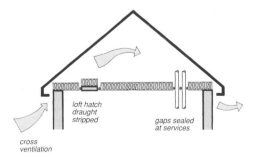

loft hatch
draught
stripped

gaps sealed
at services

cross
ventilation

The guidance above will assist in reducing the risk of condensation occuring but is not acceptable as an alternative to cross ventilation of the roof space.

Performance Standards

Guidance

To reduce the risk of freezing and condensation on pipework, the following precautions should be taken:
- place roof insulation *above and around* water tanks but not below them
- locate water pipes below the main roof insulation whenever possible
- insulate *all* water pipes above the main roof insulation. It is recommended that the cold rising main be insulated above ceiling level even if it is below the main roof insulation (condensation that forms on uninsulated cold water pipes located below the main roof insulation can result in damage to ceilings and decorations).

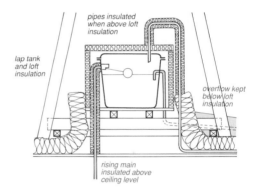

pipes insulated when above loft insulation

lap tank and loft insulation

overflow kept below loft insulation

rising main insulated above ceiling level

ROOF DRAINAGE

7.2 - S15 **Roof drainage shall adequately carry rainwater to an outfall**

Items to be taken into account include:

(a) fixing and jointing gutters and downpipes

Rainwater gutters and downpipes should be fixed in the positions indicated by the design using the correct type of fittings for internal and external angles, outlets, etc to ensure efficient drainage of the roof. Gutters and downpipes should be supported and jointed in accordance with the manufacturer's recommendations.

(b) falls

Gutters should be laid with sufficient fall towards the outlet, unless designed to be flat, and be provided with stop ends.

(c) satisfactory outfall

If a downpipe discharges above ground level or above a drainage gully, a shoe should be fixed to the end of the pipe to prevent walls becoming saturated.

Statutory references

The following table lists references to building legislation and associated documents applicable at August 1990.

Clause	Subject	Statute			
		Building [1] Regulations	Building [2] Standards (Scotland)	Building [3] Regulations (N Ireland)	Isle of Man [4] Bye-laws
D3(c)	Holding down	-	Part C	Part D	Part D
D3(f)	Timber sarking	-	Part C	Part B	Part B
D4(c)	Restraint to walls	A1/2	Part C	Part D	Part D
D6	Traditional cut roofs	A1/2	Part C	Part D	Part D
D7	House Longhorn Beetle	AD to support Regulation 7	-	Part B	Part B
D12	Thatch, etc	B2/3/4	Part D	Part E	Part E
D15	Roof drains	H3	Part M	Part N	Part N
M2	Timber sizes	A1/2	Part C	Part D	Part D
M2	Timber sizes	**Associated documents** BS 5268 : Part 2 : Table 3			

[1] Approved Documents to the Building Regulations 1985 for England and Wales (and 1990 edition).
[2] Building Standards (Scotland) Regulations 1981 and all published amendments.
[3] Building Regulations (Northern Ireland) 1990.
[4] Isle of Man Bye-laws 1976, amended 1980 and 1987.

Guidance

Protection from corrosion of metal components embedded in masonry

Metal components, other than wall ties built into masonry, should be made of a material listed below and protected in the way described in Table 1.

Reference should be made to Table 2 for guidance on which category of material and protection to use.

Table 1 - Anchorages, dowels and fixings

Category	Base material	Form	Grade and standard to be complied with	Protective measures to be carried out after fabrication
A	Hot-dip galvanized low carbon steel	Sheet	BS 2989, Z1 or Z2, coating type G 600. Minimum mass of coating 600 g/m^2 including both sides	All external cut edges to be protected using a one-pack chemical-resistant paint complying with HF1A to HF2F in part 4 of table 4H of BS 5493 : 1977 and modified to give adequate adhesion to the fixing
			BS 2989, Z1 or Z2, coating type G 275. Minimum mass of coating 275 g/m^2 including both sides	Coating to be applied after fabrication to the external surfaces and consisting of either: (a) bituminous solution complying with types 1 or 2 of BS 3416 and of minimum thickness 25 μm; or (b) a one-pack chemical-resistant paint complying with HF1A to HF2F in part 4 of table 4H of BS 5493 : 1977 and modified to give adequate adhesion to the fixing. Where the zinc is removed on internal surfaces during fabrication, e.g. by welding, further protection should be applied to these areas
B	Low carbon steel	Strip	BS 1449 : Part 1 : 1983 (mechanical requirements in table 11 only) BS 4360 grade 43A	Post-galvanizing complying with BS 729. Minimum mass of coating 460 g/m^2 including both sides
C	Low carbon steel	Strip	BS 1449 : Part 1 : 1983 (mechanical requirements in table 11 only) BS 4360 grade 43A	Post-galvanizing complying with BS 729. Minimum mass of coating 940 g/m^2 including both sides
D	Copper		BS 6017	
	Copper alloys		BS 2870 : 1980, grades listed in tables 8 and 12 BS 2873 : 1969, grades listed in tables 4 and 6 BS 2874 : 1968, grades listed in tables 6, 8 and 9 except CA 106	Material other than phosphor bronze to be formed either: (a) by bending at dull red heat and allowing to cool in still air; or (b) by cold forming and subsequently stress relief annealing at 250 °C to 300 °C for 30 min to 1 h. Effectiveness of stress relieving of cold formed components to be tested by the supplier using the mercurous nitrate test described in clause 11 of BS 2874 : 1969
	Austenitic stainless steel, minimum 18/8 composition and excluding free machining specifications	Strip	BS 1449 : Part 2	
		Bar Rod	BS 970 : Part 1	
		Tube	BS 6323 : Part 8	
		Wire	BS 1554 BS 3111 : Part 2	

Reproduced from BS 5628 : Part 3 by permission of BSI.

Table 2 - Protection of metal components (other than wall ties) built into masonry

Type of component	Situation	Category given in table 1 (material and recommended protective measures)	
		Three storeys or less	More than three storeys
Anchorages, bonding ties, slip brick ties and continuous support angles	All	C or D	D
Dowels and restraint straps Joist hangers Reinforcement for non-structural use	Internal walls	A, B, C, D	A, B, C, D
	In contact with or embedded in inner leaf	A, B, C, D	A, B, C, D
	In contact with or embedded in outer leaf or single leaf walls	C or D	D
Lintels	All	As specified in BS 5977 : Part 2 for the appropriate type of lintel i.e. installed with or without d.p.c.	Not normally applicable. If used, special precautions may be necessary
Cavity trays	All	As specified in BS 5977 : Part 2 for lintels installed without d.p.c.	As specified in BS 5977 : Part 2 for lintels installed without d.p.c.

It is an NHBC recommendation that components in contact with, or embedded in, an inner leaf which is damp or exposed to periodic wettings (eg below dpc) should be protected in the same way as components in contact with, or embedded in, an outer leaf.

Reproduced from BS 5628 : Part 3 by permission of BSI.

APPENDIX 7.2-C

Guidance

Sizes, spacings and spans for timber roof members

Tables B5 to B20 in this Appendix are reproduced from Approved Document A1/2 to the Building Regulations.

For Tables B5 to B8, the dead load of insulation, 9.5mm plasterboard and a skim coat, may be assumed to be less than 0.25kN/m². Usually therefore, the left-hand columns should be used.

For Tables B9 to B20, the dead load of concrete interlocking tiles, battens and felt may be assumed to be in the range 0.50kN/m² to 0.75kN/m². Usually therefore, the centre columns should be used.

Table B5 Ceiling joists

Timber of strength class **SC3** *(see Table B1)*

Size of joist [mm × mm]	Dead load† [kN/m²]					
	Not more than 0.25			More than 0.25 but not more than 0.50		
	Spacing of joists [mm]					
	400	450	600	400	450	600
	Maximum clear span of joist [m]					
38 × 75	1.21	1.20	1.17	1.17	1.16	1.12
38 × 89*	1.54	1.53	1.48	1.48	1.46	1.41
38 × 100	1.81	1.79	1.74	1.74	1.71	1.64
38 × 125	2.45	2.41	2.32	2.32	2.28	2.18
38 × 140*	2.84	2.79	2.68	2.68	2.63	2.51
38 × 150	3.10	3.05	2.93	2.93	2.87	2.73
38 × 175	3.77	3.70	3.54	3.54	3.46	3.28
38 × 184*	4.01	3.94	3.76	3.76	3.68	3.48
38 × 200	4.44	4.36	4.15	4.15	4.06	3.83
38 × 225	5.11	5.02	4.77	4.77	4.66	4.39
47 × 75	1.35	1.33	1.30	1.30	1.28	1.24
47 × 100	2.00	1.98	1.91	1.91	1.88	1.80
47 × 125	2.69	2.65	2.55	2.55	2.50	2.38
47 × 150	3.39	3.34	3.19	3.19	3.13	2.97
47 × 175	4.10	4.03	3.85	3.85	3.77	3.56
47 × 200	4.82	4.73	4.50	4.50	4.41	4.16
47 × 225	5.54	5.43	5.16	5.16	5.04	4.75
50 × 75	1.39	1.38	1.34	1.34	1.32	1.28
50 × 100	2.06	2.03	1.96	1.96	1.93	1.85
50 × 125	2.76	2.72	2.61	2.61	2.57	2.45
50 × 150	3.48	3.42	3.28	3.28	3.21	3.05
50 × 175	4.21	4.13	3.94	3.94	3.86	3.65
50 × 200	4.94	4.85	4.61	4.61	4.51	4.25
50 × 225	5.66	5.56	5.28	5.28	5.16	4.86

Notes

* North American surfaced size

† Dead load is the load supported by the joist, excluding the mass of the joist

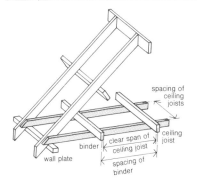

spacing of ceiling joists

ceiling joist

clear span of ceiling joist

binder

wall plate

spacing of binder

take the clear span for the binder as the clear dimension between supporting struts and/or walls

Notes

1 Tables B5 to B8 inclusive give sizes, spacings and spans for ceiling joists and binders supporting ceiling joists. The sizes, spacings and spans given will support the dead loads given in the tables and a maximum imposed load of 0.75kN/m² and a concentrated load of 0.9kN acting together.

   In calculating the ceiling joist sizes no account has been taken of trimming (e.g. around flues) or other loads (e.g. water tanks).

2 When spans for ceiling joists, and spacings for binders are unequal, the section sizes should be determined by the longer span.

3 See paragraph A2 which gives guidance on the need for bracing roof structures.

Reproduced from Approved Document A1/2 by permission of HMSO.

APPENDIX 7.2-C

Guidance

Sizes, spacings and spans for timber roof members (continued)

Table **B6** **Binders** supporting ceiling joists

Timber of strength class **SC3** *(see Table B1)*

	Dead load† [kN/m²]											
	Not more than 0.25						More than 0.25 but not more than 0.50					
	Spacing of binders [mm]											
	1200	1500	1800	2100	2400	2700	1200	1500	1800	2100	2400	2700
Size of binder [mm × mm]	Maximum clear span of binder [m]											
38 × 89*	1.05	1.00	0.97	0.93	0.90	0.88	0.98	0.93	0.89	0.86	0.83	0.80
38 × 100	1.21	1.16	1.11	1.07	1.04	1.01	1.13	1.07	1.02	0.98	0.95	0.92
38 × 125	1.60	1.52	1.46	1.40	1.35	1.31	1.47	1.39	1.33	1.27	1.23	1.18
38 × 140*	1.83	1.74	1.66	1.60	1.54	1.49	1.68	1.59	1.51	1.45	1.39	1.34
38 × 150	1.99	1.88	1.80	1.73	1.67	1.61	1.82	1.72	1.64	1.56	1.50	1.45
38 × 175	2.38	2.25	2.15	2.06	1.98	1.91	2.18	2.05	1.94	1.86	1.78	1.72
38 × 184*	2.52	2.38	2.27	2.18	2.09	2.02	2.30	2.17	2.05	1.96	1.88	1.80
38 × 200	2.77	2.62	2.49	2.39	2.30	2.22	2.53	2.38	2.25	2.15	2.06	1.94
38 × 225	3.17	2.99	2.84	2.72	2.61	2.52	2.88	2.70	2.56	2.44	2.31	2.17
47 × 100	1.33	1.27	1.22	1.18	1.14	1.11	1.24	1.17	1.12	1.08	1.04	1.01
47 × 125	1.75	1.66	1.59	1.53	1.48	1.43	1.61	1.52	1.45	1.39	1.34	1.29
47 × 150	2.17	2.06	1.96	1.89	1.82	1.76	1.99	1.88	1.78	1.71	1.64	1.58
47 × 175	2.59	2.45	2.34	2.24	2.16	2.09	2.37	2.23	2.12	2.02	1.94	1.87
47 × 200	3.01	2.85	2.71	2.60	2.50	2.41	2.75	2.58	2.45	2.34	2.24	2.16
47 × 225	3.44	3.24	3.08	2.95	2.84	2.74	3.13	2.93	2.78	2.65	2.54	2.42
50 × 100	1.37	1.31	1.26	1.21	1.17	1.14	1.27	1.21	1.15	1.11	1.07	1.03
50 × 125	1.80	1.71	1.63	1.57	1.52	1.47	1.65	1.56	1.49	1.43	1.37	1.33
50 × 150	2.22	2.11	2.01	1.93	1.86	1.80	2.04	1.92	1.83	1.75	1.68	1.62
50 × 175	2.66	2.51	2.39	2.30	2.21	2.14	2.43	2.28	2.17	2.07	1.99	1.92
50 × 200	3.09	2.91	2.78	2.66	2.56	2.47	2.81	2.64	2.51	2.39	2.30	2.21
50 × 225	3.52	3.32	3.16	3.02	2.90	2.80	3.20	3.00	2.85	2.72	2.61	2.49
63 × 100	1.51	1.44	1.39	1.34	1.29	1.25	1.40	1.33	1.27	1.22	1.18	1.14
63 × 125	1.97	1.88	1.79	1.73	1.67	1.61	1.82	1.72	1.64	1.57	1.51	1.46
63 × 150	2.44	2.31	2.21	2.12	2.04	1.98	2.24	2.11	2.00	1.92	1.84	1.78
63 × 175	2.90	2.75	2.62	2.51	2.42	2.34	2.65	2.50	2.37	2.27	2.18	2.10
63 × 200	3.37	3.18	3.03	2.90	2.79	2.70	3.07	2.89	2.74	2.62	2.51	2.42
63 × 225	3.83	3.62	3.44	3.29	3.17	3.06	3.49	3.28	3.11	2.96	2.85	2.74
75 × 125	2.12	2.01	1.92	1.85	1.79	1.73	1.95	1.84	1.75	1.68	1.62	1.56
75 × 150	2.61	2.47	2.36	2.26	2.18	2.11	2.39	2.25	2.14	2.05	1.97	1.90
75 × 175	3.10	2.93	2.80	2.68	2.58	2.50	2.83	2.67	2.53	2.42	2.33	2.25
75 × 200	3.59	3.39	3.23	3.10	2.98	2.88	3.28	3.08	2.92	2.79	2.68	2.59
75 × 225	4.08	3.85	3.66	3.51	3.38	3.26	3.72	3.49	3.31	3.16	3.04	2.93

Notes
* North American surfaced size
† Dead load is the load supported by the joist, excluding the mass of the joist as calculated for the purpose of Table B5

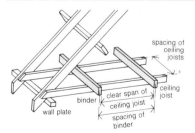

spacing of ceiling joists

ceiling joist

binder

clear span of ceiling joist

wall plate

spacing of binder

take the clear span for the binder as the clear dimension between supporting struts and/or walls

Notes

1 Tables B5 to B8 inclusive give sizes, spacings and spans for ceiling joists and binders supporting ceiling joists. The sizes, spacings and spans given will support the dead loads given in the tables and a maximum imposed load of 0.75kN/m² and a concentrated load of 0.9kN acting together.

In calculating the ceiling joist sizes no account has been taken of trimming (e.g. around flues) or other loads (e.g. water tanks).

2 When spans for ceiling joists, and spacings for binders are unequal, the section sizes should be determined by the longer span.

3 See paragraph A2 which gives guidance on the need for bracing roof structures.

Reproduced from Approved Document A1/2 by permission of HMSO.

Guidance

Table **B7** **Ceiling joists**

Timber of strength class **SC4** *(see Table B1)*

	Dead load† [kN/m²]					
	Not more than 0.25			More than 0.25 but not more than 0.50		
	Spacing of joists [mm]					
	400	450	600	400	450	600
Size of joist [mm × mm]	Maximum clear span of joist [m]					
38 × 75	1.29	1.28	1.24	1.24	.123	1.19
38 × 89*	1.63	1.62	1.57	1.57	1.55	1.49
38 × 100	1.92	1.89	1.83	1.83	1.80	1.73
38 × 125	2.58	2.54	2.45	2.45	2.40	2.29
38 × 140*	2.99	2.94	2.82	2.82	2.77	2.63
38 × 150	3.26	3.21	3.07	3.07	3.01	2.86
38 × 175	3.95	3.89	3.71	3.71	3.63	3.44
38 × 184*	4.21	4.13	3.94	3.94	3.86	3.64
38 × 200	4.65	4.57	4.35	4.35	4.25	4.01
38 × 225	5.35	5.25	4.99	4.99	4.87	4.59
47 × 75	1.43	1.41	1.37	1.37	1.36	1.31
47 × 100	2.11	2.08	2.01	2.01	1.98	1.90
47 × 125	2.83	2.79	2.68	2.68	2.63	2.50
47 × 150	3.56	3.50	3.35	3.35	3.29	3.12
47 × 175	4.30	4.23	4.03	4.03	3.95	3.73
47 × 200	5.05	4.95	4.71	4.71	4.61	4.35
47 × 225	5.79	5.68	5.39	5.39	5.27	4.96
50 × 75	1.47	1.45	1.41	1.41	1.40	1.35
50 × 100	2.17	2.14	2.07	2.07	2.04	1.95
50 × 125	2.90	2.86	2.75	2.75	2.70	2.57
50 × 150	3.65	3.59	3.44	3.44	3.37	3.19
50 × 175	4.41	4.33	4.13	4.13	4.04	3.82
50 × 200	5.16	5.07	4.82	4.82	4.72	4.45
50 × 225	5.92	5.80	5.51	5.51	5.39	5.07

Notes

* North American surfaced size

† Dead load is the load supported by the joist, excluding the mass of the joist

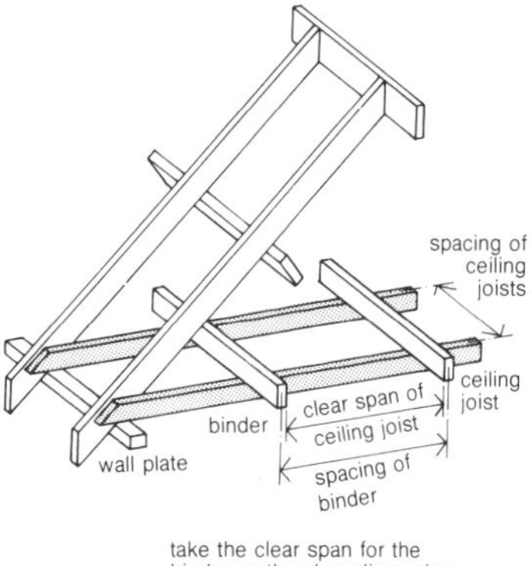

take the clear span for the binder as the clear dimension between supporting struts and/or walls

Notes

1 Tables B5 to B8 inclusive give sizes, spacings and spans for ceiling joists and binders supporting ceiling joists. The sizes, spacings and spans given will support the dead loads given in the tables and a maximum imposed load of 0.75kN/m² and a concentrated load of 0.9kN acting together.

In calculating the ceiling joist sizes no account has been taken of trimming (e.g. around flues) or other loads (e.g. water tanks).

2 When spans for ceiling joists, and spacings for binders are unequal, the section sizes should be determined by the longer span.

3 See paragraph A2 which gives guidance on the need for bracing roof structures.

Reproduced from Approved Document A1/2 by permission of HMSO.

Guidance

Sizes, spacings and spans for timber roof members (continued)

Table **B8** **Binders** supporting ceiling joists

Timber of strength class **SC4** *(see Table B1)*

	Dead load† [kN/m²]											
	Not more than 0.25						More than 0.25 but not more than 0.50					
	Spacing of binders [mm]											
	1200	1500	1800	2100	2400	2700	1200	1500	1800	2100	2400	2700
Size of binder [mm × mm]	Maximum clear span of binder [m]											
38 × 89*	1.11	1.06	1.02	0.99	0.95	0.93	1.03	0.98	0.94	0.90	0.87	0.85
38 × 100	1.28	1.22	1.18	1.13	1.10	1.06	1.19	1.13	1.08	1.04	1.00	0.97
38 × 125	1.68	1.60	1.53	1.47	1.42	1.38	1.55	1.47	1.40	1.34	1.29	1.25
38 × 140*	1.93	1.83	1.75	1.68	1.62	1.57	1.77	1.67	1.59	1.52	1.46	1.41
38 × 150	2.09	1.98	1.89	1.82	1.75	1.69	1.92	1.81	1.72	1.65	1.58	1.53
38 × 175	2.50	2.36	2.25	2.16	2.08	2.01	2.29	2.15	2.04	1.95	1.87	1.80
38 × 184*	2.65	2.50	2.38	2.28	2.20	2.12	2.42	2.27	2.16	2.06	1.98	1.91
38 × 200	2.91	2.75	2.61	2.50	2.41	2.32	2.65	2.49	2.36	2.26	2.16	2.08
38 × 225	3.32	3.13	2.97	2.85	2.74	2.64	3.02	2.83	2.68	2.56	2.46	2.36
47 × 100	1.41	1.34	1.29	1.24	1.20	1.17	1.31	1.24	1.18	1.14	1.10	1.06
47 × 125	1.84	1.75	1.67	1.61	1.55	1.50	1.70	1.60	1.53	1.46	1.41	1.36
47 × 150	2.28	2.16	2.06	1.98	1.91	1.84	2.09	1.97	1.87	1.79	1.72	1.66
47 × 175	2.72	2.57	2.45	2.35	2.26	2.18	2.49	2.34	2.22	2.12	2.04	1.96
47 × 200	3.16	2.98	2.84	2.72	2.61	2.52	2.88	2.71	2.57	2.45	2.35	2.27
47 × 225	3.60	3.39	3.23	3.09	2.97	2.86	3.28	3.07	2.91	2.78	2.67	2.57
50 × 100	1.44	1.38	1.32	1.28	1.23	1.20	1.34	1.27	1.21	1.17	1.12	1.09
50 × 125	1.89	1.79	1.72	1.65	1.59	1.54	1.74	1.64	1.57	1.50	1.44	1.40
50 × 150	2.34	2.21	2.11	2.03	1.95	1.89	2.14	2.02	1.92	1.84	1.77	1.70
50 × 175	2.78	2.63	2.51	2.40	2.32	2.24	2.55	2.40	2.27	2.17	2.09	2.01
50 × 200	3.23	3.05	2.90	2.78	2.68	2.59	2.95	2.77	2.63	2.51	2.41	2.32
50 × 225	3.68	3.47	3.30	3.16	3.04	2.93	3.35	3.15	2.98	2.85	2.73	2.63
63 × 100	1.59	1.52	1.46	1.40	1.36	1.32	1.48	1.40	1.34	1.28	1.24	1.20
63 × 125	2.07	1.97	1.88	1.81	1.75	1.69	1.91	1.80	1.72	1.65	1.58	1.53
63 × 150	2.56	2.42	2.31	2.22	2.14	2.07	2.34	2.21	2.10	2.01	1.93	1.87
63 × 175	3.04	2.87	2.74	2.63	2.53	2.44	2.78	2.62	2.48	2.37	2.28	2.20
63 × 200	3.52	3.33	3.17	3.03	2.92	2.82	3.22	3.02	2.87	2.74	2.63	2.53
63 × 225	4.01	3.78	3.59	3.44	3.31	3.20	3.65	3.43	3.25	3.10	2.98	2.87
75 × 125	2.22	2.11	2.02	1.94	1.87	1.81	2.04	1.93	1.84	1.76	1.70	1.64
75 × 150	2.73	2.59	2.47	2.37	2.28	2.21	2.51	2.36	2.25	2.15	2.07	1.99
75 × 175	3.24	3.07	2.92	2.80	2.70	2.61	2.97	2.79	2.65	2.54	2.44	2.35
75 × 200	3.75	3.54	3.38	3.23	3.11	3.01	3.43	3.22	3.06	2.92	2.81	2.71
75 × 225	4.26	4.02	3.83	3.66	3.52	3.40	3.88	3.65	3.46	3.31	3.17	3.06

Notes

* North American surfaced size
† Dead load is the load supported by the joist, excluding the mass of the joist as calculated for the purpose of Table B7

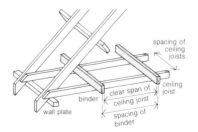

spacing of ceiling joists

ceiling joist

binder clear span of ceiling joist

wall plate spacing of binder

take the clear span for the binder as the clear dimension between supporting struts and/or walls

Notes

1 Tables B5 to B8 inclusive give sizes, spacings and spans for ceiling joists and binders supporting ceiling joists. The sizes, spacings and spans given will support the dead loads given in the tables and a maximum imposed load of 0.75kN/m² and a concentrated load of 0.9kN acting together.

In calculating the ceiling joist sizes no account has been taken of openings (e.g. around flues) or other loads (e.g. water tanks).

2 When spans for ceiling joists, and spacings for binders are unequal, the section sizes should be determined by the longer span.

3 See paragraph A2 which gives guidance on the need for bracing roof structures.

Reproduced from Approved Document A1/2 by permission of HMSO.

Table **B9** **Common or jack rafters** for roofs having a pitch more than 10° but not more than 22½° with access only for purposes of maintenance or repair

Timber of strength class **SC3** *(see Table B1)*

Size of rafter [mm × mm]	Dead load† [kN/m²]								
	Not more than 0.50			More than 0.50 but not more than 0.75			More than 0.75 but not more than 1.00		
	Spacing of rafters [mm]								
	400	450	600	400	450	600	400	450	600
	Maximum clear span of rafter [m]								
38 × 89*	1.54	1.51	1.44	1.44	1.41	1.33	1.36	1.33	1.24
38 × 100	1.85	1.82	1.72	1.72	1.68	1.57	1.62	1.57	1.46
38 × 125	2.50	2.44	2.30	2.30	2.24	2.08	2.15	2.08	1.92
38 × 140*	2.87	2.80	2.62	2.63	2.55	2.37	2.44	2.37	2.18
38 × 150	3.10	3.03	2.76	2.84	2.76	2.53	2.64	2.55	2.34
47 × 100	2.19	2.15	2.03	2.03	1.98	1.85	1.90	1.85	1.71
47 × 125	2.91	2.84	2.66	2.67	2.59	2.40	2.48	2.40	2.21
47 × 150	3.56	3.47	3.05	3.25	3.15	2.80	3.01	2.91	2.60
50 × 100	2.30	2.25	2.13	2.13	2.07	1.93	1.99	1.93	1.78
50 × 125	3.03	2.96	2.74	2.78	2.70	2.50	2.58	2.50	2.30
50 × 150	3.70	3.56	3.13	3.37	3.27	2.88	3.13	3.03	2.68

Notes
* North American surfaced size
† Dead load is the load supported by the rafter, excluding the mass of the rafter

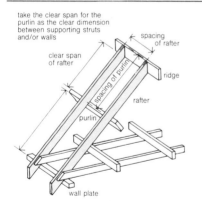

take the clear span for the purlin as the clear dimension between supporting struts and/or walls

clear span of rafter

spacing of rafter

spacing of purlin

ridge

rafter

purlin

wall plate

Notes

1 Tables B9 to B20 inclusive give sizes, spacings and spans for rafters and purlins supporting rafters. The sizes, spacings and spans given will support the dead loads given in the tables and also the following maximum imposed loads:

(a) up to 30° pitch
0.75kN/m² or a concentrated load of 0.9kN

(b) greater than 30° pitch
0.75kN/m² (the loading is reduced by 50N/m² for every 3° pitch over 30° pitch).

2 When spans for rafters, and spacings for purlins are unequal, the section sizes should be determined by the longer span.

3 See paragraph A2 which gives guidance on the need for bracing roof structures.

Guidance

Sizes, spacings and spans for timber roof members (continued)

Table **B10** **Purlins** supporting rafters to which Table B9 refers

Timber of strength class **SC3** *(see Table B1)*

	Dead load† [kN/m²]		
	Not more than 0.50	More than 0.50 but not more than 0.75	More than 0.75 but not more than 1.00
	Spacing of purlins [mm]		
Size of purlin [mm × mm]	1500 1800 2100 2400 2700 3000	1500 1800 2100 2400 2700 3000	1500 1800 2100 2400 2700 3000
	Maximum clear span of purlin [m]		
50 × 100	1.27 1.16 1.07 1.00 0.94 0.89	1.16 1.06 0.98 0.91 0.86 0.81	1.07 0.98 0.90 0.84 0.79 0.75
50 × 125	1.58 1.44 1.33 1.25 1.17 1.11	1.44 1.32 1.22 1.14 1.07 1.01	1.34 1.22 1.13 1.05 0.99 0.94
50 × 150	1.89 1.72 1.59 1.49 1.40 1.33	1.73 1.58 1.46 1.36 1.28 1.21	1.60 1.46 1.35 1.26 1.18 1.12
50 × 175	2.20 2.00 1.85 1.73 1.63 1.55	2.01 1.83 1.69 1.58 1.49 1.41	1.86 1.70 1.57 1.46 1.38 1.30
50 × 200	2.50 2.28 2.11 1.97 1.86 1.76	2.29 2.09 1.93 1.80 1.70 1.61	2.12 1.93 1.79 1.67 1.57 1.49
50 × 225	2.80 2.56 2.37 2.21 2.09 1.98	2.56 2.34 2.16 2.02 1.90 1.80	2.38 2.17 2.00 1.87 1.76 1.67
63 × 100	1.41 1.29 1.19 1.11 1.05 0.99	1.29 1.18 1.09 1.02 0.96 0.91	1.20 1.09 1.01 0.94 0.89 0.84
63 × 125	1.76 1.60 1.48 1.39 1.31 1.24	1.61 1.46 1.36 1.27 1.19 1.13	1.49 1.36 1.25 1.17 1.10 1.05
63 × 150	2.10 1.92 1.77 1.66 1.56 1.48	1.92 1.75 1.62 1.52 1.43 1.35	1.78 1.62 1.50 1.40 1.32 1.25
63 × 175	2.44 2.23 2.06 1.93 1.82 1.72	2.23 2.04 1.89 1.76 1.66 1.57	2.07 1.89 1.75 1.63 1.54 1.46
63 × 200	2.78 2.54 2.35 2.20 2.07 1.96	2.54 2.32 2.15 2.01 1.89 1.79	2.36 2.15 1.99 1.86 1.75 1.66
63 × 225	3.12 2.85 2.64 2.47 2.32 2.20	2.85 2.61 2.41 2.25 2.12 2.01	2.65 2.42 2.23 2.09 1.97 1.86
75 × 125	1.90 1.73 1.61 1.50 1.42 1.34	1.74 1.59 1.47 1.37 1.29 1.23	1.61 1.47 1.36 1.27 1.20 1.13
75 × 150	2.27 2.07 1.92 1.80 1.69 1.61	2.08 1.90 1.76 1.64 1.55 1.47	1.93 1.76 1.63 1.52 1.43 1.36
75 × 175	2.64 2.41 2.23 2.09 1.97 1.87	2.42 2.21 2.04 1.91 1.80 1.71	2.24 2.05 1.89 1.77 1.67 1.58
75 × 200	3.01 2.75 2.55 2.38 2.25 2.13	2.75 2.52 2.33 2.18 2.05 1.95	2.55 2.33 2.16 2.02 1.90 1.80
75 × 225	3.37 3.08 2.86 2.67 2.52 2.39	3.09 2.82 2.61 2.44 2.30 2.18	2.87 2.62 2.42 2.27 2.13 2.02

Note

† Dead load is the load supported by the rafter as calculated for the purposes of Table B9

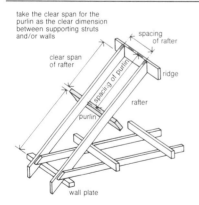

take the clear span for the purlin as the clear dimension between supporting struts and/or walls

clear span of rafter

spacing of rafter

ridge

spacing of purlin

rafter

purlin

wall plate

Notes

1 Tables B9 to B20 inclusive give sizes, spacings and spans for rafters and purlins supporting rafters. The sizes, spacings and spans given will support the dead loads given in the tables and also the following maximum imposed loads:

(a) up to 30° pitch
0.75kN/m² or a concentrated load of 0.9kN

(b) greater than 30° pitch
0.75kN/m² (the loading is reduced by 50N/m² for every 3° pitch over 30° pitch).

2 When spans for rafters, and spacings for purlins are unequal, the section sizes should be determined by the longer span.

3 See paragraph A2 which gives guidance on the need for bracing roof structures.

Reproduced from Approved Document A1/2 by permission of HMSO.

Table **B11** **Common or jack rafters** for roofs having a pitch more than 10° but not more than 22½° with access only for purposes of maintenance or repair

Timber of strength class **SC4** (see Table B1)

Size of rafter [mm × mm]	Dead load† [kN/m²]								
	Not more than 0.50			More than 0.50 but not more than 0.75			More than 0.75 but not more than 1.00		
	Spacing of rafters [mm]								
	400	450	600	400	450	600	400	450	600
	Maximum clear span of rafter [m]								
38 × 89*	1.98	1.94	1.84	1.84	1.79	1.68	1.73	1.68	1.55
38 × 100	2.36	2.31	2.18	2.18	2.12	1.97	2.03	1.97	1.82
38 × 125	3.09	3.01	2.75	2.82	2.74	2.52	2.62	2.54	2.33
38 × 140*	3.49	3.40	2.99	3.18	3.09	2.75	2.95	2.85	2.55
38 × 150	3.74	3.57	3.14	3.40	3.29	2.89	3.15	3.05	2.69
47 × 100	2.76	2.70	2.53	2.53	2.46	2.29	2.36	2.29	2.10
47 × 125	3.54	3.45	3.04	3.23	3.14	2.79	3.00	2.90	2.59
47 × 150	4.11	3.91	3.45	3.80	3.61	3.18	3.56	3.38	2.97
50 × 100	2.88	2.82	2.64	2.64	2.57	2.38	2.46	2.38	2.19
50 × 125	3.68	3.55	3.12	3.36	3.26	2.87	3.11	3.01	2.67
50 × 150	4.22	4.01	3.55	3.90	3.71	3.27	3.65	3.47	3.05

Notes

* North American surfaced size
† Dead load is the load supported by the rafter, excluding the mass of the rafter

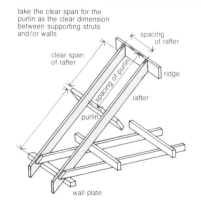

take the clear span for the purlin as the clear dimension between supporting struts and/or walls

Notes

1 Tables B9 to B20 inclusive give sizes, spacings and spans for rafters and purlins supporting rafters. The sizes, spacings and spans given will support the dead loads given in the tables and also the following maximum imposed loads:

(a) up to 30° pitch
0.75kN/m² or a concentrated load of 0.9kN

(b) greater than 30° pitch
0.75kN/m² (the loading is reduced by 50N/m² for every 3° pitch over 30° pitch).

2 When spans for rafters, and spacings for purlins are unequal, the section sizes should be determined by the longer span.

3 See paragraph A2 which gives guidance on the need for bracing roof structures.

Guidance

Sizes, spacings and spans for timber roof members (continued)

Table **B12** **Purlins** supporting rafters to which Table B11 refers

Timber of strength class **SC4** *(see Table B1)*

Size of purlin [mm × mm]	Dead load[†] [kN/m²]																	
	Not more than 0.50						More than 0.50 but not more than 0.75						More than 0.75 but not more than 1.00					
	Spacing of purlins [mm]																	
	1500	1800	2100	2400	2700	3000	1500	1800	2100	2400	2700	3000	1500	1800	2100	2400	2700	3000
	Maximum clear span of purlin [m]																	
50 × 100	1.50	1.37	1.27	1.19	1.12	1.06	1.38	1.25	1.16	1.08	1.02	0.97	1.28	1.16	1.07	1.00	0.93	0.84
50 × 125	1.87	1.71	1.58	1.48	1.39	1.32	1.71	1.56	1.45	1.35	1.27	1.20	1.59	1.45	1.34	1.25	1.16	1.04
50 × 150	2.24	2.04	1.89	1.77	1.67	1.58	2.05	1.87	1.73	1.62	1.52	1.44	1.90	1.73	1.60	1.50	1.39	1.25
50 × 175	2.60	2.38	2.20	2.06	1.94	1.84	2.38	2.17	2.01	1.88	1.77	1.68	2.21	2.01	1.86	1.74	1.62	1.46
50 × 200	2.96	2.71	2.51	2.34	2.21	2.09	2.71	2.48	2.29	2.14	2.02	1.91	2.52	2.30	2.12	1.98	1.85	1.67
50 × 225	3.32	3.03	2.81	2.63	2.47	2.35	3.04	2.78	2.57	2.40	2.26	2.14	2.82	2.57	2.38	2.22	2.08	1.87
63 × 100	1.67	1.53	1.41	1.32	1.24	1.18	1.53	1.40	1.29	1.21	1.14	1.08	1.42	1.29	1.20	1.12	1.05	1.00
63 × 125	2.08	1.90	1.76	1.64	1.55	1.47	1.90	1.74	1.61	1.50	1.42	1.34	1.77	1.61	1.49	1.39	1.31	1.24
63 × 150	2.49	2.27	2.10	1.97	1.85	1.76	2.28	2.08	1.92	1.80	1.69	1.61	2.11	1.93	1.78	1.67	1.57	1.49
63 × 175	2.89	2.64	2.45	2.29	2.16	2.04	2.65	2.42	2.24	2.09	1.97	1.87	2.46	2.24	2.08	1.94	1.83	1.73
63 × 200	3.29	3.01	2.79	2.61	2.46	2.33	3.02	2.76	2.55	2.39	2.25	2.13	2.80	2.56	2.37	2.21	2.08	1.97
63 × 225	3.69	3.37	3.13	2.93	2.76	2.62	3.38	3.09	2.86	2.68	2.52	2.39	3.14	2.87	2.65	2.48	2.34	2.21
75 × 125	2.25	2.06	1.90	1.78	1.68	1.59	2.06	1.88	1.74	1.63	1.54	1.46	1.91	1.75	1.62	1.51	1.42	1.35
75 × 150	2.69	2.46	2.28	2.13	2.01	1.90	2.46	2.25	2.08	1.95	1.84	1.74	2.29	2.09	1.93	1.81	1.70	1.61
75 × 175	3.13	2.86	2.65	2.48	2.34	2.22	2.87	2.62	2.42	2.27	2.14	2.03	2.66	2.43	2.25	2.10	1.98	1.88
75 × 200	3.56	3.26	3.02	2.82	2.66	2.53	3.26	2.98	2.76	2.58	2.44	2.31	3.03	2.77	2.56	2.40	2.26	2.14
75 × 225	3.99	3.65	3.38	3.17	2.99	2.83	3.66	3.35	3.10	2.90	2.73	2.59	3.40	3.11	2.88	2.69	2.53	2.40

Note

† Dead load is the load supported by the rafter as calculated for the purposes of Table B11.

take the clear span for the purlin as the clear dimension between supporting struts and/or walls

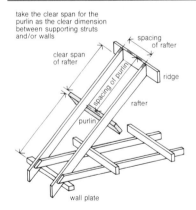

Notes

1 Tables B9 to B20 inclusive give sizes, spacings and spans for rafters and purlins supporting rafters. The sizes, spacings and spans given in the tables will support the dead loads given in the tables and also the following maximum imposed loads:

(a) up to 30° pitch
0.75kN/m² or a concentrated load of 0.9kN

(b) greater than 30° pitch
0.75kN/m² (the loading is reduced by 50N/m² for every 3° pitch over 30° pitch).

2 When spans for rafters, and spacings for purlins are unequal, the section sizes should be determined by the longer span.

3 See paragraph A2 which gives guidance on the need for bracing roof structures.

Guidance

Table **B13** **Common or jack rafters** for roofs having a pitch more than 22½° but not more than 30° with access only for purposes of maintenance or repair

Timber of strength class **SC3** *(see Table B1)*

Size of rafter [mm × mm]	Dead load† [kN/m²]								
	Not more than 0.50			More than 0.50 but not more than 0.75			More than 0.75 but not more than 1.00		
	Spacing of rafters [mm]								
	400	450	600	400	450	600	400	450	600
	Maximum clear span of rafter [m]								
38 × 89*	1.77	1.74	1.66	1.66	1.62	1.52	1.56	1.52	1.42
38 × 100	2.13	2.08	1.97	1.97	1.92	1.80	1.85	1.80	1.67
38 × 125	2.89	2.82	2.65	2.65	2.58	2.39	2.47	2.39	2.20
38 × 140*	3.34	3.26	3.01	3.05	2.96	2.74	2.83	2.74	2.51
38 × 150	3.63	3.54	3.19	3.30	3.21	2.91	3.06	2.96	2.70
47 × 100	2.51	2.46	2.32	2.32	2.26	2.10	2.17	2.10	1.94
47 × 125	3.36	3.28	3.03	3.07	2.98	2.76	2.85	2.76	2.53
47 × 150	4.17	4.00	3.51	3.78	3.67	3.22	3.50	3.38	2.99
50 × 100	2.63	2.57	2.42	2.42	2.36	2.20	2.26	2.20	2.03
50 × 125	3.51	3.42	3.12	3.20	3.11	2.86	2.97	2.87	2.63
50 × 150	4.33	4.11	3.62	3.93	3.78	3.31	3.63	3.51	3.07

Notes

* North American surfaced size
† Dead load is the load supported by the rafter, excluding the mass of the rafter

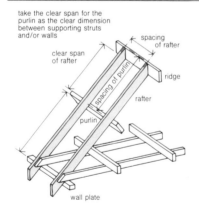

take the clear span for the purlin as the clear dimension between supporting struts and/or walls

spacing of rafter

clear span of rafter

ridge

spacing of purlin

rafter

purlin

wall plate

Notes

1 Tables B9 to B20 inclusive give sizes, spacings and spans for rafters and purlins supporting rafters. The sizes, spacings and spans given will support the dead loads given in the tables and also the following maximum imposed loads:

   (a) up to 30° pitch
   0.75kN/m² or a concentrated load of 0.9kN

   (b) greater than 30° pitch
   0.75kN/m² (the loading is reduced by 50N/m² for every 3° pitch over 30° pitch).

2 When spans for rafters, and spacings for purlins are unequal, the section sizes should be determined by the longer span.

3 See paragraph A2 which gives guidance on the need for bracing roof structures.

Guidance

Sizes, spacings and spans for timber roof members (continued)

Table **B14** **Purlins** supporting rafters to which Table B13 refers

Timber of strength class **SC3** *(see Table B1)*

	Dead load† [kN/m²]		
	Not more than 0.50	More than 0.50 but not more than 0.75	More than 0.75 but not more than 1.00
	Spacing of purlins [mm]		
Size of purlin [mm × mm]	1500 1800 2100 2400 2700 3000	1500 1800 2100 2400 2700 3000	1500 1800 2100 2400 2700 3000
	Maximum clear span of purlin [m]		
50 × 100	1.23 1.12 1.04 0.97 0.91 0.87	1.12 1.02 0.95 0.88 0.83 0.79	1.04 0.95 0.87 0.82 0.77 0.73
50 × 125	1.53 1.40 1.29 1.21 1.14 1.08	1.40 1.27 1.18 1.10 1.04 0.98	1.29 1.18 1.09 1.02 0.96 0.91
50 × 150	1.83 1.67 1.55 1.45 1.36 1.29	1.67 1.53 1.41 1.32 1.24 1.17	1.55 1.41 1.30 1.22 1.14 1.08
50 × 175	2.13 1.95 1.80 1.68 1.59 1.50	1.95 1.77 1.64 1.53 1.44 1.37	1.80 1.64 1.52 1.42 1.33 1.26
50 × 200	2.43 2.22 2.05 1.92 1.81 1.71	2.22 2.02 1.87 1.75 1.65 1.56	2.05 1.87 1.73 1.61 1.52 1.44
50 × 225	2.73 2.49 2.30 2.15 2.03 1.92	2.49 2.27 2.10 1.96 1.85 1.75	2.30 2.10 1.94 1.81 1.71 1.61
63 × 100	1.38 1.26 1.16 1.09 1.02 0.97	1.25 1.14 1.06 0.99 0.93 0.88	1.16 1.06 0.98 0.91 0.86 0.81
63 × 125	1.71 1.56 1.44 1.35 1.27 1.20	1.56 1.42 1.31 1.23 1.16 1.10	1.44 1.31 1.21 1.13 1.07 1.01
63 × 150	2.04 1.86 1.72 1.61 1.52 1.44	1.86 1.70 1.57 1.47 1.38 1.31	1.72 1.57 1.45 1.36 1.28 1.21
63 × 175	2.37 2.16 2.00 1.87 1.76 1.67	2.16 1.97 1.83 1.71 1.61 1.52	2.00 1.82 1.69 1.58 1.49 1.41
63 × 200	2.70 2.46 2.28 2.14 2.01 1.91	2.46 2.25 2.08 1.95 1.83 1.74	2.28 2.08 1.92 1.80 1.69 1.60
63 × 225	3.03 2.77 2.56 2.40 2.26 2.14	2.76 2.52 2.34 2.18 2.06 1.95	2.56 2.34 2.16 2.02 1.90 1.80
75 × 125	1.85 1.69 1.56 1.46 1.38 1.31	1.69 1.54 1.43 1.33 1.26 1.19	1.56 1.43 1.32 1.23 1.16 1.10
75 × 150	2.21 2.01 1.87 1.75 1.65 1.56	2.01 1.84 1.70 1.59 1.50 1.42	1.86 1.70 1.57 1.47 1.39 1.31
75 × 175	2.56 2.34 2.17 2.03 1.91 1.81	2.34 2.14 1.98 1.85 1.74 1.65	2.17 1.98 1.83 1.71 1.61 1.53
75 × 200	2.92 2.67 2.47 2.31 2.18 2.07	2.66 2.43 2.25 2.11 1.99 1.88	2.47 2.25 2.09 1.95 1.84 1.74
75 × 225	3.27 2.99 2.77 2.59 2.45 2.32	2.99 2.73 2.53 2.37 2.23 2.11	2.77 2.53 2.34 2.19 2.06 1.95

Note
† Dead load is the load supported by the rafter as calculated for the purposes of Table B13

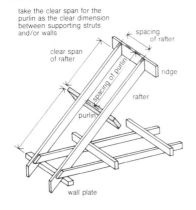

take the clear span for the purlin as the clear dimension between supporting struts and/or walls

Notes

1 Tables B9 to B20 inclusive give sizes, spacings and spans for rafters and purlins supporting rafters. The sizes, spacings and spans given in the tables will support the dead loads given in the tables and also the following maximum imposed loads:

(a) up to 30° pitch
0.75kN/m² or a concentrated load of 0.3kN

(b) greater than 30° pitch
0.75kN/m² (the loading is reduced by 50N/m² for every 3° pitch over 30° pitch).

2 When spans for rafters, and spacings for purlins are unequal, the section sizes should be determined by the longer span.

3 See paragraph A2 which gives guidance on the need for bracing roof structures.

Reproduced from Approved Document A1/2 by permission of HMSO.

Table **B15** **Common or jack rafters** for roofs having a pitch more than 22½° but not more than 30° with access only for purposes of maintenance or repair

Timber of strength class **SC4** *(see Table B1)*

	Dead load† [kN/m²]								
	Not more than 0.50			More than 0.50 but not more than 0.75			More than 0.75 but not more than 1.00		
	Spacing of rafters [mm]								
	400	450	600	400	450	600	400	450	600
Size of rafter [mm × mm]	Maximum clear span of rafter [m]								
38 × 89*	2.30	2.25	2.13	2.13	2.08	1.94	2.00	1.94	1.80
38 × 100	2.74	2.68	2.52	2.52	2.45	2.27	2.35	2.27	2.10
38 × 125	3.62	3.53	3.18	3.30	3.20	2.91	3.06	2.95	2.69
38 × 140*	4.12	3.96	3.48	3.74	3.62	3.18	3.46	3.34	2.95
38 × 150	4.40	4.17	3.67	4.02	3.83	3.36	3.71	3.57	3.12
47 × 100	3.19	3.12	2.92	2.92	2.84	2.63	2.71	2.63	2.41
47 × 125	4.16	4.00	3.51	3.78	3.66	3.21	3.49	3.37	2.98
47 × 150	4.82	4.58	4.04	4.44	4.22	3.71	4.14	3.93	3.45
50 × 100	3.34	3.25	3.02	3.05	2.96	2.74	2.83	2.74	2.51
50 × 125	4 33	4.11	3.61	3.92	3.77	3.31	3.62	3.50	3.07
50 × 150	4.95	4.70	4.15	4.56	4.33	3.81	4.25	4.04	3.54

Notes
* North American surfaced size
† Dead load is the load supported by the rafter, excluding the mass of the rafter

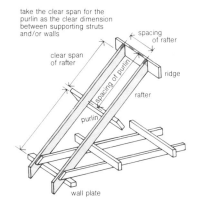

take the clear span for the purlin as the clear dimension between supporting struts and/or walls

clear span of rafter

spacing of rafter

ridge

rafter

spacing of purlin

purlin

wall plate

Notes

1   Tables B9 to B20 inclusive give sizes, spacings and spans for rafters and purlins supporting rafters. The sizes, spacings and spans given in the tables and also the following maximum imposed loads:

(a) up to 30° pitch
0.75kN/m² or a concentrated load of 0.9kN

(b) greater than 30° pitch
0.75kN/m² (the loading is reduced by 50N/m² for every 3° pitch over 30° pitch).

2   When spans for rafters, and spacings for purlins are unequal, the section sizes should be determined by the longer span.

3   See paragraph A2 which gives guidance on the need for bracing roof structures.

Guidance

Sizes, spacings and spans for timber roof members (continued)

Table **B16** **Purlins** supporting rafters to which Table B15 refers

Timber of strength class **SC4** *(see Table B1)*

Size of purlin [mm × mm]	Dead load† [kN/m²]																	
	Not more than 0.50						More than 0.50 but not more than 0.75						More than 0.75 but not more than 1.00					
	Spacing of purlins [mm]																	
	1500	1800	2100	2400	2700	3000	1500	1800	2100	2400	2700	3000	1500	1800	2100	2400	2700	3000
	Maximum clear span of purlin [m]																	
50 × 100	1.46	1.33	1.23	1.15	1.09	1.03	1.33	1.22	1.12	1.05	0.99	0.94	1.23	1.12	1.04	0.97	0.91	0.86
50 × 125	1.82	1.66	1.54	1.43	1.35	1.28	1.66	1.51	1.40	1.31	1.23	1.17	1.53	1.40	1.29	1.21	1.14	1.07
50 × 150	2.17	1.98	1.84	1.72	1.62	1.53	1.98	1.81	1.67	1.56	1.47	1.40	1.84	1.67	1.55	1.45	1.36	1.28
50 × 175	2.53	2.31	2.14	2.00	1.88	1.78	2.31	2.11	1.95	1.82	1.71	1.62	2.14	1.95	1.80	1.68	1.58	1.50
50 × 200	2.88	2.63	2.44	2.28	2.15	2.03	2.63	2.40	2.22	2.08	1.95	1.85	2.43	2.22	2.05	1.92	1.81	1.71
50 × 225	3.23	2.95	2.73	2.56	2.41	2.28	2.95	2.69	2.49	2.33	2.19	2.08	2.73	2.49	2.30	2.15	2.03	1.92
63 × 100	1.63	1.49	1.38	1.29	1.21	1.15	1.49	1.36	1.26	1.17	1.11	1.05	1.38	1.26	1.16	1.09	1.02	0.97
63 × 125	2.02	1.85	1.71	1.60	1.51	1.43	1.85	1.68	1.56	1.46	1.37	1.30	1.71	1.56	1.44	1.35	1.27	1.20
63 × 150	2.41	2.21	2.04	1.91	1.80	1.71	2.20	2.01	1.86	1.74	1.64	1.55	2.04	1.86	1.72	1.61	1.52	1.44
63 × 175	2.81	2.56	2.37	2.22	2.09	1.98	2.56	2.34	2.17	2.03	1.91	1.81	2.37	2.17	2.00	1.87	1.76	1.67
63 × 200	3.20	2.92	2.71	2.53	2.39	2.26	2.92	2.67	2.47	2.31	2.18	2.06	2.71	2.47	2.29	2.14	2.01	1.91
63 × 225	3.58	3.28	3.04	2.84	2.68	2.54	3.28	2.99	2.77	2.59	2.44	2.32	3.04	2.77	2.57	2.40	2.26	2.14
75 × 125	2.19	2.00	1.86	1.74	1.64	1.55	2.00	1.83	1.69	1.58	1.49	1.41	1.85	1.69	1.57	1.46	1.38	1.31
75 × 150	2.61	2.39	2.21	2.07	1.95	1.85	2.39	2.18	2.02	1.89	1.78	1.69	2.21	2.02	1.87	1.75	1.65	1.56
75 × 175	3.03	2.77	2.57	2.41	2.27	2.15	2.77	2.53	2.35	2.19	2.07	1.96	2.57	2.35	2.17	2.03	1.91	1.81
75 × 200	3.45	3.16	2.93	2.74	2.58	2.45	3.16	2.89	2.67	2.50	2.36	2.24	2.93	2.67	2.48	2.31	2.18	2.07
75 × 225	3.87	3.54	3.28	3.07	2.90	2.75	3.54	3.24	3.00	2.81	2.65	2.51	3.28	3.00	2.78	2.60	2.45	2.32

Note

† Dead load is the load supported by the rafter as calculated for the purposes of Table B15

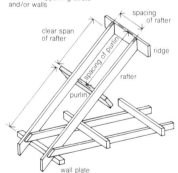

take the clear span for the purlin as the clear dimension between supporting struts and/or walls

clear span of rafter

spacing of rafter

spacing of purlin

ridge

rafter

purlin

wall plate

Notes

1 Tables B9 to B20 inclusive give sizes, spacings and spans for rafters and purlins supporting rafters. The sizes, spacings and spans given will support the dead loads given in the tables and also the following maximum imposed loads:

(a) up to 30° pitch
0.75kN/m² or a concentrated load of 0.9kN

(b) greater than 30° pitch
0.75kN/m² (the loading is reduced by 50N/m² for every 3° pitch over 30° pitch).

2 When spans for rafters, and spacings for purlins are unequal, the section sizes should be determined by the longer span.

3 See paragraph A2 which gives guidance on the need for bracing roof structures.

Guidance

Table **B17**   **Common or jack rafters** for roofs having a pitch more than 30° but not more than 42½° with access only for purposes of maintenance or repair

Timber of strength class **SC3** *(see Table B1)*

Size of rafter [mm × mm]	Dead load† [kN/m²]								
	Not more than 0.50			More than 0.50 but not more than 0.75			More than 0.75 but not more than 1.00		
	Spacing of rafters [mm]								
	400	450	600	400	450	600	400	450	600
	Maximum clear span of rafter [m]								
38 × 89*	2.64	2.49	2.17	2.40	2.27	1.97	2.22	2.09	1.82
38 × 100	2.94	2.78	2.42	2.68	2.53	2.20	2.47	2.34	2.03
38 × 125	3.54	3.36	2.93	3.23	3.06	2.67	2.99	2.83	2.46
38 × 140*	3.89	3.68	3.22	3.55	3.36	2.94	3.29	3.11	2.71
38 × 150	4.10	3.89	3.41	3.75	3.56	3.11	3.48	3.29	2.87
47 × 100	3.25	3.08	2.68	2.96	2.80	2.44	2.74	2.59	2.25
47 × 125	3.91	3.70	3.24	3.57	3.38	2.95	3.31	3.13	2.73
47 × 150	4.51	4.28	3.76	4.13	3.92	3.43	3.84	3.64	3.18
50 × 100	3.34	3.17	2.76	3.05	2.89	2.51	2.82	2.67	2.32
50 × 125	4.02	3.81	3.34	3.67	3.48	3.04	3.40	3.22	2.81
50 × 150	4.63	4.40	3.87	4.25	4.03	3.53	3.95	3.74	3.27

Notes
* North American surfaced size
† Dead load is the load supported by the rafter, excluding the mass of the rafter

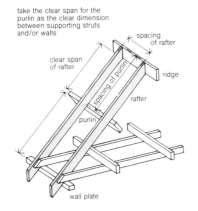

take the clear span for the purlin as the clear dimension between supporting struts and/or walls

spacing of rafter

clear span of rafter

ridge

spacing of purlin

rafter

purlin

wall plate

Notes

1   Tables B9 to B20 inclusive give sizes, spacings and spans for rafters and purlins supporting rafters. The sizes, spacings and spans given will support the dead loads given in the tables and also the following maximum imposed loads:
   (a) up to 30° pitch
   0.75kN/m² or a concentrated load of 0.9kN
   (b) greater than 30° pitch
   0.75kN/m² (the loading is reduced by 50N/m² for every 3° pitch over 30° pitch).

2   When spans for rafters, and spacings for purlins are unequal, the section sizes should be determined by the longer span.

3   See paragraph A2 which gives guidance on the need for bracing roof structures.

Guidance

Sizes, spacings and spans for timber roof members (continued)

Table **B18** **Purlins** supporting rafters to which Table B17 refers

Timber of strength class **SC3** *(see Table B1)*

Size of purlin [mm × mm]	Not more than 0.50						More than 0.50 but not more than 0.75						More than 0.75 but not more than 1.00					
	1500	1800	2100	2400	2700	3000	1500	1800	2100	2400	2700	3000	1500	1800	2100	2400	2700	3000
50 × 100	1.16	1.07	0.99	0.93	0.87	0.83	1.04	0.97	0.90	0.84	0.79	0.75	0.96	0.90	0.83	0.77	0.73	0.69
50 × 125	1.45	1.32	1.23	1.15	1.08	1.02	1.31	1.20	1.11	1.04	0.97	0.92	1.21	1.10	1.02	0.95	0.89	0.85
50 × 150	1.73	1.58	1.46	1.37	1.29	1.22	1.57	1.43	1.32	1.23	1.16	1.10	1.44	1.31	1.21	1.13	1.07	1.01
50 × 175	2.01	1.83	1.70	1.59	1.49	1.42	1.82	1.66	1.54	1.43	1.35	1.28	1.67	1.53	1.41	1.32	1.24	1.17
50 × 200	2.29	2.09	1.93	1.81	1.70	1.61	2.07	1.89	1.75	1.64	1.54	1.46	1.91	1.74	1.61	1.50	1.41	1.34
50 × 225	2.57	2.34	2.17	2.03	1.91	1.81	2.33	2.12	1.96	1.84	1.73	1.64	2.14	1.95	1.81	1.69	1.59	1.50
63 × 100	1.33	1.22	1.13	1.05	0.99	0.94	1.21	1.10	1.02	0.95	0.90	0.85	1.11	1.01	0.94	0.88	0.82	0.78
63 × 125	1.63	1.49	1.38	1.29	1.21	1.15	1.48	1.35	1.25	1.16	1.10	1.04	1.36	1.24	1.15	1.07	1.01	0.95
63 × 150	1.93	1.76	1.63	1.53	1.44	1.36	1.75	1.60	1.48	1.38	1.30	1.23	1.61	1.47	1.36	1.27	1.20	1.13
63 × 175	2.23	2.04	1.89	1.77	1.67	1.58	2.03	1.85	1.71	1.60	1.51	1.43	1.87	1.70	1.58	1.47	1.39	1.31
63 × 200	2.54	2.32	2.15	2.01	1.90	1.80	2.30	2.10	1.95	1.82	1.72	1.63	2.12	1.94	1.79	1.68	1.58	1.50
63 × 225	2.85	2.60	2.41	2.26	2.13	2.02	2.58	2.36	2.18	2.04	1.93	1.83	2.38	2.17	2.01	1.88	1.77	1.68
75 × 125	1.79	1.63	1.51	1.41	1.33	1.26	1.62	1.48	1.37	1.28	1.21	1.14	1.49	1.36	1.26	1.18	1.11	1.05
75 × 150	2.10	1.92	1.78	1.67	1.57	1.49	1.91	1.74	1.61	1.51	1.42	1.35	1.76	1.60	1.49	1.39	1.31	1.24
75 × 175	2.43	2.22	2.06	1.92	1.81	1.72	2.20	2.01	1.86	1.74	1.64	1.56	2.03	1.85	1.71	1.60	1.51	1.43
75 × 200	2.75	2.52	2.33	2.18	2.06	1.95	2.50	2.28	2.11	1.98	1.86	1.77	2.30	2.10	1.95	1.82	1.72	1.63
75 × 225	3.08	2.82	2.61	2.45	2.31	2.19	2.80	2.56	2.37	2.22	2.09	1.98	2.58	2.36	2.18	2.04	1.92	1.82

Table header (above spacing rows): Dead load† [kN/m²] ; Spacing of purlins [mm] ; Maximum clear span of purlin [m]

Note

† Dead load is the load supported by the rafter as calculated for the purposes of Table B17

take the clear span for the purlin as the clear dimension between supporting struts and/or walls

clear span of rafter

spacing of rafter

spacing of purlin

ridge

rafter

purlin

wall plate

Notes

1 Tables B9 to B20 inclusive give sizes, spacings and spans for rafters and purlins supporting rafters. The sizes, spacings and spans given will support the dead loads given in the tables and also the following maximum imposed loads:

(a) up to 30° pitch
0.75kN/m² or a concentrated load of 0.9kN

(b) greater than 30° pitch
0.75kN/m² (the loading is reduced by 50N/m² for every 3° pitch over 30° pitch).

2 When spans for rafters, and spacings for purlins are unequal, the section sizes should be determined by the longer span.

3 See paragraph A2 which gives guidance on the need for bracing roof structures.

Table **B19** **Common or jack rafters** for roofs having a pitch more than 30° but not more than 42½° with access only for purposes of maintenance or repair

Timber of strength class **SC4** *(see Table B1)*

Size of rafter [mm × mm]	Dead load† [kN/m²]								
	Not more than 0.50			More than 0.50 but not more than 0.75			More than 0.75 but not more than 1.00		
	Spacing of rafters [mm]								
	400	450	600	400	450	600	400	450	600
	Maximum clear span of rafter [m]								
38 × 89*	3.07	2.91	2.54	2.80	2.65	2.31	2.59	2.45	2.13
38 × 100	3.43	3.24	2.83	3.13	2.96	2.57	2.89	2.73	2.38
38 × 125	4.10	3.89	3.41	3.75	3.55	3.10	3.48	3.29	2.87
38 × 140*	4.48	4.25	3.73	4.10	3.89	3.40	3.81	3.61	3.15
38 × 150	4.72	4.48	3.94	4.33	4.10	3.60	4.02	3.81	3.33
47 × 100	3.78	3.58	3.13	3.45	3.27	2.85	3.16	3.02	2.64
47 × 125	4.51	4.28	3.76	4.13	3.92	3.43	3.83	3.63	3.18
47 × 150	5.17	4.92	4.33	4.75	4.51	3.97	4.42	4.19	3.68
50 × 100	3.89	3.68	3.22	3.53	3.36	2.94	3.22	3.10	2.72
50 × 125	4.63	4.40	3.87	4.25	4.03	3.53	3.94	3.74	3.27
50 × 150	5.31	5.05	4.45	4.88	4.64	4.08	4.54	4.31	3.79

Notes

* North American surfaced size
† Dead load is the load supported by the rafter, excluding the mass of the rafter

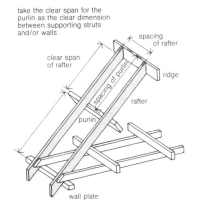

take the clear span for the purlin as the clear dimension between supporting struts and/or walls

spacing of rafter

clear span of rafter

spacing of purlin

ridge

rafter

purlin

wall plate

Notes

1 Tables B9 to B20 inclusive give sizes, spacings and spans for rafters and purlins supporting rafters. The sizes, spacings and spans given in the tables will support the dead loads given in the tables and also the following maximum imposed loads:

   (a) up to 30° pitch
   0.75kN/m² or a concentrated load of 0.9kN

   (b) greater than 30° pitch
   0.75kN/m² (the loading is reduced by 50N/m² for every 3° pitch over 30° pitch).

2 When spans for rafters, and spacings for purlins are unequal, the section sizes should be determined by the longer span.

3 See paragraph A2 which gives guidance on the need for bracing roof structures.

Guidance

Sizes, spacings and spans for timber roof members (continued)

Table **B20** **Purlins** supporting rafters to which Table B19 refers

Timber of strength class **SC4** *(see Table B1)*

Size of purlin [mm × mm]	Not more than 0.50						More than 0.50 but not more than 0.75						More than 0.75 but not more than 1.00					
	Spacing of purlins [mm]																	
	1500	1800	2100	2400	2700	3000	1500	1800	2100	2400	2700	3000	1500	1800	2100	2400	2700	3000
	Maximum clear span of purlin [m]																	
50 × 100	1.40	1.27	1.18	1.10	1.04	0.98	1.26	1.15	1.07	1.00	0.94	0.89	1.16	1.06	0.98	0.92	0.86	0.82
50 × 125	1.72	1.57	1.45	1.36	1.28	1.21	1.56	1.42	1.32	1.23	1.16	1.10	1.43	1.31	1.21	1.13	1.06	1.01
50 × 150	2.05	1.87	1.73	1.62	1.53	1.45	1.86	1.69	1.57	1.47	1.38	1.31	1.71	1.56	1.44	1.35	1.27	1.20
50 × 175	2.38	2.17	2.01	1.88	1.77	1.68	2.16	1.97	1.82	1.70	1.60	1.52	1.99	1.81	1.68	1.57	1.47	1.40
50 × 200	2.71	2.48	2.29	2.14	2.02	1.92	2.46	2.24	2.08	1.94	1.83	1.73	2.26	2.07	1.91	1.79	1.68	1.59
50 × 225	3.04	2.78	2.57	2.41	2.27	2.15	2.76	2.52	2.33	2.18	2.05	1.95	2.54	2.32	2.15	2.00	1.89	1.79
63 × 100	1.58	1.44	1.34	1.25	1.18	1.12	1.43	1.31	1.21	1.13	1.07	1.01	1.32	1.20	1.11	1.04	0.98	0.93
63 × 125	1.93	1.76	1.63	1.53	1.44	1.36	1.75	1.60	1.48	1.38	1.30	1.23	1.61	1.47	1.36	1.27	1.20	1.13
63 × 150	2.29	2.09	1.93	1.81	1.71	1.62	2.07	1.89	1.75	1.64	1.54	1.46	1.91	1.74	1.61	1.51	1.42	1.35
63 × 175	2.65	2.42	2.24	2.10	1.98	1.87	2.40	2.19	2.03	1.90	1.79	1.70	2.21	2.02	1.87	1.75	1.65	1.56
63 × 200	3.01	2.75	2.55	2.39	2.25	2.13	2.73	2.50	2.31	2.16	2.04	1.93	2.52	2.30	2.13	1.99	1.87	1.78
63 × 225	3.37	3.08	2.86	2.67	2.52	2.39	3.06	2.80	2.59	2.42	2.28	2.17	2.82	2.58	2.39	2.23	2.10	1.99
75 × 125	2.12	1.93	1.79	1.68	1.58	1.50	1.92	1.75	1.62	1.52	1.43	1.36	1.77	1.62	1.49	1.40	1.32	1.25
75 × 150	2.49	2.28	2.11	1.98	1.86	1.77	2.26	2.07	1.91	1.79	1.69	1.60	2.09	1.90	1.76	1.65	1.55	1.47
75 × 175	2.87	2.63	2.44	2.28	2.15	2.04	2.61	2.39	2.21	2.07	1.95	1.85	2.41	2.20	2.04	1.90	1.79	1.70
75 × 200	3.26	2.98	2.76	2.59	2.44	2.32	2.96	2.71	2.51	2.35	2.21	2.10	2.73	2.50	2.31	2.16	2.04	1.93
75 × 225	3.65	3.34	3.09	2.90	2.73	2.59	3.31	3.03	2.81	2.63	2.48	2.35	3.06	2.79	2.59	2.42	2.28	2.16

Note

† Dead load is the load supported by the rafter as calculated for the purposes of Table B19

take the clear span for the purlin as the clear dimension between supporting struts and/or walls

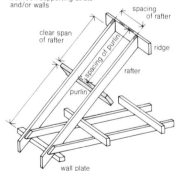

Notes

1 Tables B9 to B20 inclusive give sizes, spacings and spans for rafters and purlins supporting rafters. The sizes, spacings and spans given in the tables and also the following maximum imposed loads:

(a) up to 30° pitch
0.75kN/m² or a concentrated load of 0.9kN

(b) greater than 30° pitch
0.75kN/m² (the loading is reduced by 50N/m² for every 3° pitch over 30° pitch).

2 When spans for rafters, and spacings for purlins are unequal, the section sizes should be determined by the longer span.

3 See paragraph A2 which gives guidance on the need for bracing roof structures.

Guidance

Roof tile fixings

Table 1 - Recommended limits of pitch, gauge and lap for roof tiles

Type of tile	Gauge	Minimum head-lap [mm]	Minimum permissible pitch [°]
Plain (double-lap)	not more than ½ length-lap	65 normally for clay tiles 75 in severe exposure conditions	40 (clay) 35 (plain concrete)
Concrete (single-lap interlocking)	determined by design to comply with manufacturers' recommendations	75 or to manufacturers' specific recommendations	30 (Note: For pitches below 30, evidence shall be provided as to suitable performance)
Slates (double-lap)	not more than ½ length-lap	65 minimum, increase with lower pitch and severe exposure conditions	30 normally 40 for severe exposure

Table 2 - Minimum fixings for single-lap interlocking concrete tiles

Nail or clip tiles as follows:

Location	Fixings
Verges, abutments and each side of valleys and hips	the end tile in each course
Eaves and top edges	every tile in first course

Note

Additional nails or clips may be required depending on pitch and degree of exposure. Follow the manufacturer's recommendations. Evidence of calculations in compliance with Technical Requirement R5 may be required.

Table 3 - Minimum fixings for plain, double-lap tiles with nibs

Nail with two nails per tile as follows:

Location	Fixings
Verges, abutments and each side of valleys and hips	the end tile in each course
Eaves and top edges	every tile in first two courses
General roof area	up to 60° - 2 nails per tile every fifth course over 60° - 2 nails per tile in every course

Guidance

BRACING REQUIREMENTS FOR TRUSSED RAFTER ROOFS

Type of bracing	Position of bracing	Where applicable
A Diagonal rafter bracing (at approx 45° on plan)	Truss Span — or — or Alternative styles of bracing for roofs that are approximately square Truss Span — or — or Alternative styles of bracing for larger roofs Truss Span — X Bracing for narrow fronted roofs (less than 6.6m wide) of detached or staggered/ stepped buildings **Intersection detail 'X'** 22 x 97 x 600mm long timber splice plate nailed using minimum of 4 No. 3.35mm x 65mm long galvanised round wire nails each side of intersection diven through bracing and clenched over Truss Span Alternative styles for monopitch trusses	All trussed rafter roofs unless rigid sarking such as timber boarding or plywood is used.
B Longitudinal bracing member at ridge node point		All trussed rafter roofs
C Longitudinal binders at ceiling node points	less than 3.7m	All ceiling node points, but may be omitted where spacing between braced nodes does not exceed 3.7m
D Longitudinal bracing member at rafter node point	less than 4.2m	All rafter node points, but may be omitted where spacing between braced nodes does not exceed 4.2m
E Chevron bracing between webs	more than 8m	Where the span exceeds 8m. For monopitch roofs of any span and duopitch roofs over 11m span, bracing should be designed by an Engineer in accordance with Technical Requirement R5.
F Diagonal bracing to end vertical of monopitch trusses		Where not restrained by masonry wall, or cladding in plywood or similar rigid sheet material

Guidance

CONDITIONS AND LIMITATIONS ON THE USE OF STANDARD TRUSSED RAFTER BRACING

1 The use of standard bracing does not apply to buildings erected on long stretches of open, level or near level country with no shelter. Examples include flat coastal fringes, fens, airfields and moorland.

The height and location of the building, roof pitch and span are also important. Appendix A of BS : 5268 : Part 3 : 1985 (AMD.5931) gives full details but as a general guide standard bracing is acceptable for the following situations:

Roof type	Max pitch [°]	No of storeys	Maximum span [m]		
			England & Wales	Scotland	N Ireland & the Isle of Man
Duo-pitch	35	1	10.6	9.8 (8.6)	9.8 (8.6)
		2	9.1	7.7 (7.2)	7.7 (7.2)
		3	8.5	7.2 (6.0)	7.2 (6.0)
	30	1	12.0	11.6 (10.6)	11.6 (10.6)
		2	11.5	10.0 (8.7)	10.0 (8.7)
		3	10.2	8.8 (7.5)	8.8 (7.5)
Mono-pitch	35	1	5.6	4.9 (4.3)	4.9 (4.3)
		2	4.5	4.2 (3.6)	4.2 (3.6)
		3	4.3	3.6 (3.0)	3.6 (3.0)
	30	1	6.6	5.8 (5.1)	5.8 (5.1)
		2	5.8	5.0 (4.4)	5.0 (4.4)
		3	5.1	4.4 (3.7)	4.4 (3.7)
	25	1	8.1	7.3 (6.5)	7.3 (6.5)
		2	7.2	6.4 (5.6)	6.4 (5.6)
		3	6.4	5.6 (4.5)	5.6 (4.5)

Figures in brackets apply to areas of Scotland either north or west of Ullapool and to areas of Northern Ireland north of Londonderry.

2 The maximum span of the trussed rafters is 12m, the maximum height of the building is 8.4m to the underside of ceiling tie and the maximum rafter spacing is 600mm.

3 The maximum length of unsupported masonry between buttressing walls, piers or chimneys is 9m.

4 The bracing is for either duo-pitched or mono-pitched roofs.

5 The minimum size for bracing members is nominal 25mm x 100mm (3mm tolerance).

6 All bracing members to be nailed with 2 No 3.35mm diameter x 65mm long galvanized round nails to every trussed rafter they cross.

7 The trusses are supported only at their ends.

8 The roof (including hip ends) is rectangular in shape.

APPENDIX 7.2-E

Guidance

BRACING REQUIREMENTS FOR TRUSSED RAFTER ROOFS (continued)

9 Longitudinal bracing members may be lap-jointed provided the overlap is nailed to at least two trussed rafters. They should extend the full length of the roof and tightly abut gable and party walls. Longitudinal bracing members should permit diagonal bracing to pass.

10 At least four diagonal rafter braces are required in every roof. In narrow fronted roofs and mono-pitched roofs, where braces cross, use the intersection detail 'x' above.

11 Diagonal rafter bracing should be at approximately 45° to the rafters on plan. Chevron bracing should be at approximately 45° to the web members. Diagonal bracing and chevron bracing should be across all trussed rafters, but small gaps (2 trussed rafters between sets of bracing and 1 trussed rafter adjacent to gable or separating walls) are permitted in the middle of an otherwise fully braced roof.

12 All trusses should have a plasterboard ceiling. (For trussed rafters at 600mm centres, 12.5mm plasterboard is required.) Where there is no plasterboard, such as in garages, longitudinal binder bracing (Type C above) is to be used at all ceiling node points and additional diagonal ceiling bracing is required.

13 Bracing to satisfy particular conditions shall be in addition to that detailed in the above table.

14 The ITPA Technical Handbook gives further details and advice on construction.

Tank support details

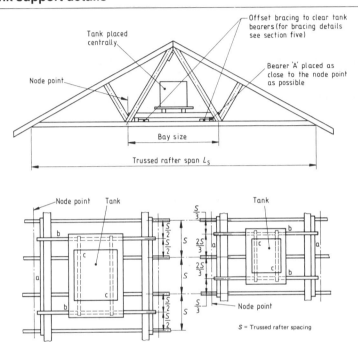

Sizes for support members				
Total tank capacity to marked waterline	Min. member sizes		Max. trussed rafter span for Fink configuration	Max. bay size for other configurations
	a and c	b		
	mm		m	m
Detail A Not more than 300 L supported on four trussed rafters	47 × 72	2/35 × 97 or 1/47 × 120	6.50	2.20
	47 × 72	2/35 × 120 or 1/47 × 145	9.00	2.80
	47 × 72	2/35 × 145	12.00	3.80
Detail B Not more than 230 L supported on three trussed rafters	47 × 72	1/47 × 97	6.50	2.20
	47 × 72	2/35 × 97 or 1/47 × 120	9.00	2.80
	47 × 72	2/35 × 120 or 1/47 × 145	12.00	3.80

NOTE. Support members may be of any species with a permissible bending stress not less than that of European redwood/whitewood of GS stress grade (see **14.1**).

Reproduced from BS 5268 : Part 3 by permission of BSI.

BUILDMARK™

Part 8 SERVICES AND INTERNAL FINISHING

P
A
R
T

8

informing the industry

| CI/SfB | 81 | (5-)(6-) | |
| CAWS | S12 | T32 | V21 |

Operative from January 1992

Chapter 8.1

NHBC STANDARDS

Internal services

This Chapter gives the Technical Requirements and recommendations for internal services, including plumbing, hot and cold water supply, and gas, electric and solid fuel heating installations.

LIST OF CHAPTERS

THE STANDARDS

The NHBC Standards give:
● Technical Requirements in red
● Performance Standards in dark blue
● Guidance in light blue
for the design and construction of dwellings acceptable to NHBC.

Diagrams may contain text in red. This is to highlight points but has no mandatory significance.

The Standards come into effect for every NHBC registered home whose foundations are concreted on or after the publication date shown on the cover of each Chapter and apply throughout the UK, unless otherwise stated.

COMPOSITION OF THE STANDARDS

The Standards are divided into 10 Parts, each containing one or more Chapters covering a particular aspect. The Parts follow the usual construction process.

In general, each Chapter is made up of sections dealing with Design, Materials and Sitework. In some cases one or more of these aspects may not be included.

TECHNICAL REQUIREMENTS

Each Chapter (except former Practice Notes) contains the five mandatory Technical Requirements which MUST be met by the Builder.

The Technical Requirements are printed in red. Chapter 1.1 'Introduction to the Standards and Technical Requirements' contains full details.

PERFORMANCE STANDARDS

Most Chapters consist of detailed Performance Standards printed in dark blue, normally in the left-hand column of each Design, Materials or Sitework page, subdivided into Clauses designated D, M or S, respectively.

Alternative standards of performance will be acceptable ONLY if, in the opinion of NHBC, the Technical Requirements are met and the standard achieved is not lower than the stated Performance Standard.

GUIDANCE

Guidance on how the Performance Standard may be met is normally shown, printed in light blue, in the right-hand column opposite the relevant Performance Standard. Some Chapters contain pages which are all Guidance.

Guidance is based on normal procedures and recommended practices shown by experience to be satisfactory and acceptable. NHBC will consider alternative methods to meet specific requirements, subject to prior consultation and evaluation.

SCOPE

This Chapter gives the Technical Requirements and recommendations for internal services, including plumbing, hot and cold water supply, and gas, electric and solid fuel heating installations.

NHBC Standards do not cover aspects of health and safety relating to building operations and to the handling and use of certain building materials. Such matters are covered by statutory requirements.

FINDING INFORMATION

To find information on a particular subject, the following procedure is recommended:

1 Identify the **Part** most appropriate for the subject.

2 Identify the **Chapter** which deals with the particular element of construction.

3 Decide whether the information required relates to the Design, Materials or Sitework **Section** of the Chapter.

4 Decide from the Contents list the **heading** under which the required information is most likely to be found.

5 Review the **clauses** listed against the heading to see which has the relevant Performance Standard.

6 Review the **items** under the Performance Standards and decide which is relevant.

7 Review the guidance in the right-hand column opposite the item most relevant to the subject. If a clause number is known, use the above procedure to find the clause.

For example: **8.1 - S8(b)** means:

8	Part 8	Services and internal finishing
1	Chapter 1	Internal services
S	Section	SITEWORK
8	Clause 8	SOIL AND WASTE SYSTEMS
(b)	Item (b)	sanitary fittings.

CONTENTS

TECHNICAL REQUIREMENTS

Technical Requirements	Performance Standards

R1 Statutory requirements

Work shall comply with all relevant Building Regulations and other statutory requirements

Chapter 1.1 gives the detailed Performance Standards which relate to these Technical Requirements.

R2 Design requirement

Design and specification shall provide satisfactory performance

R3 Materials requirement

All materials, products and building systems shall be suitable for their intended purpose

R4 Workmanship requirement

All work shall be carried out in a proper, neat and workmanlike manner

R5 Structural design requirement

Structural design shall be carried out by suitably qualified persons in accordance with British Standards and Codes of Practice

Performance Standards	Guidance

DESIGN STANDARD

8.1 - D1 Design shall meet the Technical Requirements

Design that follows the guidance below will be acceptable for internal services.

Design of internal services should take account of the recommendations and specifications set out in Chapter 1.2 'The home - its accommodation and services'.

STATUTORY REQUIREMENTS

8.1 - D2 Design shall comply with all relevant statutory requirements

A list of statutory references applicable to this Chapter is given in Appendix 8.1-A.

STRUCTURAL STABILITY

8.1 - D3 The design of internal services shall not adversely affect the stability of the dwelling

Notching, drilling and chasing to accommodate service pipes and cables should either:

● comply with Sitework clauses 8.1 - S2(d) and (e), or

● be designed by an Engineer.

PRECAUTIONS AGAINST GROUND HAZARDS

8.1 - D4 Design of service entries shall take account of ground hazards

In certain parts of the country, special precautions may be necessary to reduce the entry of radon gas. Details of geographical areas where special precautions are necessary may be obtained from the Department of the Environment.

PRECAUTIONS AGAINST CHEMICAL ATTACK

8.1 - D5 Materials for internal services shall be selected to ensure satisfactory service taking suitable precautions against chemical attack

WATER SERVICES

Pipes and fittings for water services should be of materials which are safe and minimise the risk of corrosion. The recommendations of the local Water Authority should be followed as to the compatibility of the water supply with materials and fittings.

In districts where pitting corrosion of copper cylinders occurs, it may be necessary to fit aluminium protector rods. These should be fitted during manufacture in accordance with the relevant British Standard.

The use of lead in pipes, joints or storage cisterns is not permitted.

Avoid mixing materials in water services. Further guidance is given in BS 6700.

ELECTRICITY SERVICES

PVC covered cables should not touch polystyrene insulation.

DESIGN

Performance Standards	Guidance

COLD WATER SERVICE

8.1 - D6 An adequate cold water service shall be provided in accordance with statutory requirements, bye-laws and codes

Statutory requirements for water services are given in Appendix 8.1-A.

Performance Standards and Guidance for domestic water services are given in Chapter 1.2 'The home - its accommodation and services' and BS 6700.

8.1 - D7 Adequate cold water services shall be provided

Items to be taken into account include:

(a) cold water supply

The incoming service pipe should:
- enter the dwelling through a sleeve
- be laid at sufficient depth to avoid mechanical damage
- be protected against frost damage (see Sitework clauses 8.1 - S3(a) and (b)).

Where external meter chambers are to be used, they should be in accordance with the recommendations of BS 6700.

(b) drinking water

A drinking water point off the incoming main should be provided:
- in the kitchen
- elsewhere, as required.

(c) cold water storage

Cold water storage should be provided:
- to supply a conventional hot water storage system
- in areas with low water pressure
- to supply those cold water outlets not connected directly to the main.

The cold water storage capacity should take account of the guidance in BS 6700, which recommends:
"In small houses it is usual for storage cisterns supplying only cold water fittings to have a capacity of 100L to 150L, and double this capacity if supplying all water outlets, hot and cold. In larger houses a total storage capacity of 100L per bedroom is recommended".

Primary feed cisterns for indirect water heating systems should be of adequate capacity.

Cold water storage cisterns may not be required for some unvented systems.

Performance Standards	Guidance

Cold water storage cisterns should be:
- accessible, *and*
- at a level which permits inspection and maintenance.

Storage cisterns should have rigid close fitting covers (which are not airtight) and which exclude light and insects.

(d) overflow discharge

Warning pipes and overflows of adequate size should be provided from all cold water cisterns to an easily observed discharge point.

(e) reducing risk of freezing

Pipes and cisterns should be located within the warm envelope of the home to reduce the risk of freezing.

Where water services are placed in unheated spaces they should be:
- placed on the warm side of the insulation so that heat from the home helps protect them from frost
- placed at least 100 mm away from external walls
- protected by insulation of suitable thickness. Ceiling insulation taken over tanks and cisterns is suitable.

Where it is not possible to locate pipes and cisterns within the warm envelope of the home, they should be insulated to meet the requirements of the local Water Authority Bye-laws (see Appendix 8.1-B).

No insulation should be placed beneath a cold water cistern located in an unheated roof space. Insulated storage cisterns are available.

Where possible, overflow pipes from cold water storage cisterns should be run below the loft insulation. Where this is not possible, they should be insulated (see Appendix 8.1-B).

Performance Standards

Guidance

HOT WATER SERVICE

8.1 - D8   **An adequate hot water service shall be provided in accordance with statutory requirements, bye-laws and codes**

Statutory requirements for hot water services are given in Appendix 8.1-A.

8.1 - D9   **Adequate hot water services shall be provided**

Items to be taken into account include:

(a) hot water storage

Hot water systems may be either:

- storage systems, or
- instantaneous types.

Hot water storage vessels should be correctly installed in an accessible location.

Sufficient hot water should be available, as follows:

- hot water storage should not be less than 115L, except in the case of systems using off-peak electricity which should generally have at least 200L capacity.

The Electricity Board Medallion Scheme permits the following storage capacities:

- one or two person dwellings without bath but with instantaneous shower may have a minimum storage of 109L
- one or two person dwellings with bath may have a minimum storage of 144L.

Guidance on hot water storage capacity for homes with more than one bathroom is given in BS 6700. This recommends that where a dwelling has:

- one bathroom, it should be assumed that immediately after filling a bath some hot water may be required for kitchen use, but a second bath will not be required for another 20 minutes to 30 minutes
- two or more bathrooms, it should be assumed that all the installed baths will be filled in succession and that hot water will be required immediately for kitchen use.

Performance Standards

Guidance

(b) flow rates

FLOW RATES, TEMPERATURE AND QUANTITY

The following flow rates, water temperatures and quantities should be available:

Outlet	Minimum flow rate [Litres/second]	Supply temperature [°C]	Volume [Litres]
Bath	0.25	60	60
or	0.25	40	100
Shower	0.05	40	
Wash basin	0.15	60	
Sink	0.15	60	

These flow rates should be available to each outlet when only that outlet is open.

INSTANTANEOUS WATER HEATERS, INCLUDING COMBI BOILERS

In the case of instantaneous systems which have no hot water storage, the above flow rates may not be achieved. Where such systems are proposed, the choice of the appliance should be considered in relation to the likely hot water demand. The manufacturer's recommendations or those of authoritative organisations, such as British Gas, should be followed.

The choice of hot water supply systems should take account of limitations in the mains supply, including size of mains, feed pipes and available water pressure.

Designers should check to make certain that appliances will work efficiently on the available water pressure.

(c) indirect hot water systems

Cylinders should be indirect where the:

● water is corrosive, hard or likely to cause furring

● hot water supply and space heating are a composite system, unless the manufacturer recommends otherwise.

(d) expansion

Vented hot water systems should be provided with an expansion pipe, which is:

● insulated (when in unheated roof voids)

● terminated above the cold feed cistern.

DESIGN

Performance Standards	Guidance

HOT WATER SERVICE (continued)

8.1 - D9   **(e) unvented hot water systems**

Unvented pressurised hot water systems may be installed if permitted by the relevant Water Authority. The assembled system with all its components must be covered by a BBA certificate and installed by an approved installer.

The above requirements do not apply to a:
- system having a storage capacity of less than 15L
- space heating system.

(f) safety in showers

Where a shower is installed, adequate provision should be made to ensure that the outlet temperature of the water is not seriously affected by the use of other hot or cold outlets in the dwelling. This may be achieved by the provision of a thermostatic shower mixing valve, appropriate design of pipe sizes or dedicated supplies.

(g) towel rails

Where heated towel rails are installed they should be provided with control valves and aircocks.

(h) thermal insulation

All hot water cylinders and central heating pipes and hot water supply pipes in unheated spaces should be protected with insulation to meet the recommendations of BS 5422 or BS 5615.

Performance Standards	Guidance

ELECTRICAL SERVICE

8.1 - D10 Electrical supply shall be provided in accordance with relevant regulations and codes for safe design and installation

All electrical installations should comply with the Institution of Electrical Engineers (IEE) Wiring Regulations, current on the date when the foundations of the dwelling are laid.

In particular, the need to de-rate cables which are covered or surrounded by thermal insulation should be checked. Guidance is available in the BRE Report 'Thermal insulation: avoiding risks'.

British Standards relevant to design of electrical installations and appliances include BS 3456 and BS 3955.

8.1 - D11 Adequate electrical services shall be provided

Items to be taken into account include:

(a) meters

Meters and associated equipment should be located where they are reasonably accessible and not subject to damage. Domestic meters may be of the following types:

1 Built-in - to the outer leaf of the wall

2 Surface-mounted - on an external wall

3 Semi-concealed - sunk into the groundwork adjacent to the outer wall

4 Individually purpose-made compartments - in accordance with the requirements specified in BS 6400.

Purpose-designed boxes are supplied by Electricity Boards. They do not require a lintel but should be provided with a cavity tray, where appropriate. Lintels may be required over other approved meter boxes.

(b) cooking

In all dwellings, a 30A electricity supply, suitably switched and terminated, should be provided to the cooker space.

If a cooker panel is provided, it should be located to the side of the cooker position.

Where a gas supply is provided to the dwelling, a 13A socket outlet should be positioned at the cooker space.

Performance Standards	Guidance

ELECTRICAL SERVICE (continued)

8.1 - D11 (c) socket outlets

Rooms should be provided with not less than the following 13A sockets. Dual outlets count as two.

Room	Outlets	Notes
Kitchen/utility	6	where homes have separate areas, the kitchen should have a minimum of 4 outlets, and the utility room 2
		where appliances are provided, at least 3 outlets should be free for general use
Dining room	2	
Living or family room	4	at least one double outlet should be near the TV aerial outlet
Bedrooms	3 (2)	3 for main bedroom 2 for other bedrooms
Landing	1	
Hall	1	

Combined rooms shall have sockets equal to the summation of the number for the individual rooms, with a minimum of 7 in the case of a kitchen/utility room and another room.

It is an IEE Regulation that socket outlets which reasonably might be used for outside appliances should be protected by a residual current circuit breaker.

(d) lighting

Every room should have at least one lighting outlet. Within dwellings, there should be provision for lighting to halls, landings and staircases. Two-way switching should be provided to staircases.

Where the Public Lighting Authority specify and maintain control of entrance lighting their requirements should be met. Otherwise, entrances, halls, corridors, landings and staircases forming common areas to dwellings should be provided with artificial lighting. Manual two-way switching controlled by persons using these areas is acceptable. Automatic light sensitive controls may be used, provided lights can also be switched two-way manually.

Unless the area of a dwelling is less than 60m², at least two final sub-circuits for lighting should be provided.

Performance Standards

Guidance

(e) fixed appliances

IMMERSION HEATERS

Immersion heaters, where provided, should be:

- fitted with a clearly indicated on/off switch
- appropriate for the type of water supplied to the dwelling
- chemically protected, if necessary, for water conditions
- thermostatically controlled
- located so that they can be withdrawn for replacement.

EXTRACT FAN SYSTEMS

Where the Builder supplies and fits a fan extractor, fan extract cooker hood or another similar appliance, the extraction should be ducted to the outside air by the shortest route, except when part of a heat recovery unit.

ELECTRIC SUPPLY FOR GAS APPLIANCES

Where a gas appliance requires an electric supply to be installed, for example a boiler, a suitable fixed spur or socket outlet should be provided.

(f) television reception

A concealed co-axial cable should be provided from the roof void to a terminal outlet in the main living room. Where the co-axial cable is not provided, a conduit and draw wire or an alternative should be provided. The provision of an aerial is not required.

DESIGN

Performance Standards	Guidance

GAS SERVICE

8.1 - D12 Where provided, gas services shall be in accordance with relevant standards and codes

All gas services must comply with the Gas Safety Regulations 1972 and the Gas Safety (Installation and Use) Regulations 1984 and with any requirements of British Gas plc.

British Standards relevant to design of gas installations include BS 6891, and for Butane and Propane gas, BS 5482.

8.1 - D13 Where provided, gas services shall be adequate

Items to be taken into account include:

(a) meters

Meters and associated equipment should be located where they are reasonably accessible and not subject to damage. Domestic meters may be of the following types:

1 Built-in - to the outer leaf of the wall

2 Surface-mounted - on an external wall

3 Semi-concealed - sunk into the groundwork adjacent to the outer wall

4 Individually purpose-made compartments - in accordance with the requirements specified in BS 6400.

Purpose-designed boxes are supplied by British Gas plc. They do not require a lintel but should be provided with a cavity tray, where appropriate. Lintels may be required over other approved meter boxes.

(b) cooking

Where a gas supply is provided, there should be a gas point at the cooker space.

(c) flues and air supply

Flues and chimneys for gas appliances should be in accordance with BS 5440 : Part 1, and the air supply requirements should be in accordance with BS 5440 : Part 2.

Performance Standards	Guidance

SPACE HEATING

8.1 - D14 Where space heating is provided it shall be in accordance with statutory regulations, standards and codes

Statutory references on space heating services are given in Appendix 8.1-A.

Heating systems must, in addition, comply with the provisions of the Clean Air Act 1956 or the Clean Air Act (Northern Ireland) 1964. This requirement applies to all dwellings whether or not within the area to which the Clean Air Act applies.

British Standards relevant to heating system design include BS 5449, BS 5410 and BS 8303.

8.1 - D15 Space heating shall be adequate

Items to be taken into account include:

(a) minimum standards for living room heating

The main living room of a dwelling should have a heating appliance or a heat output as part of a central, or whole home, heating system which is capable of maintaining a design temperature of at least 21°C in the room when the outside temperature is -1°C.

(b) minimum standards for whole home heating

The provision of central, or whole home, heating is discretionary. Where it is provided, it should be designed to a recognised standard such as BS 5449 'Code of Practice for central heating for domestic premises' and based generally on the following as a minimum:

● external temperature -1°C

● the design temperatures and ventilation rates given in the table below:

Room	Design temperature [°C]	Air changes per hour
Living room	21	1 ½
Dining room	21	1 ½
Bedsitting room	21	1 ½
Bedroom	18	1
Hall and Landing	18	1 ½
Kitchen	18	2
Bathroom	22	2
Toilet	18	2

DESIGN

Performance Standards	Guidance

SPACE HEATING (continued)

8.1 - D15(b) (continued)

The number of air changes per hour from kitchens and bathrooms should take account of any mechanical or passive system required by statute for the control of condensation.

Homes designed with a lower number of air changes are permitted, provided the means of air supply and quality comply with Building Regulations.

In case of dispute, the design temperatures adopted should be verified by calculations and not by temperature performance tests.

(c) safe operation of heating appliances

Reference should be made to Sitework clause 8.1 - S7 for guidance on:

- location of appliances
- provision for supply of combustion air and removal of combustion products
- separation from combustible materials.

The required height and position of flue pipes should be specified. The free air space required to separate appliances and flue pipes from combustible material should be stated, where appropriate (see Sitework clauses 8.1 - S7(b) and (c)).

Performance Standards	Guidance

SOIL AND WASTE SYSTEMS

8.1 - D16 Internal soil and waste systems shall be designed in accordance with relevant statutory requirements

Statutory references on internal soil and waste systems are given in Appendix 8.1-A.

8.1 - D17 Internal soil and waste systems shall be adequate

Items to be taken into account include:

(a) disposal of effluent from the building

Soil and waste systems should comply with any specific requirements from the local Water Authority.

Guidance and recommendations for building drainage and sanitation are given in BS 8301 and BS 5572.

(b) entry of foul air from the drainage system to the building

Soil and waste systems should be arranged so that:
- each branch is adequately ventilated
- foul air from the drainage system cannot enter the dwelling.

Ventilation should be provided at the head of underground drains. This may be by a soil pipe, separate ventilation pipe or an air admittance valve.

Where a ventilation pipe is less than 3m away from an opening into the building, it should extend at least 900mm above that opening.

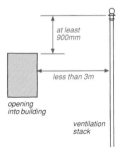

at least 900mm

less than 3m

opening into building

ventilation stack

When air admittance valves are used, they should be assessed in accordance with the Technical Requirements. Valves within the building should be:
- positioned in areas which are not liable to freezing
- fixed above the flood level of the highest sanitary fitting being served.

DESIGN

Performance Standards	Guidance

SOIL AND WASTE SYSTEMS (continued)

8.1 - D17 (c) entry of vermin

Entry of vermin should be prevented. Design in accordance with current Codes of Practice will be acceptable.

(d) noise transmission

Precautions should be taken to limit noise transmission from rooms containing WCs, for example:

- soil pipes passing through living rooms should be encased and insulated; the insulation should be continued through the thickness of any sound-insulating floor
- walls between living rooms and rooms containing WCs can be insulated as recommended in Chapter 6.3 'Internal walls' (Design).

Sound insulation should be detailed in accordance with Sitework clause 8.1 - S8(c) where:

- soil pipes pass through bedrooms or living rooms
- soil or vent pipes pass through a sound-resisting floor.

PROVISION OF INFORMATION

8.1 - D18 Designs and specifications shall be produced in a clearly understandable format and include all relevant information

Drawings should show:

- location of sanitary fittings
- drainage runs
- location and size of cold water storage cisterns
- location and size of hot water storage cylinder
- hot and cold water pipe runs
- heating boiler and heat emitters
- central heating pipe runs
- gas supply pipe runs
- electrical outlets, switches and consumer unit.

8.1 - D19 All relevant information shall be distributed to appropriate personnel

Ensure that design and specification information is issued to site supervisors and relevant specialist subcontractors and/or suppliers.

Performance Standards	Guidance

MATERIALS STANDARDS

8.1 - M1 All materials shall:
(a) meet the Technical Requirements
(b) take account of the design

Materials that comply with the design and the guidance below will be acceptable for internal services.

Materials for internal services should comply with all relevant standards, including those listed below. Where no standards exist, Technical Requirement R3 applies (see Chapter 1.1 'Introduction to the Standards and Technical Requirements').

References to British Standards and Codes of Practice include those made under the Construction Products Directive (89/106/EEC) and, in particular, appropriate European Technical Specifications approved by a European Committee for Standardisation (CEN).

PRECAUTIONS AGAINST CORROSION

8.1 - M2 Materials for internal water services shall be selected to ensure satisfactory service for the life of the systems, taking suitable precautions against corrosion

Pipes and fittings for water services should be of materials which are safe and minimise the risk of corrosion. The recommendations of the local Water Authority should be followed as to the compatibility of the water supply with materials and fittings.

In districts where pitting corrosion of copper cylinders occurs, it may be necessary to fit aluminium protector rods. These should be fitted during manufacture in accordance with the relevant British Standard.

The use of lead in pipes, joints or storage cisterns is not permitted.

Avoid mixing materials in water services. Further guidance is given in BS 6700.

Local Water Authorities may require a sacrificial anode to be fitted.

MATERIALS

Performance Standards	Guidance

MATERIALS : GENERAL

8.1 - M3 **Materials and components shall comply with relevant codes and standards and be approved by relevant authoritative organisations**

Items to be taken into account include:

(a) water services

BS 6700 Specification for design, installation, testing and maintenance of services supplying water for domestic use within buildings and their curtilages.

(b) electrical service

Relevant Electricity Authority and IEE Regulations.

(c) gas service

BS 6400 (1985) Specification for installation of domestic gas meters (2nd family gases)

BS 6891 (1988) Specification for installation of low pressure gas pipework of up to 28mm (R1) in domestic premises (2nd family gases).

(d) space heating

BS 5410 Code of Practice for oil firing

BS 5449 Code of Practice for central heating for domestic premises

BS 8303 Code of Practice for installation of domestic heating and cooking appliances burning solid mineral fuels.

(e) space heating appliances

Space heating appliances, including all components and controls should be a type approved by the relevant authority, including:

- *Solid fuel*   Solid Fuel Advisory Service, *or* Solid Smokeless Fuel Federation
- *Electricity*   British Electrotechnical Approvals Board for Household Equipment, *or* IEE ANT Scheme
- *Gas*   British Gas plc
- *Oil*   BSI's 'List of tested and approved domestic oil-burning appliances'
- *LPG*   Lists of tested and approved domestic LPG appliances issued by BSI, British Gas plc, Calor Gas, etc.

(f) soil and waste systems

BS 5572 Code of Practice for sanitary pipework

BS 6465 Sanitary installations.

Performance Standards	Guidance

SITEWORK STANDARDS

8.1 - S1 **All sitework shall:**
(a) **meet the Technical Requirements**
(b) **take account of the design**
(c) **follow established good practice and workmanship**

Sitework that follows the design and the guidance below will be acceptable for internal services.

INSTALLATION : GENERAL

8.1 - S2 **All services shall be installed to ensure satisfactory operation**

Items to be taken into account include:
(a) **location and fitting of pipes and cables**

Service entries through the substructure should be constructed as described in Chapter 5.1 'Substructure and ground bearing floors' (Design and Sitework).

Ensure that:
● no service is solidly embedded in a structural element
● any services passing through structural elements are sleeved or ducted
● no cables, other than electricity meter tails, are located in the cavity of an external wall
● where electricity meter tails are located in an external wall cavity, a damp-proof membrane is provided on the inside face of the cavity
● metal in screeds, plaster or the like, is protected against any adverse effects of chemical action and thermal movement
● the only pipes buried in screeds are part of a closed circuit, eg a central heating wet radiator system (Note: Burying water pipes in screeds is *not* acceptable in Scotland)
● all open circuit systems are accessible.

Where pipes are permitted in floor screeds they should be:
● sleeved or wrapped so that they can move freely along the length and at joints and bends
● jointed with capillary joints.

SITEWORK

Performance Standards   **Guidance**

INSTALLATION : GENERAL (continued)

8.1 - S2   **(b) jointing of pipes and fittings**

Proprietary joints should be made strictly in accordance with the manufacturer's instructions.

Only fluxes recommended by the pipe manufacturer should be used and all traces should be removed immediately after jointing. Fluxes containing lead are not acceptable.

(c) fixing of pipes

Pipes should be adequately secured with suitable clips or brackets. Fixings should be installed neatly and spaced closely enough to prevent sagging or unreasonable movement.

Pipe runs should be fixed to falls, where appropriate. Sufficient room should be allowed for thermal expansion and contraction to avoid damage and noise from pipe movement.

(d) notching and drilling of timber

Timber joists and studs should only be notched and drilled within the limits shown in the table below:

Item	Location	Maximum size
Notching joists up to 250mm depth	top edge 0.1 to 0.2 of span	0.15 x depth of joist
Drilling joists up to 250mm depth	centre line 0.25 to 0.4 of span	0.25 x depth of joist
Drilling studs	centre line 0.25 to 0.4 of height	0.25 x depth of stud

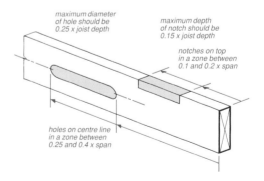

maximum diameter of hole should be 0.25 x joist depth

maximum depth of notch should be 0.15 x joist depth

notches on top in a zone between 0.1 and 0.2 x span

holes on centre line in a zone between 0.25 and 0.4 x span

Performance Standards

Guidance

Notches and drillings in the same joist should be at least 100mm apart horizontally.

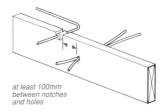

at least 100mm between notches and holes

Any other notching, drilling or cutting should be designed by an Engineer in accordance with Technical Requirement R5.

(e) concealed services

Services concealed in walls or floors should be located so that significant cracking of the surface does not occur.

WALLS

If chases in walls are necessary, their depth should not exceed:
- one-sixth the thickness of the single leaf for horizontal chases
- one-third the thickness for horizontal chases.

Hollow blocks should not be chased unless specifically permitted by the manufacturer.

FLOORS

Pipes under floor screeds should be protected by wrapping or ducting. Room should be allowed for thermal expansion, especially at changes of direction.

The cover over a pipe or any insulating material should be at least 25mm. If it is necessary to form a duct to obtain adequate cover in a suspended concrete floor, the location and depth should be approved by the Engineer, unless the floor is in accordance with Chapter 5.2 'Suspended ground floors' (Design and Sitework).

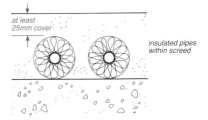

at least 25mm cover

insulated pipes within screed

Performance Standards	Guidance

INSTALLATION : GENERAL (continued)

8.1 - S2(e) (continued)

Where floors are built in accordance with the tables given in Chapter 5.2 'Suspended ground floors' (Design), ducts should not be larger than 150mm wide x 38mm deep.

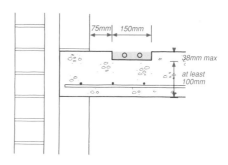

(f) firestopping

Firestopping must be provided around any services which penetrate fire-resisting floors, walls or partitions. Where a proprietary system is used, such as an intumescent seal, it should be installed in accordance with the manufacturer's instructions.

(g) compliance with codes and standards

Builders should note that installation contractors registered with the National Inspection Council for Electrical Installation Contracting (NICEIC) or the Confederation for the Registration of Gas Installers (CORGI) undertake to comply with the relevant codes and regulations and are subject to inspection by those bodies.

Performance Standards   Guidance

HOT AND COLD WATER SERVICES

8.1 - S3   **Hot and cold water services shall be installed to avoid mechanical, frost and corrosive damage**

Items to be taken into account include:

(a) protection of the incoming service

Any stop valve within the curtilage and outside the dwelling should be protected by a shaft or a box.

Service pipes should be at least 750mm below the ground surface. Where this is not possible, adequate precautions should be taken against frost and mechanical damage.

Any underground duct shall be sealed to be gastight.

(b) insulation of the incoming service

If the incoming service pipe rises vertically within 750mm of the external wall and the floor is a ground bearing slab, the incoming water pipe should be insulated within the underfloor duct.

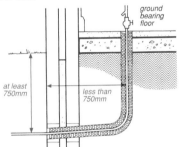

If the floor is of suspended construction, the underfloor water service should be insulated as it passes through the ground and the ventilated space.

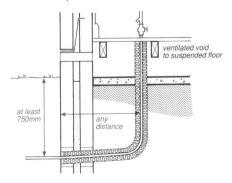

Performance Standards

Guidance

HOT AND COLD WATER SERVICES (continued)

8.1 - S3 **(c) location of meters**

If a water meter is supplied and built into the external wall of the dwelling, it should comply with Clause S6.

(d) provision of cold water storage

Cold water storage cisterns should have the capacity specified in the design.

Adequate support should be provided for the cistern filled with water.

Water cisterns installed in roof spaces should be supported as described in Chapter 7.2 'Pitched roofs' (Design and Sitework).

Continous support should be provided, where necessary, to prevent the cistern bottom being deformed. Suitable materials for support platforms are:

● softwood boarding
● marine plywood
● chipboard Type C4 to BS 5669.

All water tanks should be accessible. Gangway boarding should be provided from the roof space access opening to each cistern. An area of 1m² of boarding should be provided around each cistern.

Water storage cisterns should be protected from contamination by a rigid close fitting cover (which is not airtight) and which excludes light and insects.

Galvanized cisterns should be painted inside with non-toxic bitumen after all debris and loose material has been removed.

Holes should be formed with a cutter in the positions shown in the design. Turn down overflows or warning pipes within the cistern and terminate below water level to avoid cold draughts from the outside. Alternatively, the pipe should terminate vertically downwards or a tee should be fitted horizontally at the discharge end.

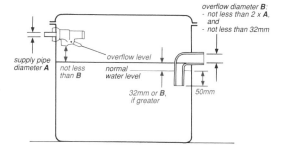

overflow diameter **B**:
- not less than 2 x **A**, and
- not less than 32mm

supply pipe diameter **A**

not less than **B**

overflow level

normal water level

32mm or **B**, if greater

50mm

Performance Standards

Guidance

(e) hot water storage

Hot water cylinders should be supported on bearers and should be at least 50mm clear of timber or similar floors.

Cylinders should be installed vertically, unless designed otherwise, and should be accessible. The positioning should allow immersion heaters and thermostats to be withdrawn for maintenance or replacement.

Cylinders should be insulated as specified in the design.

(f) thermal insulation of water services

All water services in unheated spaces, including cisterns, warning pipes, overflows and vent pipes, should be insulated against freezing as specified in the design. Do not insulate beneath a cold water tank in an unheated roof space.

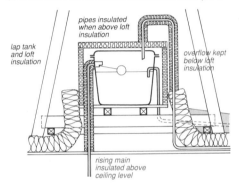

All bends and junctions should be insulated all round, especially near openings to the outside air, such as the eaves, where there is an increased risk of freezing. If possible, avoid locating water pipes within the loft space where they could be affected by cold ventilation air.

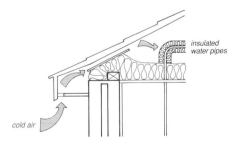

SITEWORK

Performance Standards | **Guidance**

HOT AND COLD WATER SERVICES (continued)

8.1 - S3 **(g) provision for expansion**

Vented systems should be provided with an expansion pipe.

(h) unvented hot water systems

When an unvented hot water system with a storage capacity greater than 15 litres is required by the design, it must be covered by a BBA certificate and be installed by a BBA approved installer.

(i) draining down facility

Each installation, whether in a house, flat or maisonette, should be capable of being separately drained down.

(j) use of materials

Pipes and fittings for water services should be of materials which are safe and minimise the risk of corrosion. The recommendations of the local Water Authority should be followed as to the compatibility of the water supply with materials and fittings.

In districts where pitting corrosion of copper cylinders occurs, it may be necessary to fit aluminium protector rods. These should be fitted during manufacture in accordance with the relevant British Standard.

The use of lead in pipes, joints or storage cisterns is not permitted.

Avoid mixing materials in water services. Further guidance is given in BS 6700.

Local Water Authorities may require a sacrificial anode to be fitted.

Performance Standards

Guidance

ELECTRICAL SERVICE

8.1 - S4 **Electrical services shall be installed to comply with relevant codes and standards and ensure safe and satisfactory operation**

Items to be taken into account include:

(a) compliance with IEE Regulations

Electrical installations should comply with that edition of the Regulations for the Electrical Equipment of Buildings, published by the Institution of Electrical Engineers, which is current on the date when the foundations of the dwelling are laid.

(b) manufacturers' recommendations

Any work involving material or equipment installed as part of the supply or use of electricity should be carried out in accordance with manufacturers' recommendations.

(c) location of electric cables

In order to comply with the IEE Regulations, cables without special protection, such as an earthed metal conduit, must be positioned as follows:

● vertically from the outlet or switch being served, or

● horizontally from the outlet or switch being served, or

● within the shaded zone in the diagram below

● not closer than 50mm to any ceiling where cables are within a timber floor or below a concrete floor.

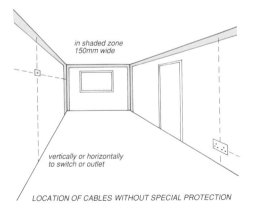

in shaded zone 150mm wide

vertically or horizontally to switch or outlet

LOCATION OF CABLES WITHOUT SPECIAL PROTECTION

Where cables are fixed vertically to studs, fixings should be not more than 500mm apart.

SITEWORK

Performance Standards   **Guidance**

ELECTRICAL SERVICE (continued)

8.1 - S4 **(d) location of cables in relation to insulation**

Cables should not be placed under, against or within thermal insulation, unless de-rated in accordance with the IEE Wiring Regulations. For further guidance, refer to the BRE Report 'Thermal insulation: avoiding risks'.

PVC covered cables should not be in contact with polystyrene insulation.

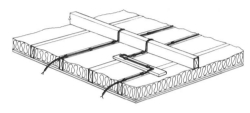

cables above insulation do not need de-rating

(e) location of socket outlets

Socket outlets on walls should be at least 150mm above floor or work surface level, as appropriate, measured from the bottom of the socket plate.

(f) fitting of immersion heaters

Where an immersion heater is fitted, it should be:
- appropriate for the type of water supplied to the dwelling
- chemically protected, if necessary, for the water conditions
- thermostatically controlled
- located so that it can be withdrawn for replacement
- fitted with an on/off switch.

Performance Standards

Guidance

GAS SERVICE

8.1 - S5 **Where a gas service is installed, it shall comply with relevant codes and standards to ensure safe and satisfactory operation**

Items to be taken into account include:

(a) adherence to standards for mains gas installations

Where gas is to be supplied by British Gas plc, piping, appliances and flues should be in accordance with the requirements of British Gas plc which are current on the date when the foundations of the dwelling are laid.

(b) adherence to standards or recommendations for other gases

Piping, appliances and flues should comply with the manufacturer's recommendations and comply with the requirements of the gas supplier which are current on the date when the foundations of the dwelling are laid.

METERING

8.1 - S6 **Openings for metering equipment shall be structurally adequate and prevent dampness entering the dwelling**

EXTERNAL ELECTRICITY AND GAS METERS

Openings for electricity and gas meter-reading cabinets in-set into external walls should be provided with dpcs and cavity trays, as specified in the design, and lintels, if required.

Purpose-designed built-in meter boxes provided by British Gas plc and Electricity Boards do not require lintels.

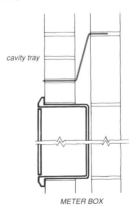

cavity tray

METER BOX

EXTERNAL WATER METERS

Meter chambers for external water meters below ground should be provided in accordance with the design and manufacturer's recommendations.

SITEWORK

Performance Standards   **Guidance**

SPACE HEATING

8.1 - S7 Installation of space heating systems shall comply with relevant codes and standards and ensure safe and satisfactory operation

Items to be taken into account include:

(a) location and fitting of appliances

Appliances should be installed strictly in accordance with:
- relevant regulations and codes of practice
- the design
- manufacturers' instructions.

Appliances should be positioned as shown on the drawings, keeping the specified distance from any combustible materials.

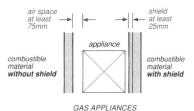

GAS APPLIANCES

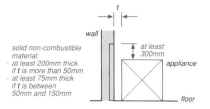

SOLID FUEL AND OIL FIRED APPLIANCES

Appliances should be located to allow inspection, service and replacement. Water-carrying appliances should be positioned so that they can be drained down.

Incandescent heating appliances should not be chosen for small rooms where, because the freedom to arrange furniture is limited, there may be a risk of fire caused by radiant heat.

Any appliance location where heat can cause excessive shrinkage of timber or joinery should be avoided.

Performance Standards

Guidance

(b) provision for supply of combustion air and removal of combustion products

Provision for the supply of combustion air and the removal of combustion products from appliances should be made in accordance with:
- relevant regulations and codes of practice
- the design
- manufacturers' instructions.

For gas systems, check that terminals of balanced flue appliances are located correctly.

It is important that when manufacturers give specific dimensions for siting balanced flue terminals, their dimensions should be followed. However, if the appliance manufacturers do not give specific siting dimensions, the dimensions shown on the following chart should be used for appliances with maximum heat input up to 60kW:

		MINIMUM DISTANCE	
	TERMINAL POSITION	Natural Draught	Fanned Draught
A	Directly below an openable window or other opening e.g. air brick	300mm	300mm
B	Below gutters, soil pipes or drain pipes	300mm*	75mm*
C	Below eaves	300mm*	200mm*
D	Below balconies	600mm	200mm
E	Beside vertical drain pipe and soil pipes	75mm	75mm
F	Beside internal or external corners	600mm	300mm
G	Above ground or balcony level	300mm**	300mm**
H	From a surface facing a terminal	600mm	600mm
I	Where a terminal faces a terminal	600mm	1.2m

* *If the terminal is fitted within 850mm of a plastic or painted gutter or 450mm of painted eaves, an aluminium shield at least 750mm long should be fitted to the underside of the gutter or painted surface.*

** *If a terminal is fitted less than 2m above either a balcony or ground level, or a flat roof to which people have access, then a suitable terminal guard should be provided.*

Reproduced from 'Gas in Housing' by permission of British Gas plc.

SITEWORK

Performance Standards

Guidance

SPACE HEATING (continued)

8.1 - S7(b) (continued)

Flue pipes passing through floors or walls should be separated from adjacent combustible materials in accordance with the design.

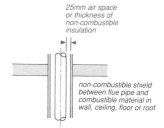

25mm air space or thickness of non-combustible insulation

non-combustible shield between flue pipe and combustible material in wall, ceiling, floor or roof

GAS FLUE PIPE PASSING THROUGH WALL, CEILING, FLOOR OR ROOF

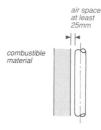

air space at least 25mm

combustible material

GAS FLUE PIPE ADJACENT TO COMBUSTIBLE MATERIAL

(c) location of warm air ducts

Warm air ducts for gas-fired air heaters should be installed in accordance with the design, and follow the manufacturer's recommendations. Underfloor ducts below ground floors should be installed so that water cannot drain into them, and arranged so that access for inspection and repair does not impair the structural stability of the floor. Reference should also be made to Chapter 5.1 'Substructure and ground bearing floors' (Design).

(d) thermal insulation of heating services

All pipework and ductwork should be insulated as specified in the design.

Performance Standards   Guidance

SOIL AND WASTE SYSTEMS

8.1 - S8   **Soil and waste systems shall be installed to ensure that effluent is removed without affecting health or creating unnecessary noise and smell**

Items to be taken into account include:

(a) pipework

Soil and waste pipes should be installed to serve all sanitary fittings shown on the drawings.

Pipes should be fixed neatly and securely to provide correct falls. All traps should be accessible.

(b) sanitary fittings

Fixings to walls and floors should be appropriate for the weight of fittings and the surface to receive the fixing. Excess packing should be avoided under sanitary fittings.

All sanitary fittings, cisterns, basin brackets and the like should be fixed with non-ferrous screws or fixings.

(c) sound insulation of pipes

Insulation should be provided where specified in the design.

Sound insulation should be provided for soil pipes passing through bedrooms or living rooms.

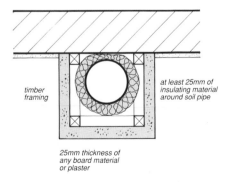

timber framing

at least 25mm of insulating material around soil pipe

25mm thickness of any board material or plaster

Performance Standards   **Guidance**

SOIL AND WASTE SYSTEMS (continued)

8.1 - S8(c) (continued)

Where soil or vent pipes pass through sound-resisting floors, the insulation should be carried through the floor and should seal all gaps in the duct to prevent sound transmission between dwellings.

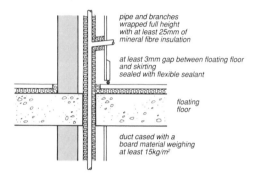

pipe and branches
wrapped full height
with at least 25mm of
mineral fibre insulation

at least 3mm gap between floating floor
and skirting
sealed with flexible sealant

floating
floor

duct cased with a
board material weighing
at least 15kg/m²

(d) flexible joints/sealants

Junctions with wall tiling around baths and showers on joisted floors should be made with watertight flexible sealant to accommodate movement. Manufacturers' instructions should be followed.

(e) accessories

All specified accessories, such as chains, plugs, silencing tubes, etc should be provided and installed in accordance with the design. WC lids and seats should be stable when open.

(f) waste disposal units

Waste disposal units should have adequate provision for support and should be fitted with a tubular trap (not bottle or re-sealing) and be connected directly to a stack or drain.

Performance Standards

Guidance

TESTING

8.1 - S9 **All services shall be tested at least once**

Testing should be carried out in accordance with all relevant regulations and codes of practice as appropriate for the service system.

Tests for formal acceptance of work should be carried out as directed by the Building Control inspector or NHBC inspector, as appropriate. Testing can take place either before covering up or before handover.

If possible, pipes to be located under screeds should be air or water tested before the screed is laid.

Every service installation should be tested and any leaks or other defects made good prior to the application of finishes and handover of the building.

Guidance

Statutory references

The following table lists references to building legislation and associated documents applicable at August 1990.

Clause	Subject	Building [1] Regulations	Building [2] Standards (Scotland)	Building [3] Regulations (N Ireland)	Isle of Man [4] Bye-laws
			Statute		
D2	Firestopping between floors	B2/3/4	Part D	-	-
D6	Cold water service	G2	Part Q	Part N	Part N
D7	Insulation of pipes and cisterns	L1	Part J	Part S	Part F
D8	Hot water service	-	Part P Part Q	-	-
D10	Electrical installation	-	Part N	-	-
D14	Space heating	J1/2/3	Part F Part P	Part M	Part M
		L4	Part N Part Q	-	-
		L5			
D16	Soil and waste systems	G3 H1 E1/2/3	Part M	Part N	Part N

Associated documents

IEE Regulations
Water Authority Bye-laws
Water Bye-laws under Section 70, Water (Scotland) Act 1980
BRE Report 'Thermal insulation: avoiding risks'
Clean Air Act 1956
Clean Air Act (Northern Ireland) 1964
HMSO No 34 "Installation of LPG in fixed position in N Ireland"

[1] Approved Documents to the Building Regulations 1985 for England and Wales (and 1990 edition).
[2] Building Standards (Scotland) Regulations 1981 and all published amendments.
[3] Building Regulations (Northern Ireland) 1990.
[4] Isle of Man Bye-laws 1976, amended 1980 and 1987.

Guidance

Thermal insulation of water pipes to prevent freezing

Table 9. Minimum thickness of thermal insulating material to delay freezing for frost protection

Nominal outside diameter of pipe	Thermal conductivity of insulating material not exceeding:							
	0.035 W/(m·K)	0.04 W/(m·K)	0.055 W/(m·K)	0.07 W/(m·K)	0.035 W/(m·K)	0.04 W/(m·K)	0.055 W/(m·K)	0.07 W/(m·K)
	Indoor installations				Outdoor installations			
mm	mm	mm	mm	mm	mm	mm	mm	mm
Up to and including 15	22	32	50	89	27	38	63	100
Over 15 up to and including 22	22	32	50	75	27	38	63	100
Over 22 up to and including 42	22	32	50	75	27	38	63	89
Over 42 up to and including 54	16	25	44	63	19	32	50	75
Over 54 up to and including 76.1	13	25	32	50	16	25	44	63
Over 76.1 and flat surfaces	13	19	25	38	16	25	32	50

NOTE 1. This table is based on discussions with the manufacturers pending revision of BS 5422. It lists the thermal conductivity value with an air temperature of 0 °C and the minimum thickness of insulating material that will afford worthwhile protection against freezing during normal occupation of buildings.

NOTE 2. Storage cisterns and pipework in roof spaces are considered as indoor installations except where otherwise specified in **10.3.4**.

NOTE 3. Pipework in the air space beneath a suspended ground floor or in a detached garage should be protected as outdoor installations.

Table 10. Examples of insulating materials

Thermal conductivity	Material
W/(m·K)	
Less than 0.035	Polyurethane foam
	Foamed or expanded plastics including rigid and flexible preformed pipe insulation of these materials.
0.04 to 0.055	Corkboard
0.055 to 0.07	Exfoliated vermiculite (loose fill)

Reproduced from Section 2 of BS 6700 : 1987 by permission of BSI.

BUILDMARK™

NHBC, Buildmark House, Chiltern Avenue, Amersham, Bucks HP6 5AP

NHBC, 5 Manor Place, Edinburgh, Scotland EH3 7DH

NHBC, Holyrood Court, 59 Malone Road, Belfast BT9 6SA

informing the industry

CI/SfB	81	(42)		
CAWS	K10	M20	M40	

Operative from January 1992

Chapter **8.2**

NHBC STANDARDS

Wall and ceiling finishes

This Chapter gives the Technical Requirements and
recommendations for internal wall and ceiling finishes.

LIST OF CHAPTERS

THE STANDARDS

The NHBC Standards give:
- Technical Requirements in red
- Performance Standards in dark blue
- Guidance in light blue

for the design and construction of dwellings acceptable to NHBC.

Diagrams may contain text in red. This is to highlight points but has no mandatory significance.

The Standards come into effect for every NHBC registered home whose foundations are concreted on or after the publication date shown on the cover of each Chapter and apply throughout the UK, unless otherwise stated.

COMPOSITION OF THE STANDARDS
The Standards are divided into 10 Parts, each containing one or more Chapters covering a particular aspect. The Parts follow the usual construction process.

In general, each Chapter is made up of sections dealing with Design, Materials and Sitework. In some cases one or more of these aspects may not be included.

TECHNICAL REQUIREMENTS
Each Chapter (except former Practice Notes) contains the five mandatory Technical Requirements which MUST be met by the Builder.

The Technical Requirements are printed in red. Chapter 1.1 'Introduction to the Standards and Technical Requirements' contains full details.

PERFORMANCE STANDARDS
Most Chapters consist of detailed Performance Standards printed in dark blue, normally in the left-hand column of each Design, Materials or Sitework page, subdivided into Clauses designated D, M or S, respectively.

Alternative standards of performance will be acceptable ONLY if, in the opinion of NHBC, the Technical Requirements are met and the standard achieved is not lower than the stated Performance Standard.

GUIDANCE
Guidance on how the Performance Standard may be met is normally shown, printed in light blue, in the right-hand column opposite the relevant Performance Standard. Some Chapters contain pages which are all Guidance.

Guidance is based on normal procedures and recommended practices shown by experience to be satisfactory and acceptable. NHBC will consider alternative methods to meet specific requirements, subject to prior consultation and evaluation.

SCOPE

This Chapter gives the Technical Requirements and recommendations for internal wall and ceiling finishes.

NHBC Standards do not cover aspects of health and safety relating to building operations and to the handling and use of certain building materials. Such matters are covered by statutory requirements.

FINDING INFORMATION

To find information on a particular subject, the following procedure is recommended:

1 Identify the **Part** most appropriate for the subject.

2 Identify the **Chapter** which deals with the particular element of construction.

3 Decide whether the information required relates to the Design, Materials or Sitework **Section** of the Chapter.

4 Decide from the Contents list the **heading** under which the required information is most likely to be found.

5 Review the **clauses** listed against the heading to see which has the relevant Performance Standard.

6 Review the **items** under the Performance Standards and decide which is relevant.

7 Review the guidance in the right-hand column opposite the item most relevant to the subject. If a clause number is known, use the above procedure to find the clause.

For example: **8.2 - S3(b)** means:

8	Part 8	Services and internal finishing
2	Chapter 2	Wall and ceiling finishes
S	Section	SITEWORK
3	Clause 3	PLASTERBOARD AND DRY LINING
(b)	Item (b)	surface finish.

CONTENTS

TECHNICAL REQUIREMENTS

Technical Requirements	Performance Standards

R1 Statutory requirements
Work shall comply with all relevant Building Regulations and other statutory requirements

Chapter 1.1 gives the detailed Performance Standards which relate to these Technical Requirements.

R2 Design requirement
Design and specification shall provide satisfactory performance

R3 Materials requirement
All materials, products and building systems shall be suitable for their intended purpose

R4 Workmanship requirement
All work shall be carried out in a proper, neat and workmanlike manner

R5 Structural design requirement
Structural design shall be carried out by suitably qualified persons in accordance with British Standards and Codes of Practice

Performance Standards	Guidance

DESIGN STANDARD

8.2 - D1 Design shall meet the Technical Requirements

Design that follows the guidance below will be acceptable for wall and ceiling finishes.

STATUTORY REQUIREMENTS

8.2 - D2 Design shall comply with all relevant statutory requirements

A list of statutory references applicable to this Chapter is given in Appendix 8.2-A.

PLASTERING

8.2 - D3 Design shall ensure a suitable substrate for the intended decorative finish

Items to be taken into account include:

(a) background

Backgrounds should be given appropriate treatment before plastering in accordance with BS 5492 Code of Practice for internal plastering.

HIGH DENSITY CLAY OR CONCRETE BRICKS AND BLOCKS AND DENSE CONCRETE (including floor soffits)
- suitable bonding treatment
- hacking
- spatterdash
- stipple.

MIXED BACKGROUNDS, eg CONCRETE WITH BRICKS/ BLOCKS
- may require expanded metal, to provide key for plastering and to reduce the effects of differential movement.

LIGHTWEIGHT CONCRETE BLOCKS
- plaster should not be stronger than recommended by the blockwork manufacturer.

AUTOCLAVED AERATED CONCRETE BLOCKS
- plastering should be carried out in accordance with manufacturers' recommendations, with special care taken regarding the moisture condition of the blocks.

NORMAL CLAY BRICKWORK, CONCRETE BLOCK
- may require raked joints or the use of keyed bricks.

PLASTERBOARD
- reference should be made to BS 5492 for plastering on plasterboard.

DESImGN

Performance Standards   Guidance

PLASTERING (continued)

8.2 - D3   **(b) services**

Services to be concealed by plaster should be tested, where possible, before plastering is commenced (reference should be made to Chapter 8.1 'Internal services' (Sitework)).

(c) plaster mix

Plaster mixes should be specified as appropriate for the:
- strength and surface characteristics of the background
- intended quality of the plaster surface
- application of further finishes.

Undercoats, finishing coats and mix proportions should be as recommended by the plaster manufacturer for the particular conditions of use. Portland cement and gypsum plaster should not be used in the same mix.

(d) plaster thickness

DECORATIVE FINISH
The number of plaster coats should be sufficient to achieve a reasonably plane finish in accordance with the following:

Surface to be plastered	Min no of coats	Thickness of plaster
Walls		
Metal lathing	3	13mm (nominal from lathing)
Brickwork	2	up to 13mm
Blockwork	2	up to 13mm
Plasterboard or concrete	1	sufficient to provide a crack-free surface
Ceilings		
Concrete	2	10mm (maximum)
Plasterboard	1	skimcoat

FIRE RESISTANCE AND SOUND INSULATION
Where plaster is intended to contribute to fire resistance or sound insulation, minimum requirements for plaster thickness are specified in the appropriate statutory regulations (see Appendix 8.2-A).

(e) plastic compound finish

Plastic compound finishes containing asbestos should not be specified.

Performance Standards   Guidance

PLASTERBOARD AND DRY LINING

8.2 - D4 **Dry lining shall be designed to be suitable for the intended decorative finish**

Dry lining work should be in accordance with BS 8212.

Items to be taken into account include:

(a) support of plasterboard

Supports for plasterboard should be designed so that the following span limits are not exceeded:

Plasterboard thickness [mm]	Maximum span [mm]
9.5	450
12.5	600

Unless support spacing is reduced, noggings should be provided behind all cut edges more than 50mm from a support. For plasterboard ceilings below trussed rafters, bound edges should be fixed to supports at the perimeters of all separately boarded areas.

Plasterboard to receive ceramic wall tiling should be supported in accordance with the details given in Appendix 8.2-B.

Where double layers of plasterboard are used, for example for improved sound insulation, board joints should be staggered from one layer to the other and extra noggings provided, as necessary.

(b) surface facing

Plasterboard surfaces should be specified to match the intended finish, as follows:

Finish	Plasterboard face
Plastering	plaster face (grey)
Skimming	plaster face (grey)
Direct tiling	decorative face
Decoration	decorative face

Tapered edge boards should be used for surfaces to be decorated directly on the board surface.

(c) fire resistance

Where plasterboard contributes to fire resistance, its thickness and treatment should be as specified in the appropriate statutory regulations (see Appendix 8.2-A).

Performance Standards | Guidance

PLASTERBOARD AND DRY LINING (continued)

8.2 - D4 **(d) vapour check**

Where required to control interstitial condensation, vapour checks should be incorporated. In timber frame walls, vapour checks should be in accordance with recommendations detailed in Chapter 6.2 'External timber framed walls and wall panels' (Design).

In roof constructions, vapour checks should be in accordance with the following chapters:
7.1 'Flat roofs and balconies' (Design)
7.2 'Pitched roofs' (Design).

(e) fixings

PLASTERBOARD
Plasterboard may be fixed to:
● timber, using plasterboard nails or dry wall screws
● metal, using dry wall screws.

DRY LINING
Dry lining may be fixed by:
● adhesive dabs
● nailing or screwing to timber battens
● screwing to metal channels
● proprietary fixing systems.

Where insulated dry lining is fixed with adhesive dabs, nailable plugs should also be specified in accordance with manufacturers' recommendations.

(f) gap sealing

Gap sealing should be specified, where necessary, to prevent draughts (see Sitework clause 8.2 - S3(f) for details).

(g) coving

Location, type, size and method of fixing should be specified.

CERAMIC WALL TILING

8.2 - D5 **Ceramic wall tiling shall be designed and specified to achieve a surface of acceptable appearance and adequate durability**

Items to be taken into account include:

(a) background

EVENNESS
Background surfaces for tiling should be sufficiently even to achieve a plane tiled surface.

Performance Standards   Guidance

STRENGTH
Background surfaces should be strong enough to support tiling of the specified thickness.

BOND
The background should provide adequate mechanical key. Very smooth and dense surfaces may require bonding agents or metal lathing for increased adhesion.

UNIFORMITY
Surfaces should be sufficiently uniform to avoid differential movement. Metal lathing or wire netting may be necessary to cover junctions.

SUCTION
Background surfaces should have adequate porosity for the specified method of fixing the tiles. Where cement mortar is to be used as an adhesive, a background containing soluble salts may require special precautions, such as the use of mortar with sulphate-resisting cement.

(b) tile quality

Tiles should be appropriate for their location and intended use. Specification items may include:
- surface finish
- size and thickness
- colour
- edge shape
- fittings (coves, skirtings, etc)
- accessories (soap tray, paper holder, hooks, etc).

Tiles on lightweight plasters should not be thicker than 8mm.

(c) fixing

Tiles should be fixed as appropriate for the background, using:
- cement mortar, or
- proprietary adhesive.

Tiles likely to be frequently wetted should be fixed with waterproof adhesive on a water-resistant background.

(d) joint filling

Grouting should be:
- cement-based or a proprietary material
- waterproof in and around shower enclosures where tiling can be saturated.

A sealing method should be specified for the joint between sanitary fittings and adjacent tiling - this is particularly important where movement can take place, eg where timber floors are used.

DESIGN

Performance Standards	Guidance

PROVISION OF INFORMATION

8.2 - D6 **Designs and specifications shall be produced in a clearly understandable format and include all relevant information**

Design information should include:
- schedule of finishes
- plaster thickness, mix and special requirements
- location of vapour checks behind dry lining
- extent and detail of tiled surfaces
- location of services adjacent to tiled surfaces.

8.2 - D7 **All relevant information shall be distributed to appropriate personnel**

Ensure that design and specification information is issued to site supervisors and relevant specialist subcontractors and/or suppliers.

Performance Standards	Guidance

MATERIAL STANDARDS

8.2 - M1 All materials shall:
  (a) meet the Technical Requirements
  (b) take account of the design

Materials that comply with the design and the guidance below will be acceptable for wall and ceiling finishes.

Materials for wall and ceiling finishes should comply with all relevant standards, including those listed below. Where no standard exists, Technical Requirement R3 applies (see Chapter 1.1 'Introduction to the Standards and Technical Requirements').

References to British Standards and Codes of Practice include those made under the Construction Products Directive (89/106/EEC) and, in particular, appropriate European Technical Specifications approved by a European Committee for Standardisation (CEN).

PLASTERING

8.2 - M2 Materials for plastering shall be adequate for the location and intended use

Items to be taken into account include:

(a) plasters

Relevant standards include:

BS 1191 Specification for gypsum building plasters

BS 5270 Part 1 Specification for polyvinyl acetate (PVAC) emulsion bonding agents for indoor use with gypsum building plasters.

(b) materials for render

Relevant standards include:

BS 12   Specification for Portland cements

BS 1199 and 1200 Specifications for building sands from natural sources.

(c) metal laths and beads

Relevant standards include:

BS 405   Specification for uncoated expanded metal carbon steel sheets for general purposes

BS 1369 Steel lathing for internal plastering and external rendering.

(d) plastic compound finishes

Plastic compound finishes containing asbestos should not be used.

MATERIALS

Performance Standards   **Guidance**

PLASTERBOARD AND DRY LINING

8.2 - M3   **Materials for plasterboard and dry lining shall be adequate for the location and intended use**

Relevant standards include:

BS 1230 Gypsum plasterboard

BS 6214 Specification for jointing materials for plasterboard.

Recommendations regarding materials for use in dry lining work are included in:

BS 8212 Code of Practice for dry lining and partitioning using gypsum plasterboard.

CERAMIC WALL TILING

8.2 - M4   **Materials for ceramic tiling shall be adequate for the location and intended use**

Relevant standards include:

BS 6431 Ceramic floor and wall tiles.

Performance Standards

Guidance

SITEWORK STANDARDS

8.2 - S1   **All sitework shall:**
 (a) **meet the Technical Requirements**
 (b) **take account of the design**
 (c) **follow established good practice and workmanship**

Sitework that complies with the design and the guidance below will be acceptable for wall and ceiling finishes.

PLASTERING

8.2 - S2   **Plastering shall be suitable for the intended decorative finish**

Items to be taken into account include:

 (a) **background**

EVENNESS
Background to be plastered should be sufficiently even to provide a reasonably plane plaster finish and to avoid the necessity for excessive dubbing out before the finish is applied.

BOND
The background should provide a satisfactory key. Backgrounds may be improved by:
● raking out masonry joints
● hacking and scratching
● applying a spatterdash coat or stipple coat
● applying a bonding agent.

SUCTION
Suction of the background should be checked for adequacy and should be reasonably even. Where different materials in the background could cause cracks, eg in floors of precast beams and infill blocks, metal lathing should be used or other precautions taken.

EDGE PROTECTION
Metal beads should be fixed to provide edge protection, where necessary, using zinc-plated fasteners as recommended by the manufacturer.

 (b) **services**

All services to be concealed behind plaster should be completed and protected against any adverse effects of chemical action or thermal movement. Where there appears to be a risk of insufficient plaster cover to avoid surface cracking, fix metal lathing or wire netting.

SITEWORK

Performance Standards	Guidance

PLASTERING (continued)

8.2 - S2   (c) plaster mix

Plaster should be mixed in the specified proportions or as recommended by the plaster manufacturer for the particular location and use.

Undercoats and finishing coats should be compatible. Portland cement and gypsum plaster should not be used in the same mix.

(d) plaster thickness

DECORATIVE FINISH
Plaster should be applied to a thickness, excluding any dubbing out, sufficient to achieve the required quality of finish, in accordance with the following:

Surface to be plastered	Min no of coats	Thickness of plaster
Walls		
Metal lathing	3	13mm (nominal from lathing)
Brickwork	2	up to 13mm
Blockwork	2	up to 13mm
Plasterboard or concrete	1	sufficient to provide a crack-free surface
Ceilings		
Concrete	2	10mm (maximum)
Plasterboard	1	skimcoat

(e) application

SCHEDULING OF WORK
Plastering should not be carried out in weather which could adversely affect the finished result. Any plaster damaged by frost should be removed and replaced (reference should be made to Chapter 1.4 'Cold weather working').

MIXING
Materials should be mixed thoroughly, but prolonged mixing should be avoided. Avoid mixing more plaster than can be applied before it starts to set. Plaster should not be re-tempered.

PROTECTION
The completed work of other trades, especially timber, chipboard and glazing, should be protected from damp and damage during plastering.

Performance Standards	Guidance

PREPARATION

Before plastering is started, all surfaces should be dry, clean, and free from laitance, grease, loose material or any substance likely to prove harmful to the bond or the intended finished appearance of the plaster.

Joints between boarded or slab surfaces should be scrimmed, paper taped or otherwise treated as recommended by the manufacturer.

Dubbing out should be done well in advance of the application of the first coat.

PLASTERING

The background surface should be fully set for each coat of plaster. The surface should not be overworked and adequate time should be left between coats to allow strength and suction to develop.

(f) quality of finish

All plastered surfaces should be reasonably plane and true and with a quality of finish appropriate for the location and intended use.

Reveals, soffits to openings, external angles and the like, should be reasonably plumb and level, and ceiling lines and corners should be regular.

Particular care should be taken in areas around wall light points, wall light switches and socket outlets.

(g) plastic compound finish

Plastic compound finishes should be applied by suitably trained operatives.

Performance Standards

Guidance

PLASTERBOARD AND DRY LINING

8.2 - S3 **Plasterboard and dry lining shall be suitable for the intended decorative finish**

Items to be taken into account include:

(a) background

EVENNESS AND STRENGTH

Plasterboard thickness should be correct for the support spacing. Maximum limits are as follows:

Plasterboard thickness [mm]	Maximum span [mm]
9.5	450
12.5	600

Unless the spacings between supports are reduced, noggings should be provided behind all cut edges more than 50mm from a support. For plasterboard ceilings below trussed rafters, bound edges should be fixed to supports at the perimeters of all separately boarded areas.

When double layers of plasterboard for ceilings are specified, the joints of one layer should not coincide with those of the other. Provide extra noggings, where necessary, to achieve this and maintain a flat surface.

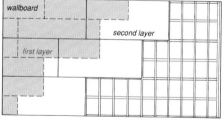

Noggings for the first layer of a 2 layer system are as follows:

Board thickness [mm]	Joist centres [mm]	Intermediate noggings required
9.5	400	no
	450	yes
12.5	450	no
	600	yes

Performance Standards

Guidance

SERVICES

There should be adequate support for:

● light points
● socket outlets
● other service installations.

Openings in plasterboard for services and electrical outlets should be accurately cut and any gaps in vapour checks taped and sealed, as detailed in Chapter 6.2 'External timber framed walls and wall panels'.

WATER VAPOUR RESISTANCE

Install vapour checks where specified. Edges should be lapped over supports and be taped or sealed.

(b) surface finish

Plasterboard facings should match the intended finish, as follows:

Finish	Plasterboard face
Plastering	plaster face (grey)
Skimming	plaster face (grey)
Direct tiling	decorative face
Decoration	decorative face

Tapered edge boards should be used for surfaces to be decorated directly on the board surface.

(c) scheduling of work

Plasterboard work should:

● not be started until the building is substantially weatherproof
● be programmed so that finishes are applied as soon as possible after completion.

Performance Standards	Guidance

PLASTERBOARD AND DRY LINING (continued)

8.2 - S3   **(d) fixing**

Fixing methods should be as follows:
- to timber : plasterboard nails or drywall screws (galvanized or zinc plated)
- to metal : drywall screws.

Fixing lengths should be as follows:
- nail lengths: 30mm for 9.5mm boards
                    40mm for 12.5mm boards
- screw lengths: 32mm for 9.5mm boards
                    36mm for 12.5mm boards

Nails or screws should be not less than:
- 10mm from paper bound edges
- 13mm from cut ends of boards
- 6mm from edges of timber members.

Nail and screw heads should not project above the board surface.

Fixing centres should be as follows:
- nailing to: walls and ceilings - approximately 150mm centres (8 per linear metre)
- screwing to: walls - approximately 300mm centres (8 per 2 linear metres)
                  ceilings - approximately 230mm centres (5 per linear metre).

In Northern Ireland and the Isle of Man, sheradised nails should not be used.

DRY LINING ON ADHESIVE DABS

Boards should be fixed to a pattern of adhesive dabs, at approximately 300mm centres vertically, and as shown in the following table:

Thickness of wall board [mm]	Width of wall board [mm]	Dabs per board [rows]
9.5	900	3
9.5	1200	4
12.5	1200	3

Dabs should be applied to one board at a time.

Performance Standards	Guidance

MECHANICAL FIXINGS FOR THERMAL WALLBOARDS

At least 2 nailable plugs should be used per board in accordance with the manufacturer's recommendations.

PROPRIETARY SYSTEMS

Proprietary dry lining systems should be fixed in accordance with the manufacturer's recommendations.

(e) jointing

Where surfaces are to receive skim coat plaster, joints should be scrimmed or paper taped in accordance with the manufacturer's recommendations. Ceiling boards should be staggered to minimise any risk of cracking.

For unskimmed surfaces, joints should be filled, taped or finished as recommended by the manufacturer.

(f) gap sealing

To prevent draughts through dry lining which could deposit moisture, all gaps at the perimeter of plasterboarded areas on external walls should be fully sealed. In addition:

● dry linings should be completely taped and filled at board joints and at abutments to ceilings and internal walls

● dry wall lining at door and window openings should be securely fixed and filled. This also applies at external and internal corners

● gaps at skirting level should be sealed with jointing compound between the bottom of the wall board and floor level

● gaps around service points, electric sockets, light switches, etc should be filled with jointing compound.

(g) appearance

Unless designed otherwise, intersections should be formed at right angles and be flush. Junctions at floors and ceilings should be neat and regular.

Dry lining to be finished fair should be of a quality recommended by the manufacturer. Damaged boards should not be used.

Performance Standards	Guidance

CERAMIC WALL TILING

8.2 - S4 Ceramic wall tiling shall provide a surface adequate for its intended use

Items to be taken into account include:

(a) background

EVENNESS

The background to be tiled should be reasonably true so that a plane tile surface can be achieved. Under a 2m straight-edge, gaps should *not* be greater than:

- 3mm - for *thin* bed adhesives
- 6mm - for *thick* bed adhesives.

STRENGTH

The surface should be strong enough to accept the specified adhesive and support the tiling. Separate coats should be well bonded.

BOND

The background should provide a satisfactory key. Backgrounds may be improved by:

- raking out masonry joints
- hacking and scratching
- applying a bonding agent.

UNIFORMITY

Metal lathing or wire netting should be fixed across junctions where differential movement might occur.

SUCTION

Suction of the background should be adequate and reasonably consistent. Where different materials could cause cracks, eg across junctions, appropriate precautions should be taken, eg by fixing metal lathing.

WETTING

Gypsum plasters should not be used where repeated or persistent wetting may occur. A moisture-resistant background should be provided.

HEATING

Gypsum plasters should not be used where repeated or persistent heating occurs, eg on flues or near heat sources.

(b) adhesives

Tiles should be fixed as specified, using cement mortar or proprietary adhesive in accordance with manufacturers' instructions. Adhesives for tiles subject to frequent wetting should be waterproof.

Performance Standards	Guidance

(c) application

PREPARATION

Before tiling is started, surfaces should be dry, clean, and free from laitance, grease, loose material or any substance likely to prove harmful to the bond or the intended finished appearance of the plaster.

FIXING

Tiles should be fixed in straight and even courses to form a plane surface. Work generally should be of a straight and regular appearance. Take particular care where lighting points are close to the tiled surface, such as above washbasins in bathrooms.

JOINTING

Joints should be even and cutting neatly carried out. Make sure that the spacing is sufficient to allow expansion.

GROUTING

Grouting should be the specified mix and colour. The specified sealing method should be used at junctions between tiling and sanitary fittings.

Proprietary waterproof grouting should be used in accordance with manufacturers' recommendations.

EDGING

A suitable proprietary edging strip should be used for exposed edges and external corners.

(d) movement

Properly designed movement joints should be built into tiling at centres not exceeding 4.5m both vertically and horizontally and also at all vertical corners in large tiled areas.

Tiles without spacer lugs should be provided with an adequate joint to relieve local stress.

Guidance

Statutory references

The following table lists references to building legislation and associated documents applicable at August 1990.

		Statute			
Clause	Subject	Building [1] Regulations	Building [2] Standards (Scotland)	Building [3] Regulations (N Ireland)	Isle of Man [4] Bye-laws
D2	Control of fire spread	B2/3/4	Part D Part E	Part E	Part E
D2	Sound insulation	E1/2/3	Part H	Part G	Part G
		Associated documents			

[1] Approved Documents to the Building Regulations 1985 for England and Wales (and 1990 edition).
[2] Building Standards (Scotland) Regulations 1981 and all published amendments.
[3] Building Regulations (Northern Ireland) 1990.
[4] Isle of Man Bye-laws 1976, amended 1980 and 1987.

Guidance

Dry lining to receive ceramic wall tiling

Table 3. Dry lining to receive ceramic wall tiling

Description	Board thickness (mm)	Support centres (mm)	Additional support	Max. height (mm)	Comments
Timber frame	12.5	400 to 450	No	3600	
		600	Timber noggins 600 mm centres vertically	3600	
Timber battens	12.5	400	Battens at head, base and intermediate positions not exceeding 1200 mm centres	3600	
Direct bond	9.5	450 dabs of adhesive	Horizontal dabs at 1/3 centres in height	3600	Complete at least 10 days before tiling
Direct bond (Thermal laminates)	12.5	600 dabs of adhesive	Horizontal dabs at 1/3 centres in height	3600	Complete at least 10 days before tiling
Metal furring	12.5	400 metal furring sections	Metal furring stops at head, base and intermediate positions not exceeding 1200 mm centres		Complete at least 10 days before tiling
Resin base adhesive (Thermal laminates)	12.5	Normal bands			
Independent steel stud lining 48 mm	2 × 12.5	400	Mid-point support	3000	
60 mm	2 × 12.5		Mid-point support	3600	
48 mm metal stud partitions	2 × 12.5	400	Additional stud at 300 mm up to tile height	3600	
70 mm metal stud partitions	2 × 12.5	400		3600	
146 mm metal stud partitions	2 × 12.5	600		3600	
Prefabricated gypsum wallboard panel partition	50 / 57 / 63	Normal specification		2400 / 2700 / 3600	
Laminated partition	50 / 65	Normal specification		2600 / 2800	Complete at least 10 days before tiling

Reproduced from Table 3 BS 8212 by permission of BSI.

BUILDMARK™

NHBC, Buildmark House, Chiltern Avenue, Amersham, Bucks HP6 5AP

NHBC, 5 Manor Place, Edinburgh, Scotland EH3 7DH

NHBC, Holyrood Court, 59 Malone Road, Belfast BT9 6SA

informing the industry

CI/SfB	81	(43)		
CAWS	M10	M40	M50	

Operative from January 1992

Chapter **8.3**

NHBC STANDARDS

Floor finishes

This Chapter gives the Technical Requirements and
recommendations for floor finishes including:

- integral insulation
- screeds
- ceramic, concrete and similar tiles

- flexible sheet and tiles
- wood block
- asphalt

8.3 | Floor finishes

LIST OF CHAPTERS

THE STANDARDS

The NHBC Standards give:
● Technical Requirements in red
● Performance Standards in dark blue
● Guidance in light blue
for the design and construction of dwellings acceptable to NHBC.

Diagrams may contain text in red. This is to highlight points but has no mandatory significance.

The Standards come into effect for every NHBC registered home whose foundations are concreted on or after the publication date shown on the cover of each Chapter and apply throughout the UK, unless otherwise stated.

COMPOSITION OF THE STANDARDS
The Standards are divided into 10 Parts, each containing one or more Chapters covering a particular aspect. The Parts follow the usual construction process.

In general, each Chapter is made up of sections dealing with Design, Materials and Sitework. In some cases one or more of these aspects may not be included.

TECHNICAL REQUIREMENTS
Each Chapter (except former Practice Notes) contains the five mandatory Technical Requirements which MUST be met by the Builder.

The Technical Requirements are printed in red. Chapter 1.1 'Introduction to the Standards and Technical Requirements' contains full details.

PERFORMANCE STANDARDS
Most Chapters consist of detailed Performance Standards printed in dark blue, normally in the left-hand column of each Design, Materials or Sitework page, subdivided into Clauses designated D, M or S, respectively.

Alternative standards of performance will be acceptable ONLY if, in the opinion of NHBC, the Technical Requirements are met and the standard achieved is not lower than the stated Performance Standard.

GUIDANCE
Guidance on how the Performance Standard may be met is normally shown, printed in light blue, in the right-hand column opposite the relevant Performance Standard. Some Chapters contain pages which are all Guidance.

Guidance is based on normal procedures and recommended practices shown by experience to be satisfactory and acceptable. NHBC will consider alternative methods to meet specific requirements, subject to prior consultation and evaluation.

SCOPE

This Chapter gives the Technical Requirements and recommendations for floor finishes, including integral insulation, screeds, ceramic, concrete and similar tiles, flexible sheet and tiles, wood block and asphalt.

NHBC Standards do not cover aspects of health and safety relating to building operations and to the handling and use of certain building materials. Such matters are covered by statutory requirements.

FINDING INFORMATION

To find information on a particular subject, the following procedure is recommended:

1 Identify the **Part** most appropriate for the subject.

2 Identify the **Chapter** which deals with the particular element of construction.

3 Decide whether the information required relates to the Design, Materials or Sitework **Section** of the Chapter.

4 Decide from the Contents list the **heading** under which the required information is most likely to be found.

5 Review the **clauses** listed against the heading to see which has the relevant Performance Standard.

6 Review the **items** under the Performance Standards and decide which is relevant.

7 Review the guidance in the right-hand column opposite the item most relevant to the subject. If a clause number is known, use the above procedure to find the clause.

For example: **8.3 - S6(a)** means:

8	Part 8	Services and internal finishing
3	Chapter 3	Floor finishes
S	Section	SITEWORK
6	Clause 6	WOOD FINISHES
(a)	Item (a)	moisture protection.

CONTENTS Clause

TECHNICAL REQUIREMENTS

Technical Requirements | Performance Standards

R1 Statutory requirements

Work shall comply with all relevant Building Regulations and other statutory requirements

Chapter 1.1 gives the detailed Performance Standards which relate to these Technical Requirements.

R2 Design requirement

Design and specification shall provide satisfactory performance

R3 Materials requirement

All materials, products and building systems shall be suitable for their intended purpose

R4 Workmanship requirement

All work shall be carried out in a proper, neat and workmanlike manner

R5 Structural design requirement

Structural design shall be carried out by suitably qualified persons in accordance with British Standards and Codes of Practice

Performance Standards	Guidance

DESIGN STANDARD

8.3 - D1 Design shall meet the Technical Requirements

Design that follows the guidance below will be acceptable for floor finishes.

STATUTORY REQUIREMENTS

8.3 - D2 Design shall comply with all relevant statutory requirements

A list of statutory references applicable to this Chapter is given in Appendix 8.3-A.

SCREEDING

8.3 - D3 Floor screeds shall be suitable for their intended use

Items to be taken into account include:

(a) background

BOND

Background surfaces for bonded screeds should provide an adequate mechanical key. If necessary, cement grouting or a bonding agent should be specified to provide adequate adhesion.

MOISTURE PROTECTION

The floor design should ensure that moisture from the ground does not enter the dwelling. For details, reference should be made to Chapters 5.1 'Substructure and ground bearing floors' (Design) and 5.2 'Suspended ground floors' (Design).

(b) services

Provision should be made for :
- thermal movement of water pipes
- protection against chemical attack, for example by using purpose-made pipe sleeves or ducts.

Note
Burying water pipes in screeds is not acceptable in Scotland.

(c) screed mix

Cement and sand screeds should normally be a mix between 1 : 3 and 1 : 4½. Screeds more than 40mm thick may be of concrete.

Proprietary additives should have been assessed in accordance with Technical Requirement R3.

| Performance Standards | Guidance |

SCREEDING (continued)

8.3 - D3   (d) screed thickness

Screeds should be not less than the following thickness:

Method of laying	Minimum thickness at any point [mm]
Laid monolithically with base	12
Laid on and bonded to a set and hardened base	20
Laid on a separating membrane (eg 1000g polyethylene)	50
Laid on resilient slabs or quilts (screed reinforced with galvanized wire mesh)	65
Above services, reinforcement or insulation	25

For concrete ground bearing floors, up to 20mm thickness of monolithic screed may be acceptable as part of the required thickness.

(e) bay size

Screeds over underfloor heating should be sub-divided into bays not exceeding 15m^2 in area. Otherwise, room size laying is preferable. Expansion joints in screeds should be consistent with joints in the slab.

(f) curing

A curing period should be allowed until the screed achieves sufficient strength to resist shrinkage stresses and other damage.

(g) surface quality

SCREEDS UNDER FINISHES

Screeds intended to be covered with floor finishes should provide an even surface as appropriate.

Recommendations for screeds suitable for various floor finishes are given in the British Standards referred to in Materials clause 8.3 - M2. BS 8204 gives recommendations for screeds to receive in-situ floorings.

POWER FLOATED FINISH

Concrete floor slabs may be suitably finished to serve directly as a wearing surface without the need for an additional topping, in accordance with recommendations of BS 8204.

USE OF SEALERS OR HARDENERS

If required, surface sealers or hardeners should only be used in accordance with manufacturers' instructions.

Performance Standards

Guidance

(h) moisture content

The moisture content of screeds to receive other finishes, should be:
- generally in accordance with relevant British Standards
- in accordance with floor finish manufacturers' recommendations, where available.

(i) thermal insulation material below screeds

Insulation below screeds should provide adequate compressive strength to support wet construction screeds and floor loads.

Suitable materials include:

Material	BS	Grade or description
EPS (expanded polystyrene)	3837	SD
Extruded polystyrene	3837	E2
PUR (rigid polyurethane) PIR (rigid polyisocyanurate)	4841	for use under screeds
Proprietary materials assessed in accordance with Technical Requirement R3	-	-

Insulants should be compatible with any dpm in contact with the insulation.

(j) sound insulation material below screeds

Screeds above compressible material in sound insulating floating floors should be laid on an isolating membrane (for example building paper) and reinforced with galvanized wire mesh.

Suitable insulation materials include:
- pre-compressed expanded polystyrene - impact sound duty (ISD) grade
- proprietary materials assessed in accordance with Technical Requirement R3.

DESIGN

Performance Standards	Guidance

CERAMIC, CONCRETE, TERRAZZO AND SIMILAR TILE FINISHES

8.3 - D4   **Tile floorings shall provide a suitable surface for the intended use**

Items to be taken into account include:

(a) background

EVENNESS

The substrate shall be sufficiently even to provide a plane surface, including falls where specified.

MOISTURE PROTECTION

Where floor tiling is laid above ground bearing floor slabs, a dpm should be incorporated below or above the floor slab.

(b) application

Floor tiling should be in accordance with the recommendations of BS 5385 : Part 3 and BS Code of Practice CP 202.

Care should be taken to ensure that:
● the concrete base or screed is true and level
● sufficient drying time has been allowed, ie at least 4 weeks for concrete base, 2 weeks for screed.

TILES ON WOOD-BASED SUBSTRATE

Tiles should be bedded on either:
● cement : sand mortar on a separating layer of:
  - bitumen felt, or
  - building paper, or
  - polyethylene sheet

or
● rubber-latex : cement mortar.

ASPHALT FINISHES

8.3 - D5   **Asphalt finishes shall be suitable for their intended use**

Asphalt floor finishes should be in accordance with BS 6925 (limestone aggregate) and BS 6577 (natural aggregate), as appropriate. Suitable thicknesses and grades include:

Use	Thickness [mm]	Grade
Floor finish	15 to 20	I or II
Underlay for other finishes (in one coat)	15 to 20	I or II

Suspended floor system manufacturers should be consulted where mastic asphalt floor finishes are to be used with such systems.

Performance Standards	Guidance

FLEXIBLE SHEET AND TILE FINISHES

8.3 - D6 **Flexible sheet and tile flooring shall provide a suitable surface for the intended use**

Items to be taken into account include:

(a) background

BS 8203 gives recommendations on the use of flexible sheet and tile floorings.

EVENNESS

Substrates should be sufficiently level to achieve an acceptable floor surface. If necessary, a levelling underlay should be provided.

Acceptable types of underlay for boarded surfaces include the following:

Type of underlay	Minimum thickness [mm]
Hardboard	3.2
Plywood	4.0
Chipboard	9.0

MOISTURE PROTECTION

Where flexible sheet or tile flooring is laid on ground bearing concrete floors, a dpm should be incorporated to prevent rising moisture adversely affecting floor finishes.

Screeds or concrete surfaces should be sufficiently dry to avoid any adverse effects on the flooring.

Where there is a risk of trapping moisture from spillage or interstitial condensation, permeable finishes should be used.

(b) laying and fixing

Flexible tiles and sheets should be laid, using the adhesive and the method recommended by the manufacturer.

Special precautions, such as welded seams, may need to be specified to prevent curling, bubbling and lifting.

(c) accessories

Skirtings should be specified, where appropriate.

DESIGN

Performance Standards	Guidance

WOOD FINISHES

8.3 - D7 **Wood and wood-based flooring shall be designed to provide a suitable wearing surface for the intended use**

Items to be taken into account include:

(a) background

BS 8201 gives recommendations on the use of wood and wood-based floorings for directly and indirectly applied finishes.

BS 5250 gives recommendations on the use of vapour barriers or vapour checks with wood and wood-based floorings.

Screeds or concrete to receive wood flooring should be sufficiently dry to avoid any adverse effects. Tests for moisture content are given in BS 8201.

A damp-proof membrane should be incorporated as appropriate.

DIRECTLY APPLIED FINISHES
(wood blocks, parquet, wood mosaic, etc)
Floor finishes should be applied with the correct adhesives, for example:

● bitumen rubber emulsion (in accordance with BS 8201)

● proprietary adhesives (assessed in accordance with Technical Requirement R3) in accordance with manufacturers' instructions.

Screeds or concrete surfaces to receive wood finishes:

● should be treated with a suitable primer where recommended by the adhesive manufacturer.

Performance Standards

Guidance

INDIRECTLY APPLIED FINISHES
(softwood boarding, wood-based panel products)

The following precautions should be taken:

● vapour checks may need to be incorporated above the insulation

● battens should be preservative treated in accordance with recommendations given in Chapter 2.3 'Timber preservation (natural solid timber)'

● provision should be made for local support for heavy items such as storage heaters, boilers, etc

● battens should be at appropriate centres, generally in accordance with the following:

Thickness of finish [mm]	Maximum batten centres [mm]
Chipboard	
18/19	450
22	600
Plywood	
12	450
16	600

● fixings to battens should prevent excessive movement and should be in accordance with manufacturers' recommendations.

(b) services

Wherever possible, services beneath the floor finish should be tested before floor laying is commenced.

8.3 | Floor finishes

Performance Standards

Guidance

WOOD FINISHES (continued)

8.3 - D7 **(c) sound insulation**

Floating floor finishes should be designed to:
- separate the floor finish from the supporting floor and all walls
- avoid excessive movement or squeaking
- avoid the use of fixings which penetrate the insulation layer.

Floors should be designed so that there are no airpaths, especially at the perimeter. This limits the transfer of airborne sound and avoids flanking transmission.

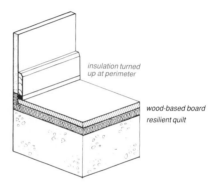

insulation turned up at perimeter

wood-based board
resilient quilt

CONCRETE STRUCTURAL FLOOR

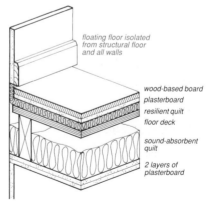

floating floor isolated from structural floor and all walls

wood-based board
plasterboard
resilient quilt
floor deck

sound-absorbent quilt

2 layers of plasterboard

TIMBER STRUCTURAL FLOOR

SOFT FLOOR COVERING
Where a floor relies on a soft floor covering to provide the minimum standard of sound insulation, the covering should be fixed permanently in position.

Performance Standards	Guidance

(d) thermal insulation

Methods of providing insulation include the following:
- insulation above in-situ concrete slab *(dpm required)*

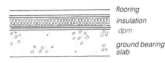

- insulation above dry, precast system *(dpm NOT required)*.

Proprietary insulated flooring should be assessed in accordance with Technical Requirement R3. Manufacturers' recommendations regarding provision of moisture barriers and damp-proof membranes should be followed.

Further information can be found in BS 5250 and the BRE Report 'Thermal insulation: avoiding risks'.

STAIRCASE FINISHES

8.3 - D8   Staircase finishes shall allow safe use of the staircase

Items to be taken into account include:

(a) rise and going

Staircase pitch and tread dimensions are specified in Chapter 6.6 'Staircases' (Design). It is important that rise and going remain consistent and are not affected by the staircase finish, particularly at the top and bottom of the flight.

(b) slip resistance

Guidance on staircase finishes of flexible sheet or tiles is included in BS 8203.

Communal staircases, such as those providing means of escape in fire, should be provided with a non-slip surface or nosing.

DESIGN

Performance Standards	Guidance

PROVISION OF INFORMATION

8.3 - D9   **Designs and specifications shall be produced in a clearly understandable format and include all necessary information**

Drawings and specifications should cover at least:
- schedule of finishes
- screed thickness and mix
- details of sound insulating floors
- extent and detail of tiled surfaces
- location of services adjacent to tiled surfaces
- details of staircase finishes.

8.3 - D10   **All relevant information shall be distributed to appropriate personnel**

Ensure that design and specification information is issued to site supervisors and relevant specialist sub-contractors and/or suppliers.

Performance Standards	Guidance

MATERIALS STANDARDS

8.3 - M1   **All materials shall:**
    (a) meet the Technical Requirements
    (b) take account of the design

Materials that comply with the design and the guidance below will be acceptable for floor finishes.

Materials for floor finishes shall comply with all relevant standards, including those listed below. Where no standard exists, Technical Requirement R3 applies (see Chapter 1.1 'Introduction to the Standards and Technical Requirements').

References to British Standards and Codes of Practice include those made under the Construction Products Directive (89/106/EEC) and, in particular, appropriate European Technical Specifications approved by a European Committee for Standardisation (CEN).

SCREEDING MATERIALS

8.3 - M2   **Materials selected for screeding shall be adequate for the location and intended use**

Relevant standards include:
BS 8204 In-situ floorings

The following standards include references to concrete and screed as sub-base:
BS 5385 Part 3 : Code of Practice for the design and installation of ceramic floor tiles and mosaics
BS 8201 Code of Practice for flooring of timber, timber products and wood-based panel products
BS 8203 Code of Practice for installation of sheet and tile flooring
CP 202 Code of Practice for tile flooring and slab flooring.

CERAMIC, CONCRETE, TERRAZZO AND SIMILAR TILE FINISHES

8.3 - M3   **Materials for tile flooring shall be adequate for the location and intended use**

CP 202 Code of Practice for tile flooring and slab flooring contains references to materials for ceramic, concrete and similar floor tiles.

Items to be taken into account include:
(a) concrete tiles

Relevant standards include:
BS 1197 Specification for concrete flooring tiles and fittings.

(b) ceramic tiles

Relevant standards include:
BS 5385 Part 3 : Code of Practice for the design and installation of ceramic floor tiles and mosaics
BS 6431 Ceramic floor and wall tiles.

(c) terrazzo tiles

Relevant standards include:
BS 4131 Specification for terrazzo tiles
BS 8204 In-situ floorings.

Performance Standards	Guidance

ASPHALT FINISHES

8.3 - M4 **Materials for asphalt flooring shall be adequate for the location and intended use**

Relevant standards include:

BS 6577 Specification for mastic asphalt for building (natural rock asphalt aggregate)

BS 6925 Specification for mastic asphalt for building and civil engineering (limestone aggregate).

FLEXIBLE SHEET AND TILE FINISHES

8.3 - M5 **Materials for flexible sheet and tile flooring shall be adequate for the location and intended use**

Relevant standards include:

BS 2592 Specification for thermoplastic flooring tiles

BS 3260 Specification for semi-flexible PVC floor tiles

BS 3261 Specification for unbacked flexible PVC flooring

BS 4902 Specification for sheet and tile flooring colours for building purposes

BS 5085 Specification. Backed flexible PVC flooring

BS 6826 Specification for linoleum and cork carpet sheet and tiles.

The following standard contains further specification details for flexible sheet and tile flooring:

BS 8203 Code of Practice for installation of sheet and tile flooring.

WOOD FINISHES

8.3 - M6 **Materials for wood flooring shall be adequate for the location and intended use**

ALL WOOD AND WOOD-BASED MATERIALS

Relevant standards include:

BS 8201 Code of Practice for flooring of timber, timber products and wood-based panel products.

DIRECTLY APPLIED FINISHES
(wood blocks, parquet, wood mosaic, etc)

Relevant standards include:

BS 1187 Specification for wood blocks for floors

BS 4050 Specification for mosaic parquet panels.

INDIRECTLY APPLIED FINISHES
(softwood and hardwood boarding, wood-based panel products, etc)

Relevant standards include:

BS 1202 Specification for nails

BS 1210 Specification for wood screws

BS 1297 Specification for tongued and grooved softwood flooring

BS 5669 Part 2 : Particleboard : Specification for wood chipboard

BS 6566 Plywood.

Performance Standards	Guidance

SOUND INSULATION

8.3 - M7   **Sound insulation materials shall provide adequate insulation standards in their intended location**

Information concerning materials and constructions that will generally be acceptable is given in statutory regulations.

Proprietary products should have been assessed in accordance with Technical Requirement R3.

Sound insulation materials include:
- flexible material
- mineral fibre at least 13mm thick, density at least $36kg/m^3$
- board material (for use under screeds)
- pre-compressed expanded polystyrene - impact sound duty (ISD) grade
- proprietary materials which have been assessed in accordance with Technical Requirement R3.

THERMAL INSULATION

8.3 - M8   **Thermal insulation materials shall provide adequate insulation standards in their intended location**

Floor insulation materials should include the following:

Material	BS	Grade or description
EPS (expanded polystyrene)	3837	SD
PUR (rigid polyurethane) PIR (rigid polyisocyanurate)	4841	for use under screeds
Fibre building board	1142 Part 3	insulating board (softboard)
Proprietary materials assessed in accordance with Technical Requirement R3	-	-

Insulation materials for use below screeds should:
- have adequate compressive strength to support wet construction screeds and floor loads
- be compatible with any dpm, where appropriate.

STRUCTURAL FLOOR DECKING

8.3 - M9   **Structural floor decking materials shall be suitable for their purpose and location**

Decking materials should be selected in accordance with the relevant parts of Chapter 6.4 'Timber and concrete upper floors' (Design and Materials).

Performance Standards	Guidance

SITEWORK STANDARDS

8.3 - S1 **All sitework shall:**

(a) **meet the Technical Requirement**

(b) **take account of the design**

(c) **follow established good practice and workmanship**

Sitework that complies with the design and the guidance below will be acceptable for floor finishes.

SCREEDING

8.3 - S2 **Floor screeds shall be laid to provide a suitable background for the intended floor finishes**

Items to be taken into account include:

(a) **background**

MOISTURE PROTECTION
Check that any specified damp-proofing treatment has been completed before screeding is commenced.

SURFACE PREPARATION
All surfaces should be clean and dust free. In particular, any traces of gypsum should have been removed. Concrete surfaces should be wetted and brushed before screeding.

BOND
Where screeds are to be bonded to the substrate, the surface should provide adequate bond. If necessary, the surface should be improved by:

● hacking

● roughening

● grouting

● application of a bonding agent.

(b) **services**

Provision should be made for:

● thermal movement of water pipes

● protection against thermal attack, for example by using purpose-made sleeves or ducts, see Chapter 8.1 'Internal services' (Design and Sitework).

There should be at least 25mm thickness of screed above the highest point of any service pipe, or insulation placed around the pipe.

In Scotland, burying services in floor screeds is not acceptable.

Performance Standards	Guidance

SCREEDING (continued)

8.3 - S2   (c) mixing

Cement and sand screeds should be mixed in the specified proportions.

Proprietary screeds should be mixed in accordance with the manufacturer's recommendations.

(d) laying

WEATHER CONDITIONS
Screeding should not be carried out under weather conditions which could adversely affect the result. The following precautions should be taken:

- *hot or dry weather* - screeds should not be laid in hot or dry weather unless precautions are taken to prevent the screed surface drying out too quickly
- *frost* - screeds should not be laid if there is a risk of freezing. Any screeds damaged by frost should be removed and replaced (reference should be made to Chapter 1.4 'Cold weather working').

TIMING
Monolithic screeds should be laid within three hours of the concrete sub-floor being poured.

Wet screeding should be programmed to allow sufficient drying out time before dry lining is to commence.

BAY SIZE
Screeds above underfloor heating should be sub-divided into bays not more than 15m^2 in area. Otherwise, room size laying is preferable.

THICKNESS
Screeds should be laid to the specified thickness.

COMPACTION
Screeds should be thoroughly compacted, using a heavy tamper or a mechanical compactor or vibrator.

Proprietary screeds should be laid in accordance with manufacturers' recommendations.

(e) protection, curing

Screed surfaces should be protected against damage from traffic and be kept continuously moist until sufficient strength has been attained to resist shrinkage stresses (at least 7 days).

Performance Standards	Guidance

(f) surface finish

SCREEDS PROVIDING A WEARING SURFACE

Floor screeds to be left as a wearing surface should be either treated with a surface hardener in accordance with manufacturers' recommendations or be power floated to a smooth and durable surface.

SCREEDS TO RECEIVE A FLOOR FINISH

Where a screed is to be used as a sub-base for a floor finish, the surface should be suitable for the required finish as specified in the design.

(g) screeds on resilient insulation materials

Screeds above resilient insulating materials should be laid on a separating membrane and reinforced as specified.

The slabs of resilient material should be tightly butted, and turned up at the room perimeter to prevent contact between the screed and the structure which could create sound transmission paths.

Joints in the isolating membrane should be lapped and taped. The membrane should be turned up at the perimeter to prevent grout seeping through.

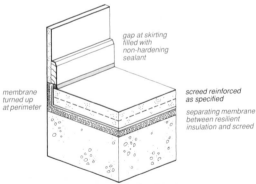

gap at skirting filled with non-hardening sealant

membrane turned up at perimeter

screed reinforced as specified

separating membrane between resilient insulation and screed

(h) screeds on thermal insulation

The procedure for laying screeds on resilient materials should be followed. Turning up insulation at perimeters prevents cold bridging.

SITEWORK

Performance Standards	Guidance

CERAMIC, CONCRETE, TERRAZZO AND SIMILAR TILE FINISHES

8.3 - S3 **Tile flooring shall provide a suitable surface for the intended use**

Items to be taken into account include:

(a) background

EVENNESS

The background to be tiled should be reasonably even and laid to falls where required.

PREPARATION

Before bedding is commenced, the following precautions should be taken:

- the surface should be clean and free from grease and loose material
- where appropriate, a damp-proof membrane should have been incorporated
- differences in level should be dubbed out
- the screed or concrete surface should be true and level (±3mm under a 3m straight edge)
- the screed or base should be sufficiently dry.

(b) bedding mix

Cement and sand mortar should normally be a mix between 1 : 3 and 1 : 4½.

Where proprietary mortars are used, manufacturers' recommendations should be followed.

(c) laying

Floor tiles should be bedded in mortar of a thickness appropriate for the material. The tiles should be arranged to minimise cutting with straight joints of even width. Any cutting necessary should be done neatly and accurately.

TILES ON WOOD-BASED SUBSTRATE

Tiles should be bedded on either:

- cement : sand mortar on a separating layer of:
  - bitumen felt, or
  - building paper, or
  - polyethylene sheet

  or
- rubber-latex : cement mortar.

(d) accessories

Any accessories, such as covings, skirtings, etc, should match the tile pattern and be fixed so that joints are aligned with those in the floor.

Performance Standards

Guidance

(e) protection

Where necessary, tile flooring should be protected until the dwelling is handed over. Temporary covering should be building paper or an alternative material which will withstand traffic from other trades and any plaster droppings or other spillage.

ASPHALT FINISHES

8.3 - S4 Asphalt and pitch mastic shall be suitable for its use

Suitable thicknesses and grades include:

Use	Thickness [mm]	Grade
Floor finish	15 to 20	I or II
Underlay for other finishes (in one coat)	15 to 20	I or II

Suspended floor system manufacturers should be consulted where mastic asphalt floor finishes are to be used with such systems.

FLEXIBLE SHEET AND TILE FINISHES

8.3 - S5 Flexible sheet and tile floor finishes shall be laid to provide a suitable wearing surface

Items to be taken into account include:

(a) background

MOISTURE PROTECTION

The substrate should be sufficiently dry to prevent any adverse effect on the flooring.

Where applicable, manufacturers' recommendations should be followed.

EVENNESS

The surface should be even and without high spots or cracks. Where a levelling underlay is needed, it should be of a type and thickness recommended by the flooring manufacturer.

Performance Standards	Guidance

FLEXIBLE SHEET AND TILE FINISHES (continued)

8.3 - S5(a) (continued)

Boarded surfaces may be covered by a sheet underlay. The following types are acceptable:

Type of underlay	Minimum thickness [mm]
Hardboard	3.2
Plywood	4.0
Chipboard	9.0

(b) laying

CONDITIONING

Flexible and sheet flooring materials should be stored in a clean and ventilated place. Unless specifically permitted by the manufacturer, materials should not be stored in cold conditions. The temperature should be not less than 18°C for at least 24 hours before and during laying.

UNDERLAYS

Plywood or hardboard underlays should be fixed with ring shank nails or staples; and chipboard with ring shank nails or screws, 2½ times the thickness of the boards.

Fixings for plywood or hardboard should be at 100mm centres at perimeters (12mm from edges) and 150mm centres across the sheets; and for chipboard, at 300mm centres at perimeters (9mm from edges) and 400mm centres across the boards.

Measures should be taken to prevent damage to underfloor services.

FLOORING

Sheet or tile flooring should be fixed with the specified adhesives and in accordance with manufacturers' instructions.

Flooring should be fully bonded, where appropriate. Adhesives should be spread evenly, and dry and contact adhesives left for the correct period of time to ensure ensure full bonding. Provision for adjustment after initial contraction or expansion should be made where necessary.

Welded joints should be provided, where specified, in accordance with manufacturers' recommendations.

The flooring should be pressed down firmly where appropriate, surplus adhesive removed, and the completed surface loaded or rolled as necessary to prevent curling or bubbling.

(c) fittings

Where specified, skirtings, coves, cover strips and other pre-formed components should be fixed in accordance with manufacturers' recommendations.

Performance Standards	Guidance

(d) quality of finish

The floor finish should be reasonably level and smooth. Particular care should be taken at doorways and junctions. Flooring should be cut so that it fits neatly around fittings, pipes, etc.

(e) protection

All sheet or tile flooring should be kept protected until handover of the dwelling. Temporary covering should be building paper or other material, which will withstand traffic from other trades and any dampness caused by plaster droppings or spillage.

WOOD FINISHES

8.3 - S6 **Wood flooring shall be laid so as to be suitable for the intended use**

Items to be taken into account include:

(a) moisture protection

For wood finishes to be laid on concrete slabs or screeds, the substrate should be sufficiently dry to prevent any adverse effects. A 50mm screed is likely to require at least 2 months to become sufficiently dry. A concrete slab requires at least 6 months to become sufficiently dry. Alternatively, it should be tested for moisture content in accordance with BS 8201.

Where specified and where timber battens are used above a dry slab, a continuous vapour barrier should be fixed under the wood flooring, with lapped and taped or sealed joints coincident with supports.

The supporting battens below the vapour barrier should be preservative treated and a dpm should have been provided below the slab.

preservative treated battens

vapour barrier to prevent condensation damaging wood flooring

dry, ground bearing slab

dpm

Wood blocks and strips should be conditioned before laying to the appropriate moisture content for the specified period.

Performance Standards	Guidance

WOOD FINISHES (continued)

8.3 - S6 **(b) services**

Underfloor heating, where installed, should be kept on before and during the floor laying.

(c) laying and fixing

PREPARATION OF SCREEDS OR CONCRETE SURFACES
Preparation should be as follows:
- high spots, nibs and major irregularities should be removed
- differences in level should be dubbed out.

DIRECTLY APPLIED FINISHES
(wood block and strip flooring)

Wood block and strip flooring should be laid and fixed in accordance with manufacturers' recommendations, using the specified or recommended adhesive as appropriate.

Adhesive should be evenly spread, and blocks laid to the specified pattern, leaving gaps around the perimeter for movement.

INDIRECTLY APPLIED FINISHES
(softwood boarding, wood-based panel products)
- *batten spacing* - battens should be at centres appropriate to the floor finish material, and generally in accordance with the following:

Thickness of finish [mm]	Maximum batten centres [mm]
Chipboard	
18/19	450
22	600
Plywood	
12	450
16	600

- *batten fixing to substrate* - battens may be shot-fired or fixed with suitable clips.

Performance Standards

Guidance

● *chipboard fixed to battens*

Fixing	Length	Centres
Flat headed ring shank nails or screws	2 ½ x board thickness	200mm to 300mm centres around perimeters
		400mm to 500mm centres on intermediate supports

or in accordance with manufacturers' recommendations

● *plywood fixed to battens*

Fixing	Centres
10 gauge nails or screws	150mm centres around perimeter
	300mm centres on intermediate supports
	nails/screws at least 10mm from edge of panel

or in accordance with manufacturers' recommendations

FLOOR COVERINGS LAID ON RESILIENT MATERIALS

Where flooring is to be laid on resilient materials, it is important that edges should be kept clear of structural elements and that skirtings do not fit tight against the flooring. All open joints should be filled with a non-hardening sealant.

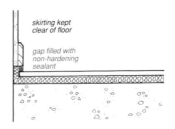

skirting kept clear of floor

gap filled with non-hardening sealant

STRUCTURAL DECKING

Floor boards and decking should be laid and fixed as described in Chapter 6.4 'Timber and concrete upper floors' (Sitework).

(d) protection

All wood flooring should be kept protected until handover of the dwelling. Temporary covering should be building paper or other material, which will withstand traffic from other trades and any dampness caused by plaster droppings or spillage.

SITEWORK

8.3 | Floor finishes

Performance Standards	Guidance

STAIRCASE FINISHES

8.3 - S7 **Staircase finishes shall be suitable for their intended use**

Items to be taken into account include:

(a) provision of slip-resistant nosings

For communal stairs, eg in escape routes in blocks of flats, non-slip nosings or inserts should be provided where specified, and fixed in accordance with manufacturers' recommendations.

(b) consistent rise and going

The rise and going should remain uniform after the application of the staircase finish. Reference should also be made to Chapter 6.6 'Staircases' (Design and Sitework).

Guidance

Statutory references

The following table lists references to building legislation and associated documents applicable at August 1990.

Clause	Subject	Statute			
		Building [1] Regulations	Building [2] Standards (Scotland)	Building [3] Regulations (N Ireland)	Isle of Man [4] Bye-laws
D2	Control of surface spread of flame	B2/3/4	Part D	Part E	Part E
D7	Sound insulation	E1/2/3	Part H	Part G	Part G
		Associated documents			

[1] Approved Documents to the Building Regulations 1985 for England and Wales (and 1990 edition).
[2] Building Standards (Scotland) Regulations 1981 and all published amendments.
[3] Building Regulations (Northern Ireland) 1990.
[4] Isle of Man Bye-laws 1976, amended 1980 and 1987.

BUILDMARK™

NHBC, Buildmark House, Chiltern Avenue, Amersham, Bucks HP6 5AP

NHBC, 5 Manor Place, Edinburgh, Scotland EH3 7DH

NHBC, Holyrood Court, 59 Malone Road, Belfast BT9 6SA

informing the industry

CI/SfB	81	(7-)		
CAWS	N11	P20	P21	

Operative from January 1992

Chapter **8.4**

NHBC STANDARDS

Finishings and fitments

This Chapter gives the Technical Requirements and
recommendations for fitments and cupboards, internal
trim and finishings.

LIST OF CHAPTERS

THE STANDARDS

The NHBC Standards give:
- Technical Requirements in red
- Performance Standards in dark blue
- Guidance in light blue

for the design and construction of dwellings acceptable to NHBC.

Diagrams may contain text in red. This is to highlight points but has no mandatory significance.

The Standards come into effect for every NHBC registered home whose foundations are concreted on or after the publication date shown on the cover of each Chapter and apply throughout the UK, unless otherwise stated.

COMPOSITION OF THE STANDARDS
The Standards are divided into 10 Parts, each containing one or more Chapters covering a particular aspect. The Parts follow the usual construction process.

In general, each Chapter is made up of sections dealing with Design, Materials and Sitework. In some cases one or more of these aspects may not be included.

TECHNICAL REQUIREMENTS
Each Chapter (except former Practice Notes) contains the five mandatory Technical Requirements which MUST be met by the Builder.

The Technical Requirements are printed in red. Chapter 1.1 'Introduction to the Standards and Technical Requirements' contains full details.

PERFORMANCE STANDARDS
Most Chapters consist of detailed Performance Standards printed in dark blue, normally in the left-hand column of each Design, Materials or Sitework page, subdivided into Clauses designated D, M or S, respectively.

Alternative standards of performance will be acceptable ONLY if, in the opinion of NHBC, the Technical Requirements are met and the standard achieved is not lower than the stated Performance Standard.

GUIDANCE
Guidance on how the Performance Standard may be met is normally shown, printed in light blue, in the right-hand column opposite the relevant Performance Standard. Some Chapters contain pages which are all Guidance.

Guidance is based on normal procedures and recommended practices shown by experience to be satisfactory and acceptable. NHBC will consider alternative methods to meet specific requirements, subject to prior consultation and evaluation.

SCOPE

This Chapter gives the Technical Requirements and recommendations for fitments and cupboards, internal trim and finishings.

NHBC Standards do not cover aspects of health and safety relating to building operations and to the handling and use of certain building materials. Such matters are covered by statutory requirements.

FINDING INFORMATION

To find information on a particular subject, the following procedure is recommended:

1 Identify the **Part** most appropriate for the subject.

2 Identify the **Chapter** which deals with the particular element of construction.

3 Decide whether the information required relates to the Design, Materials or Sitework **Section** of the Chapter.

4 Decide from the Contents list the **heading** under which the required information is most likely to be found.

5 Review the **clauses** listed against the heading to see which has the relevant Performance Standard.

6 Review the **items** under the Performance Standards and decide which is relevant.

7 Review the guidance in the right-hand column opposite the item most relevant to the subject. If a clause number is known, use the above procedure to find the clause.

For example: **8.4 - S2(b)** means:

8	Part 8	Services and internal finishing
4	Chapter 4	Finishings and fitments
S	Section	SITEWORK
2	Clause 2	CUPBOARDS AND FITMENTS
(b)	Item (b)	correct location.

CONTENTS

Technical Requirements	Performance Standards

R1 Statutory requirements
Work shall comply with all relevant Building Regulations and other statutory requirements

Chapter 1.1 gives the detailed Performance Standards which relate to these Technical Requirements.

R2 Design requirement
Design and specification shall provide satisfactory performance

R3 Materials requirement
All materials, products and building systems shall be suitable for their intended purpose

R4 Workmanship requirement
All work shall be carried out in a proper, neat and workmanlike manner

R5 Structural design requirement
Structural design shall be carried out by suitably qualified persons in accordance with British Standards and Codes of Practice

Performance Standards	Guidance

DESIGN STANDARD

8.4 - D1 **Design shall meet the Technical Requirements**

Design that follows the guidance below will be acceptable for finishings and fitments.

The Builder should provide the purchaser with information in accordance with Chapter 1.2 'The home - its accommodation and services'.

STATUTORY REQUIREMENTS

8.4 - D2 **Design shall comply with all relevant statutory requirements**

A list of statutory references applicable to this Chapter is given in Appendix 8.4-A.

CUPBOARDS AND FITMENTS

8.4 - D3 **The builder shall provide fixed and built-in fitments in accordance with the specification**

Items to be taken into account include:

(a) kitchen facilities

The specification should cover space or facilities for:
- preparation and cooking of food
- washing up, drying and storage of dishes and utensils
- storage of dry foods
- storage of perishable foods
- laundering
- storage of domestic cleaning appliances, part of which should be suitable for brooms, upright cleaners and similar equipment.

Space or facilities for laundering and cleaning items may be provided outside the kitchen area.

A circulation space of not less than one metre should be provided in front of all work surfaces, cupboards and appliances provided. For design purposes, when work surfaces, cupboards and applicances are intended (but not provided) they should be assumed to be 600mm deep.

(b) storage space

Storage space should be provided as specified in Chapter 1.2 'The home - its accommodation and services', including space or provision for:
- general storage
- storage of clothes, linen and bedding and, in homes which do not have central, or whole home, heating, their airing.

Performance Standards   **Guidance**

CUPBOARDS AND FITMENTS (continued)

8.4 - D3   **(c) airing cupboards**

In England, Wales and Scotland, airing cupboards are required in homes which do not have central, or whole home, heating. Otherwise, they are at the discretion of the Builder.

Where provided, airing cupboards should have:
- not less than 0.5m² of easily reached shelving suitable for the airing of clothes
- a vertical space between shelves of not less than 300mm
- a suitable heat source, such as a hot water cylinder or an equivalent.

Care is necessary when designing airing cupboards. To be accessible, the shelving should be placed not higher than 1.5m.

The airing area should be separated from other storage.

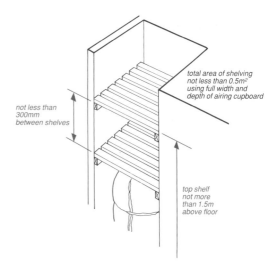

total area of shelving not less than 0.5m² using full width and depth of airing cupboard

not less than 300mm between shelves

top shelf not more than 1.5m above floor

(d) hinges

To reduce movement and shrinkage, doors should be hung on hinges as follows:

Location of door	Hinges
Airing cupboard	1½ pairs x 75mm
Other internal fitments	1 pair x 75mm

Performance Standards | Guidance

FINISHINGS AND INTERNAL TRIM

8.4 - D4   **Finishings and internal trim shall be suitable for their location and intended use**

Items to be taken into account include:

(a) wood trim

All trim should be of adequate size to mask joints around built-in fitments, etc allowing for movement and shrinkage.

Any wood trim in the vicinity of fireplaces or heating appliances should be fixed at not less than the statutory minimum distance from heat sources and be arranged to minimise movement and shrinkage.

Special consideration should be given to the positioning of finishings and trim in relation to cable runs, light points, socket outlets, door furniture, handrails, balustrades, etc.

(b) non-wood trim

Proprietary trim items should be installed in accordance with the manufacturer's recommendations.

PROVISION OF INFORMATION

8.4 - D5   **All relevant information shall be produced in a clearly understandable format and distributed to appropriate personnel**

Ensure that design and specification information is issued to site supervisors and relevant specialist subcontractors and/or suppliers.

Performance Standards	Guidance

MATERIALS STANDARDS

8.4 - M1 All materials shall:
(a) meet the Technical Requirements
(b) take account of the design

Materials that comply with the design and the guidance below will be acceptable for finishings and fitments.

Materials for finishings and fitments should comply with all relevant standards including those listed below. Where no standard exists, Technical Requirement R3 applies (see Chapter 1.1 'Introduction to the Standards and Technical Requirements').

References to British Standards and Codes of Practice include those made under the Construction Products Directive (89/106/EEC) and, in particular, appropriate European Technical Specifications approved by a European Committee for Standardisation (CEN).

JOINERY

8.4 - M2 Wood and wood-based materials shall be of the quality and dimensions required by the design

Items to be taken into account include:

(a) classification

All wood and wood-based materials should, as a minimum, comply with the requirements of:
BS 1186 Part 1 : Specification for timber: Timber for and workmanship in joinery : Class 3
BS 5669 Particleboard.

(b) workmanship

All joinery items should be constructed to a good standard of workmanship including:
- fit and construction of joints
- construction of finger joints
- glueing and laminating
- construction of moving parts
- surface finishes.

Prefabricated components should comply with the relevant parts of BS 1186 : Part 2.

(c) surface finish

The prepared surface should be such that no defects are visible after the finish is applied.

MATERIALS

Performance Standards	Guidance

IRONMONGERY

8.4 - M3   **Ironmongery shall be provided in accordance with the design and specification**

Relevant standards include:

BS 1227 Part 1A : Specification for hinges : Hinges for general building purposes.

OTHER MATERIALS

8.4 - M4   **Other materials shall be suitable for the intended use**

Materials other than wood should be of the quality and dimensions required by the design and should be chosen in accordance with manufacturers' recommendations.

PREFABRICATED ITEMS

8.4 - M5   **All prefabricated items shall be suitably protected against damage**

Appropriate protection should be specified to reasonably ensure that items are undamaged.

Performance Standards	Guidance

SITEWORK STANDARDS

8.4 - S1 **All sitework shall:**
- **(a) meet the Technical Requirements**
- **(b) take account of the design**
- **(c) follow established good practice and workmanship**

Sitework that complies with the design and the guidance below will be acceptable for finishings and fitments.

CUPBOARDS AND FITMENTS

8.4 - S2 **Cupboards and fitments shall be installed to give satisfactory appearance and performance**

Items to be taken into account include:

(a) pre-installation check

Cupboards and fitments should be checked to ensure they are undamaged before installation.

(b) correct location

Cupboards and fitments should be installed as shown in the design.

In the kitchen, a circulation space of not less than one metre should be provided in front of all work surfaces, cupboards and appliances.

(c) accurate levelling

All cupboards and worktops should be plumb and level and be scribed to wall faces, where necessary.

(d) adequate support and fixing

All wall units should be securely fixed, using:
- plugs and screws to masonry
- screws to timber studs, etc (fixings should be of appropriate size)
- appropriate proprietary fixings in accordance with manufacturers' instructions.

Use pre-drilled holes in units and brackets provided by the manufacturer, where appropriate.

Worktops spanning between units should be supported, where necessary.

Hanging rails should be provided in wardrobe cupboards, with intermediate supports, where necessary, to avoid bending.

8.4 Finishings and fitments

Performance Standards	Guidance

CUPBOARDS AND FITMENTS (continued)

8.4 - S2 **(e) edge trim**

Where worktops or unit panels are cut, edges should be sealed using a metal or plastic strip glued to the edge with waterproof adhesive. Alternatively, an appropriate waterproof joint may be used.

(f) sealing

Sinks and hob units, which are inset in worktops, and vanity units should be sealed with a waterproof joint.

Where appropriate, gaps between fitments and wall tiling should be sealed with a waterproof joint and brought to a smooth finish.

(g) operation of moving parts

For built-in fitments, doors should fit openings closely and evenly and operate freely; drawers should run smoothly, and locks and catches properly engage.

FINISHINGS AND INTERNAL TRIM

8.4 - S3 **Finishings and internal trim shall be fixed to ensure a satisfactory finish free from unsightly blemishes**

Items to be taken into account include:

(a) general workmanship

All trim should be sufficiently wide to mask joints.

Any trim in the vicinity of fireplaces, or other heat-producing appliances, should be:
● at the specified distance
● arranged to minimise movement and shrinkage.

Nails should be punched just below the timber surface and holes filled. Nails should never be driven home with the hammer head. As far as possible, any chipping, hammer marks or burrs should be avoided where easing is required and any damage made good.

(b) shelving

Shelving supports should be fixed securely and so that shelves are level. The specified distance between shelves in airing cupboards should be allowed.

(c) special features

Fireplace surrounds, panelling and other special features should be complete and joined satisfactorily to adjoining surfaces.

Performance Standards	Guidance

(d) architraves and skirtings

Architraves should be:
- parallel to frames and linings
- installed with an equal margin to each frame member
- fixed securely to linings to prevent curling.

Skirtings should be:
- mitred or scribed at external and internal angles, as appropriate
- jointed firmly with architraves to give a flush finish
- run level and scribed to floors.

Skirtings and architraves of materials other than wood, eg those designed to accommodate trunking, should be fixed in accordance with the manufacturer's recommendations.

(e) painting, etc

Painting, staining, etc should be carried out in accordance with Chapter 8.5 'Painting and decorating' (each section).

(f) completion

All work should be left in a clean state.

PROTECTION

8.4 - S4 **Completed work shall be handed over undamaged**

Items to be taken into account include:

(a) kitchens

Kitchen units and complete fitted kitchens should be protected and, wherever possible, be left in the original wrappings until shortly before handover.

(b) special features

Appropriate protection for fireplace surrounds, panelling and other special features should be provided, where necessary.

(c) trim

Make sure that all completed skirtings, architraves, etc are adequately protected against damage from other trades.

(d) removal of coverings

All temporary coverings should be removed and all fitments and finishings cleaned and dusted shortly before handover.

Guidance

Statutory references

The following table lists references to building legislation and associated documents applicable at August 1990.

		Statute			
Clause	Subject	Building [1] Regulations	Building [2] Standards (Scotland)	Building [3] Regulations (N Ireland)	Isle of Man [4] Bye-laws
D2	Provision of food storage	-	-	-	Part K
		Associated documents			

[1] Approved Documents to the Building Regulations 1985 for England and Wales (and 1990 edition).
[2] Building Standards (Scotland) Regulations 1981 and all published amendments.
[3] Building Regulations (Northern Ireland) 1990.
[4] Isle of Man Bye-laws 1976, amended 1980 and 1987.

BUILDMARK™

NHBC, Buildmark House, Chiltern Avenue, Amersham, Bucks HP6 5AP

NHBC, 5 Manor Place, Edinburgh, Scotland EH3 7DH

NHBC, Holyrood Court, 59 Malone Road, Belfast BT9 6SA

informing the industry

CI/SfB	81	(4-)	V	
CAWS	M52	M60		

Operative from January 1992

Chapter **8.5**

NHBC STANDARDS

Painting and decorating

This Chapter gives the Technical Requirements and
recommendations for painting and decorating.

LIST OF CHAPTERS

THE STANDARDS

The NHBC Standards give:
- Technical Requirements in red
- Performance Standards in dark blue
- Guidance in light blue

for the design and construction of dwellings acceptable to NHBC.

Diagrams may contain text in red. This is to highlight points but has no mandatory significance.

The Standards come into effect for every NHBC registered home whose foundations are concreted on or after the publication date shown on the cover of each Chapter and apply throughout the UK, unless otherwise stated.

COMPOSITION OF THE STANDARDS
The Standards are divided into 10 Parts, each containing one or more Chapters covering a particular aspect. The Parts follow the usual construction process.

In general, each Chapter is made up of sections dealing with Design, Materials and Sitework. In some cases one or more of these aspects may not be included.

TECHNICAL REQUIREMENTS
Each Chapter (except former Practice Notes) contains the five mandatory Technical Requirements which MUST be met by the Builder.

The Technical Requirements are printed in red. Chapter 1.1 'Introduction to the Standards and Technical Requirements' contains full details.

PERFORMANCE STANDARDS
Most Chapters consist of detailed Performance Standards printed in dark blue, normally in the left-hand column of each Design, Materials or Sitework page, subdivided into Clauses designated D, M or S, respectively.

Alternative standards of performance will be acceptable ONLY if, in the opinion of NHBC, the Technical Requirements are met and the standard achieved is not lower than the stated Performance Standard.

GUIDANCE
Guidance on how the Performance Standard may be met is normally shown, printed in light blue, in the right-hand column opposite the relevant Performance Standard. Some Chapters contain pages which are all Guidance.

Guidance is based on normal procedures and recommended practices shown by experience to be satisfactory and acceptable. NHBC will consider alternative methods to meet specific requirements, subject to prior consultation and evaluation.

SCOPE

This Chapter gives the Technical Requirements and recommendations for painting and decorating.

NHBC Standards do not cover aspects of health and safety relating to building operations and to the handling and use of certain building materials. Such matters are covered by statutory requirements.

FINDING INFORMATION

To find information on a particular subject, the following procedure is recommended:

1 Identify the **Part** most appropriate for the subject.

2 Identify the **Chapter** which deals with the particular element of construction.

3 Decide whether the information required relates to the Design, Materials or Sitework **Section** of the Chapter.

4 Decide from the Contents list the **heading** under which the required information is most likely to be found.

5 Review the **clauses** listed against the heading to see which has the relevant Performance Standard.

6 Review the **items** under the Performance Standards and decide which is relevant.

7 Review the guidance in the right-hand column opposite the item most relevant to the subject. If a clause number is known, use the above procedure to find the clause.

For example: **8.5 - S3(b)** means:

8	Part 8	Services and internal finishing
5	Chapter 5	Painting and decorating
S	Section	SITEWORK
3	Clause 3	STORAGE ON SITE
(b)	Item (b)	prefabricated components.

CONTENTS
Clause

Technical Requirements	Performance Standards

R1 Statutory requirements

Work shall comply with all relevant Building Regulations and other statutory requirements

Chapter 1.1 gives the detailed Performance Standards which relate to these Technical Requirements.

R2 Design requirement

Design and specification shall provide satisfactory performance

R3 Materials requirement

All materials, products and building systems shall be suitable for their intended purpose

R4 Workmanship requirement

All work shall be carried out in a proper, neat and workmanlike manner

R5 Structural design requirement

Structural design shall be carried out by suitably qualified persons in accordance with British Standards and Codes of Practice

Performance Standards	Guidance

DESIGN STANDARD

8.5 - D1   Design shall meet the Technical Requirements

Design that follows the guidance below will be acceptable for painting and decorating.

SELECTION OF PAINT AND DECORATIVE SYSTEMS

8.5 - D2   Paint and decorative systems shall provide an acceptable finish

When choosing paint or decorative systems account should be taken of the substrate.

Items to be taken into account include:

(a) timber

DECORATIVE SYSTEMS

Decorative systems should be compatible with the surface to be decorated which may be:

- bare timber
- stained timber
- primed timber
- preservative treated timber
- naturally durable species.

STAIN SYSTEMS

Stain systems for timber should be either:

- a 2 coat system, or
- in accordance with manufacturers' recommendations.

PAINT SYSTEMS

Paint systems for timber should be either:

- at least one priming coat, one undercoat and one finishing coat, or
- proprietary systems in accordance with manufacturers' recommendations.

PRESERVATIVE TREATMENT

Painting or staining of external timber is required to provide protection and stability even if the timber is preservative treated, unless the preservative treatment manufacturer confirms otherwise (see Clause D3).

MOISTURE CONTENT

Wood with moisture content above 18% is not suitable for priming/painting.

Performance Standards   **Guidance**

SELECTION OF PAINT AND DECORATIVE SYSTEMS (continued)

8.5 - D2 (b) masonry and rendering

Paint or decorative finishes should not be applied to external brickwork or render where the finish could trap moisture in the construction causing frost damage or sulphate attack or other detrimental effects. (This applies particularly to bricks which have no upper limit on their soluble salt content. The brick manufacturer's written agreement to the application of any finish should be obtained in such cases.)

Paint systems for external brickwork or render, including proprietary surface preparations, should be appropriate for the substrate in accordance with the manufacturer's recommendations.

Where the decorative system is part of the weather resistance of the rendering, it should be assessed in accordance with Technical Requirement R3.

(c) metal

STRUCTURAL STEEL

Guidance on the protection of structural steel is given in BS 5493.

Internal and external steel which has not been galvanized should be protected with at least two coats of zinc phosphate primer and a suitable decorative finish, where required.

Internal and external steel which has been galvanized to a rate of at least $460g/m^2$ is acceptable without further protection. Steel galvanized to a rate of less than $460g/m^2$ should be protected with at least one metal priming coat, one undercoat and one finishing coat.

Where steelwork is to be protected by intumescent paint for fire resistance, the manufacturer's recommendations should be followed.

GUTTERS

Insides of metal gutters (other than aluminium) should be painted with bituminous paint.

NON-FERROUS PIPEWORK

Copper pipes, etc should be painted with the normal decorative finishes.

(d) plaster and plasterboard

Plaster and plasterboard surfaces should be prepared in accordance with manufacturers' directions for:
- plastic compound finishes
- wallpapers
- emulsion paints, etc.

Performance Standards	Guidance

(e) proprietary building boards

Paint systems should be either:

- at least one priming coat, one undercoat and one finishing coat, or
- proprietary systems in accordance with manufacturers' recommendations.

Other finishes should be applied in accordance with manufacturers' recommendations.

COMPATIBILITY

8.5 - D3 Paint and decorative systems shall be compatible with timber species and treatments

Items to be taken into account include:

(a) preservatives

Paint and stain systems specified should be compatible with any timber preservatives that have been used. Where appropriate, manufacturers' recommendations should be obtained and followed.

(b) stains and varnishes

Stains and varnishes should be suitable for the species of timber to which they are applied. Where appropriate, manufacturers' recommendations should be obtained and followed.

BS 6952 gives recommendations on the use of exterior wood coating systems.

(c) glazing compounds

Linseed-oil putty should not be specified for glazing rebates in windows and doors treated with stains.

Appropriate sealants should be used in accordance with manufacturers' recommendations.

Performance Standards	Guidance

PROVISION OF INFORMATION

8.5 - D4 **Designs and specifications shall be produced in a clearly understandable format and include all relevant information**

Design information should include:
- specification of preparatory work
- schedule of finishes.

8.5 - D5 **All relevant information shall be distributed to appropriate personnel**

Ensure that design and specification information is issued to site supervisors and relevant specialist subcontractors and/or suppliers.

Performance Standards	Guidance

MATERIALS STANDARDS

8.5 - M1 **All materials shall:**
   (a) meet the Technical Requirements
   (b) take account of the design

Materials that comply with the design and the guidance below will be acceptable for painting and decorating.

Materials for painting and decorating should comply with all relevant standards, including those listed below. Where no standard exists, Technical Requirement R3 applies (see Chapter 1.1 'Introduction to the Standards and Technical Requirements').

References to British Standards and Codes of Practice include those made under the Construction Products Directive (89/106/EEC) and, in particular, appropriate European Technical Specifications approved by a European Committee for Standardisation (CEN).

PRESERVATIVES, STAINS AND PAINTS

8.5 - M2 **Materials for use on non-durable building elements shall be selected to provide adequate protection**

Items to be taken into account include:

(a) preservatives

Timber preservatives should be selected in accordance with Chapter 2.3 'Timber preservation (natural solid timber)' (Materials).

(b) knotting

BS 1336 Specification for knotting.

(c) stains

BS 6952 Exterior wood coating systems.

(d) primers

BS 3698 Specification for calcium plumbate priming paints
BS 4756 Specification for ready-mixed aluminium priming paints for woodwork
BS 5082 Specification for water-borne priming paints for woodwork
BS 5358 Specification for solvent-borne priming paints for woodwork.

(e) proprietary paint systems

Paint systems should be suitable in all respects for their intended use and situation. Selection should be in accordance with manufacturers' recommendations.

MATERIALS

Performance Standards	Guidance

PREFABRICATED JOINERY

8.5 - M3 **Prefabricated joinery shall be provided with adequate protection**

Protection in accordance with Clause M2 may be required.

Prefabricated joinery to be painted or stained should have been primed or given a first coat of stain or sealer before fixing.

Where primer is damaged, surfaces should be re-primed.

Performance Standards	Guidance

SITEWORK STANDARDS

8.5 - S1 **All sitework shall:**
  (a) **meet the Technical Requirements**
  (b) **take account of the design**
  (c) **follow established good practice and workmanship**

Sitework that complies with the design and the guidance below will be acceptable for painting and decorating.

PREFABRICATED COMPONENTS

8.5 - S2 **Prefabricated components to be painted or decorated shall be of suitable quality and adequately prepared**

Components to be painted, stained or sealed should have been primed (if to be painted) or given a first coat of stain or sealer before fixing.

Components supplied untreated should have been stored under cover and be primed as soon as possible after delivery.

Where primer is damaged, surfaces should be re-primed.

STORAGE ON SITE

8.5 - S3 **Materials and prefabricated components stored on site shall be adequately protected**

  Items to be taken into account include:
  (a) **painting materials**

Where it is necessary to store materials, the storage should ensure that the materials remain fit for use in the dwelling.

Water-borne paints, primers and stains should be protected against frost before use. Painting materials should not be used if they have been damaged by frost.

  (b) **prefabricated components**

Where it is necessary to store components, the storage should ensure that they remain fit for use in the dwelling.

8.5 Painting and decorating

Performance Standards	Guidance

TIMING

8.5 - S4   Work shall only be carried out when conditions and surfaces are appropriate

Items to be taken into account include:

(a) external work

External paintwork should not be carried out under weather conditions which may adversely affect the completed work.

Surfaces should be free from frost before painting commences and while paint dries.

Coatings should not be applied to moist surfaces, nor when rain is expected before the paint surface has set.

(b) internal work

When decorating internal walls, cold surfaces may cause problems with water-borne paints, even though the air temperature may be above freezing.

Surfaces should be free from condensation before applying paint. Coatings, especially those which are oil-based, should not be applied until all moisture has evaporated from the surface. Internal paintwork should be left until the risk of dust and damage is minimal.

(c) staining

Staining should be carried out when the substrate is dry to ensure adequate dispersal and absorption.

QUALITY OF FINISH

8.5 - S5   Workmanship shall ensure a satisfactory finish

Items to be taken into account include:

(a) painting on wood

SURFACE PREPARATION

Door and window furniture, sockets and light switches should be removed before painting to avoid over-painting and splashing.

Unsound wood, loose or highly resinous knots, etc should be cut out, replaced and made good.

Tool and machine marks and raised grain should be removed. Where a smooth surface is required, re-finish with glasspaper and fillers, as appropriate.

Performance Standards	Guidance

Nail holes, splits and other imperfections should be stopped. Sharp arrises should be rubbed down to ensure an even coating.

Surfaces to be painted should be free from dirt, dust and moisture.

All joinery delivered pre-primed to the site should meet the requirements given under PRIMING below.

Any surfaces showing deterioration of primer or seal coat should be rubbed down and a second coat applied.

Prefabricated joinery should have the first coat of paint or stain applied before fixing.

PRESERVATIVES

Before application, primer or paint finishes should be checked for compatibilty with any timber preservatives that have been used.

Where appropriate, manufacturers' recommendations for selection and use of materials should be obtained and followed.

KNOTTING

All knots should be sealed using knotting applied by brush.

PRIMING

One full round coat of primer should be applied to all surfaces to be painted and to hidden surfaces of external woodwork.

Cut ends of external woodwork, rebates for glazing and backs of glazing beads should be primed.

UNDERCOAT AND GLOSS

Paint should not be thinned beyond the limits recommended by the manufacturer.

Unless an alternative recommendation is made by the manufacturer, the following should be applied:
- at least one undercoat (2 coats preferred), and
- one finishing coat.

The undercoat should provide a suitable base to ensure a satisfactory finishing coat. Additional undercoats or finishing coats are at the discretion of the Builder.

SITEWORK

Performance Standards	Guidance

QUALITY OF FINISH (continued)

8.5 - S5(a) (continued)

Each application should be a full round coat.

Surfaces should be lightly rubbed down between coats with glasspaper and each coat should be applied within one month of the application of the previous coat.

(b) staining and varnishing on wood

SURFACE PREPARATION

Before application, stains should be checked for compatibility with any timber preservatives that have been used. Stains should not be applied to door or window rebates to be glazed with linseed-oil putty.

Surfaces to be stained or varnished should be prepared to provide adequate adhesion and acceptable appearance.

APPLICATION

Low-build or high-build stain should be applied as recommended by the manufacturer to provide appropriate cover.

Varnish should be applied in at least two coats. Surfaces should be sanded between coats.

(c) painting on metal

STRUCTURAL STEEL

Internal and external steel which has not been galvanized should be protected with at least two coats of zinc phosphate primer and a suitable decorative finish, where required.

Internal and external steel which has been galvanized to a rate of at least 460g/m^2 is acceptable without further protection. Steel galvanized to a rate of less than 460g/m^2 should be protected with at least one priming coat, one undercoat and one finishing coat.

Where steelwork is to be protected by intumescent paint for fire resistance, the manufacturer's recommendations should be followed.

GUTTERS

Insides of metal gutters (other than aluminium) should be painted with bituminous paint.

NON-FERROUS PIPEWORK

Copper pipes, etc should be painted with the normal decorative finishes.

Performance Standards	Guidance

(d) painting on other surfaces

EXTERNAL MASONRY AND RENDERING

Only materials specified should be used for external masonry or rendering.

Substrates should be clean and free from dust or loose deposits. Surfaces with varying suction may require stabilizing with a treatment recommended by the manufacturer.

PLASTER AND SKIM COAT ON PLASTERBOARD

Surfaces should be visibly sound and without powdering or crumbling.

Surfaces with uneven suction may require stabilizing, either with a coat of thinned paint or with a sealer recommended by the manufacturer.

All joints should be completed and any cracks, nail holes and surface imperfections filled. The surface should be rubbed down with glasspaper, if necessary, and dusted.

Paint should be applied in not less than two coats.

DRY LINING

A seal coat should be applied and surfaces prepared for decoration in accordance with manufacturers' recommendations.

BUILDING BOARD

Where painting is specified, surfaces should be primed or sealed and finished with at least two coats.

The first coat should be as recommended by the board manufacturer.

(e) surface finish

QUALITY OF COMPLETED WORK

All paintwork should be complete. Surfaces should be evenly coated and neither background nor undercoat should be visible.

Where brush marks, runs or abnormal roughness occur, work should be rubbed down and re-painted. Spilt, splashed or badly applied paint should be removed.

On completion, there should be no paintmarks on any surfaces not intended to be painted. Ironmongery removed before painting should be re-fixed afterwards.

PROTECTION

Completed work should be protected against dirt and damage until the dwelling is handed over.

8.5 | **Painting and decorating**

Performance Standards	Guidance

WALLPAPERING

8.5 - S6 **Wallpapering shall achieve a neat, consistent appearance**

Items to take into account include:

(a) surface preparation

Before any wallpapering is started, check that surfaces are dry and sufficiently even and smooth. Surfaces should be sized or sealed, if necessary.

To prevent stripping of the board lining paper, dry lining should be sized in accordance with manufacturers' recommendations.

Where proprietary coverings are used, any preparatory treatment recommended by the manufacturer should be applied.

(b) choice of adhesive

Adhesive of a type recommended by the wallpaper manufacturer should be used.

(c) workmanship

Wallpaper and coverings should be properly aligned and neatly fixed.

Electrical switch plates should be temporarily removed and the papering accurately trimmed so that it will tuck behind the switch plate on completion. Papers containing metal backings should not be tucked behind switch plates.

NHBC, Buildmark House, Chiltern Avenue, Amersham, Bucks HP6 5AP

NHBC, 5 Manor Place, Edinburgh, Scotland EH3 7DH

NHBC, Holyrood Court, 59 Malone Road, Belfast BT9 6SA

Part 9 EXTERNAL WORKS

9.1 Garages
9.2 Drives, paths, fences and landscaping

P
A
R
T

9

informing the industry

| CI/SfB | 81 | (90.2) | |
| CAWS | E10 | F10 | G20 |

Operative from January 1992

Chapter **9.1**

NHBC STANDARDS

Garages

This Chapter gives the Technical Requirements and recommendations for integral, attached and detached garages.

LIST OF CHAPTERS

THE STANDARDS

The NHBC Standards give:
● Technical Requirements in red
● Performance Standards in dark blue
● Guidance in light blue
for the design and construction of dwellings acceptable to NHBC.

Diagrams may contain text in red. This is to highlight points but has no mandatory significance.

The Standards come into effect for every NHBC registered home whose foundations are concreted on or after the publication date shown on the cover of each Chapter and apply throughout the UK, unless otherwise stated.

COMPOSITION OF THE STANDARDS
The Standards are divided into 10 Parts, each containing one or more Chapters covering a particular aspect. The Parts follow the usual construction process.

In general, each Chapter is made up of sections dealing with Design, Materials and Sitework. In some cases one or more of these aspects may not be included.

TECHNICAL REQUIREMENTS
Each Chapter (except former Practice Notes) contains the five mandatory Technical Requirements which MUST be met by the Builder.

The Technical Requirements are printed in red. Chapter 1.1 'Introduction to the Standards and Technical Requirements' contains full details.

PERFORMANCE STANDARDS
Most Chapters consist of detailed Performance Standards printed in dark blue, normally in the left-hand column of each Design, Materials or Sitework page, subdivided into Clauses designated D, M or S, respectively.

Alternative standards of performance will be acceptable ONLY if, in the opinion of NHBC, the Technical Requirements are met and the standard achieved is not lower than the stated Performance Standard.

GUIDANCE
Guidance on how the Performance Standard may be met is normally shown, printed in light blue, in the right-hand column opposite the relevant Performance Standard. Some Chapters contain pages which are all Guidance.

Guidance is based on normal procedures and recommended practices shown by experience to be satisfactory and acceptable. NHBC will consider alternative methods to meet specific requirements, subject to prior consultation and evaluation.

INTRODUCTION

Garages 9.1

SCOPE

This Chapter gives the Technical Requirements and recommendations for integral, attached and detached garages.

NHBC Standards do not cover aspects of health and safety relating to building operations and to the handling and use of certain building materials. Such matters are covered by statutory requirements.

FINDING INFORMATION

To find information on a particular subject, the following procedure is recommended:

1 Identify the **Part** most appropriate for the subject.

2 Identify the **Chapter** which deals with the particular element of construction.

3 Decide whether the information required relates to the Design, Materials or Sitework **Section** of the Chapter.

4 Decide from the Contents list the **heading** under which the required information is most likely to be found.

5 Review the **clauses** listed against the heading to see which has the relevant Performance Standard.

6 Review the **items** under the Performance Standards and decide which is relevant.

7 Review the guidance in the right-hand column opposite the item most relevant to the subject. If a clause number is known, use the above procedure to find the clause.

For example: **9.1 - D6(b)** means:

9	Part 9	External works
1	Chapter 1	Garages
D	Section	DESIGN
6	Clause 6	RESISTANCE TO FIRE SPREAD
(b)	Item (b)	door openings into the dwelling.

CONTENTS Clause

TECHNICAL REQUIREMENTS

DESIGN

Design standard	D1
Statutory requirements	D2
Garage foundations	D3
Garage floors	D4
Garage walls	D5
Resistance to fire spread	D6
Security	D7
Doors and windows	D8
Garage roofs	D9
Permanent prefabricated garages and carports	D10
Services	D11
Provision of information	D12-D13

MATERIALS

Materials standards	M1

SITEWORK

Sitework standards	S1

APPENDIX 9.1-A

Statutory references

TECHNICAL REQUIREMENTS

Technical Requirements	Performance Standards

R1   Statutory requirements
Work shall comply with all relevant Building Regulations and other statutory requirements

Chapter 1.1 gives the detailed Performance Standards which relate to these Technical Requirements.

R2   Design requirement
Design and specification shall provide satisfactory performance

R3   Materials requirement
All materials, products and building systems shall be suitable for their intended purpose

R4   Workmanship requirement
All work shall be carried out in a proper, neat and workmanlike manner

R5   Structural design requirement
Structural design shall be carried out by suitably qualified persons in accordance with British Standards and Codes of Practice

Performance Standards	Guidance

DESIGN STANDARD

9.1 - D1 Design shall meet the Technical Requirements

Design that follows the guidance below will be acceptable for garages.

STATUTORY REQUIREMENTS

9.1 - D2 Design shall comply with all relevant statutory requirements

A list of statutory references applicable to this Chapter is given in Appendix 9.1-A.

GARAGE FOUNDATIONS

9.1 - D3 Garage foundations shall transmit all loads to the ground safely and without undue movement

Garage foundations should support adequately the imposed loads, taking account of ground conditions. Further guidance is given in:

● Chapter 4.4 'Strip and trench fill foundations' (Design), *and*

● the guidance given below.

Items to be taken into account include:

(a) hazardous ground

For foundations on hazardous ground, the following Chapters are relevant:

4.1 'Foundations - finding the hazards' (Design)

4.2 'Building near trees'

4.3 'Building near trees - supplement'

4.5 'Raft, pile, pier and beam foundations' (Design).

Any existing fill on the site of the garage should be examined and identified. Where any potential health hazard or risk of damage is indicated, appropriate precautions should be taken, as described in the following Chapters:

4.1 'Foundations - finding the hazards' (Design)

5.1 'Substructure and ground bearing floors' (Design).

(b) type of foundation required for integral/ attached garages

Foundations for integral or attached garages should be the same as those for the dwelling unless proper consideration is given to each foundation and the possibility of differential movement between them.

DESIGN

9.1 Garages

GARAGE FOUNDATIONS (continued)

9.1 - D3 **(c) type of foundation required for detached garages and blocks of garages**

Design of foundations for detached individual garages or blocks of garages should avoid damage caused by differential loads and uneven settlement.

An unreinforced edge thickened concrete slab may be used where the ground is uniform and provides a satisfactory foundation bearing.

Unreinforced concrete slabs should:

● have a minimum thickness of 100mm

● have a minimum downstand thickening of 350mm below ground level around the whole perimeter of the slab

● have a minimum width of edge thickening of 300mm

● be constructed on 100mm minimum of properly compacted hardcore

● have dimensions not exceeding 6m in any direction - for dimensions greater than this, movement joints should be provided.

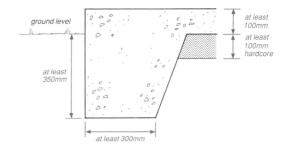

(d) adjacent structures

Foundations for garages should not impair the stability of the dwelling or any other adjacent structure.

(e) underground services

Garage foundations that are to be above or near services should be constructed so that no settlement of foundations or damage to services occurs (see Chapter 5.3 'Drainage below ground' (Design)).

(f) provision for movement

Movement joints in foundations should be provided:

● between dwellings and attached garages where there is a change of foundation type or depth

● at approximately 6m intervals where unreinforced concrete slab foundations are used.

Performance Standards	Guidance

GARAGE FLOORS

9.1 - D4 **Garage floors shall transmit all loads to either the foundations or the ground safely and without undue movement**

Garage floors will be acceptable if they are in accordance with:
- Chapters 5.1 'Substructure and ground bearing floors' (Design) and 5.2 'Suspended ground floors' (Design), *and*
- the guidance given below.

Items to be taken into account include:

(a) bearing capacity of the ground

Where the depth of fill exceeds 600mm, concrete floors should be suspended in accordance with Chapter 5.2 'Suspended ground floors' (Design).

Supporting fill should comply with the requirements of Chapter 5.1 'Substructure and ground bearing floors' (Sitework).

Where protection is needed to prevent attack by sulphates in either the ground, ground water or fill below the slab, an impervious isolating membrane should be provided between the concrete and the ground.

(b) resistance of the floor to moisture from the ground

Generally, a dpm is unnecessary except where:
- it is necessary to prevent dampness entering the dwelling, or
- the floor has to be protected against chemical attack from the ground.

Where no dpm is provided, the floor may show signs of dampness.

Where the floor is below ground level, precautions should be taken to prevent the entry of ground water by:
- tanking
- the use of dpcs and dpms
- drainage of the ground behind the wall to a level below the floor.

(c) thickness of floor slabs

Ground bearing floors, where provided, should not be less than 100mm thick, including a float finish.

(d) floor drainage

When practicable, garage floors should to be laid to falls to ensure that water or spillage is directed out of the garage via the vehicle doorway.

(e) structural topping

Where reinforced screeds are to be incorporated as structural topping, they should be designed by an Engineer in accordance with Technical Requirement R5.

Performance Standards	Guidance

GARAGE WALLS

9.1 - D5   **Walls for all garages shall transmit all loads to foundations, safely and without undue movement**

Garage walls will be acceptable if they are in accordance with:
- Chapter 5.1 'Substructure and ground bearing floors' (Design), *and*
- Chapter 6.1 'External masonry walls' (Design), *and*
- the guidance given below.

Items to be taken into account include:

(a) stability of walls above ground

Walls for detached garages and external walls for attached garages should:
- be not less than 90mm thick
- in the case of walls up to 200mm thick, have piers at corners (unless buttressed by a return) and at intermediate centres not exceeding 3m
- have adequate lateral restraint against wind loading.

(b) stability of walls retaining ground

Garage walls retaining ground should be:
- suitable for the ground conditions
- structurally adequate.

Where garage walls act as retaining walls, they should be designed in accordance with Chapter 5.1 'Substructure and ground bearing floors' or by an Engineer in accordance with Technical Requirement R5.

(c) provision for movement

Movement joints in garage walls, as described in BS 5628, should be provided:
- between dwellings and attached garages as required by Clause D3(f)
- where there are movement joints in foundations (reference should be made to Clause D3(f)).

(d) adequate resistance to rain and ground water

A damp-proof course should be provided at a level at least 150mm above the level of adjacent ground. This dpc will protect the wall from rising ground moisture.

Garage walls constructed from a single leaf of masonry, such as brickwork or blockwork approximately 100mm thick, will not be impervious to wind driven rain and consequently could become damp. In areas of *severe* exposure, single leaf walls may require a high standard of workmanship and possibly surface treatment to prevent an unacceptable level of rain penetration. Where a garage is integral or attached, the design should ensure that dampness cannot enter the dwelling.

Performance Standards	Guidance

Where a floor is below ground level, precautions should be taken to prevent the entry of ground water by:

● tanking

● use of dpcs and dpms

● drainage of ground behind the wall.

RESISTANCE TO FIRE SPREAD

9.1 - D6 Garages shall be constructed so as to prevent fire spread to the dwelling from the garage

A list of statutory references is given in Appendix 9.1-A.

Items to be taken into account include:

(a) fire resistance

Fire resistance between dwellings and integral or attached garages, may be provided by:

● a wall in brickwork, blockwork or fire-resisting studwork up to the underside of the roof covering

● a half-hour fire-resisting floor or ceiling

● any proposal which gives nominal half-hour fire resistance.

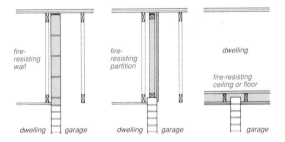

(b) door openings into the dwelling

The dimension to the top of the threshold of any opening between a dwelling and a garage is to be at least 100mm above garage floor level. The opening should be fitted with an FD20 fire-resisting door with a positive self closing device. Rising butt hinges are not acceptable as a self-closing device.

DESIGN

Performance Standards	Guidance

SECURITY

9.1 - D7 **Garages shall be constructed to provide reasonable security against unauthorised entry, in particular where garages are linked**

Where garages in different ownership are linked, walls should prevent direct access from one garage to another.

Further recommendations about garage security are given in Chapter 1.3 'Improving security'.

DOORS AND WINDOWS

9.1 - D8 **Garage doors and windows shall be adequate for their purpose**

Doors and windows will be acceptable if they are in accordance with:
- Chapter 2.3 'Timber preservation (natural solid timber)' (Design), and
- Chapter 6.7 'Doors, windows and glazing' (Design), and
- the guidance given below.

Items to be taken into account include:

(a) robustness

Frames should be selected and fixed having regard to the type and weight of the garage door.

(b) ease of operation

Proprietary doors and door gear should be installed in accordance with manufacturers' recommendations.

Care should be taken to ensure that garage doors are in proper working order at the time of handover of the dwelling.

GARAGE ROOFS

9.1 - D9 **Garage roofs shall satisfactorily resist the passage of rain and snow to the inside of the building, support applied loads and self weight and transmit the loads to the walls safely and without undue movement**

Garage roofs will be acceptable if they are in accordance with:
- Chapter 7.1 'Flat roofs and balconies' (Design), and
- Chapter 7.2 'Pitched roofs' (Design), and
- the guidance given below

Items to be taken into account include:

(a) holding down

Where the dead weight of the roof is less than the uplift, holding down straps should be provided at not more than 2m centres where the roof members bear on the supporting wall. Straps should have a cross sectional area of 150mm^2, be at least one metre long and have three fixings to the wall. Straps may also be necessary in areas of *Moderate* or *Severe* exposure.

Performance Standards	Guidance

(b) bracing

Trussed rafter roofs should be braced. In garages without a ceiling of plasterboard or similar lining, longitudinal bracing is required at ceiling joist level in all situations (reference should be made to Chapter 7.2 'Pitched roofs' (Design)).

(c) fixing of corrugated roof coverings

Framing for corrugated coverings should be constructed and sheets laid to falls in accordance with manufacturers' recommendations.

(d) detailing at abutments

The following precautions should be taken at abutments between a garage roof and the main building or between stepped garages:

- flashings and weatherproofing should allow for differential movement
- cover flashings should be of metal or other approved material
- aprons and eaves fillers for corrugated coverings should fit the corrugation profile of the roofing
- cavity trays should divert water from inside the cavity to the external surface of the roof.

(e) movement

Movement joints should be provided:

- between dwellings and attached garages which have different types or depths of foundations (reference should be made to Clause D3(f))
- at approx 6m intervals where unreinforced slab foundations are used (reference should be made to Chapter 7.1 'Flat roofs and balconies' (Design)).

Movement joints in roofs should be continued through roof coverings and be provided with appropriate weather protection.

(f) adequate disposal of rainwater

The provision of rainwater disposal is at the discretion of the Builder, subject to statutory requirements (see Appendix 9.1-A) and the paragraphs below.

Individual roofs, or combinations of roofs that drain from one to another with a total area greater than $6m^2$, should have a rainwater drainage system.

Where rainwater from a large roof surface discharges onto a garage roof, precautions should be taken to prevent premature erosion of the lower surface.

Rainwater should not discharge from the roof directly to a drive or path.

Performance Standards	Guidance

GARAGE ROOFS (continued)

9.1 - D9(f) (continued)

For details on the design of rainwater disposal systems, reference should be made to the following Chapters, as appropriate:

7.1 'Flat roofs and balconies' (Design)

7.2 'Pitched roofs' (Design).

(g) acceptable forms of construction

Garage roofs should be designed, specified and constructed as described in Chapter 7.1 'Flat roofs and balconies' (each section) or Chapter 7.2 'Pitched roofs' (each section), as appropriate.

PERMANENT PREFABRICATED GARAGES AND CARPORTS

9.1 - D10 Permanent prefabricated garages and carports shall be suitable for their intended purpose

Permanent prefabricated garages and carports should:
- have appropriate foundations
- be structurally adequate
- provide appropriate weathertightness
- provide adequate separation between linked garages in different ownership.

Prefabricated garages should be erected in accordance with manufacturers' recommendations.

Particular care should be taken to ensure adequate holding down of carports and other light structures against wind action.

SERVICES

9.1 - D11 The provision of any service or appliance within a garage shall be in accordance with relevant regulations

Where services or appliances are provided in garages, they should comply with the guidance below and with the following Chapters, as appropriate:

5.3 'Drainage below ground' (Design)

8.1 'Internal services' (Design).

Items to be taken into account include:

(a) protection of water services against frost

A rising main should not be located within a garage.

A water supply or outlet in a garage should have adequate provision for isolating and draining down.

Pipes should be insulated and located so as to minimise the risk of freezing.

Performance Standards	Guidance

(b) provision of electricity

The provision of electric lighting and socket outlets in a garage is at the discretion of the Builder.

Electrical installations should comply with the current IEE Wiring Regulations. It should be noted that socket outlets which 'may reasonably be expected to' be used for outside appliances should be protected by an RCD, unless supplied by circuits exempted by the IEE Wiring Regulations.

It is not practicable to include the full IEE Wiring Regulations on RCDs for outside appliances.

(c) risk of fire or explosion

Installation in a garage of an oil or gas burning boiler or heating appliance should be in accordance with any relevant Statutory Regulations.

PROVISION OF INFORMATION

9.1 - D12 Designs and specifications shall be produced in a clearly understandable format and include all relevant information

Design information should include all necessary details of the following:

- exact location of garages
- all relevant levels, related to an agreed reference point
- foundations
- waterproofing, where applicable
- walls
- roof structure and coverings
- external and internal finishes
- services, where applicable.

9.1 - D13 All relevant information shall be distributed to appropriate personnel

Ensure that design and specification information is issued to site supervisors and relevant specialist subcontractors and/or suppliers.

Performance Standards	Guidance

MATERIALS STANDARDS

9.1 - M1   All materials shall:
(a) **meet the Technical Requirements**
(b) **take account of the design**

Materials that comply with the design and the guidance given in the Chapters listed below will be acceptable for garages.

FOUNDATIONS

4.4 'Strip and trench fill foundations' (Materials)

4.5 'Raft, pile, pier and beam foundations' (Materials)

5.1 'Substructure and ground bearing floors' (Materials)

6.1 'External masonry walls' (Materials).

FLOORS

5.1 'Substructure and ground bearing floors' (Materials)

5.2 'Suspended ground floors' (Materials).

WALLS

5.1 'Substructure and ground bearing floors' (Materials)

6.1 'External masonry walls' (Materials).

ROOFS

7.1 'Flat roofs and balconies' (Materials)

7.2 'Pitched roofs' (Materials).

Performance Standards	Guidance

SITEWORK STANDARDS

9.1 - S1 **All sitework shall:**

(a) **meet the Technical Requirements**

(b) **comply with the design**

(c) **follow established good practice and workmanship**

Sitework that complies with the design and the guidance given in the Chapters listed below will be acceptable for garages.

FOUNDATIONS

4.4 'Strip and trench fill foundations' (Sitework)

4.5 'Raft, pile, pier and beam foundations' (Sitework)

5.1 'Substructure and ground bearing floors' (Sitework)

6.1 'External masonry walls' (Sitework).

FLOORS

5.1 'Substructure and ground bearing floors' (Sitework)

5.2 'Suspended ground floors' (Sitework).

WALLS

5.1 'Substructure and ground bearing floors' (Sitework)

6.1 'External masonry walls' (Sitework).

ROOFS

7.1 'Flat roofs and balconies' (Sitework)

7.2 'Pitched roofs' (Sitework).

Statutory references

The following table lists references to building legislation and associated documents applicable at August 1990.

		Statute			
Clause	Subject	Building [1] Regulations	Building [2] Standards (Scotland)	Building [3] Regulations (N Ireland)	Isle of Man [4] Bye-laws
D2	Structure	A1/2/3	Part C	Part D	Part D
D6	Fire spread	B2/3/4	Part D	Part E	Part E
D9(f)	Rainwater drainage	H3	Part N	Part N	Part N
D11(b)	Provision of electricity	**Associated documents** IEE Wiring Regulations			

[1] Approved Documents to the Building Regulations 1985 for England and Wales (and 1990 edition).
[2] Building Standards (Scotland) Regulations 1981 and all published amendments.
[3] Building Regulations (Northern Ireland) 1990.
[4] Isle of Man Bye-laws 1976, amended 1980 and 1987.

BUILDMARK™

informing the industry

CI/SfB	81	(90)	
CAWS	Q2	Q3	Q4

Operative from January 1992

Chapter **9.2**

NHBC STANDARDS

Drives, paths, fences and landscaping

This Chapter gives the Technical Requirements and recommendations for drives, paths, fences and landscaping.

LIST OF CHAPTERS

Volume 1

THE STANDARDS

The NHBC Standards give:
- Technical Requirements in red
- Performance Standards in dark blue
- Guidance in light blue

for the design and construction of dwellings acceptable to NHBC.

Diagrams may contain text in red. This is to highlight points but has no mandatory significance.

The Standards come into effect for every NHBC registered home whose foundations are concreted on or after the publication date shown on the cover of each Chapter and apply throughout the UK, unless otherwise stated.

COMPOSITION OF THE STANDARDS
The Standards are divided into 10 Parts, each containing one or more Chapters covering a particular aspect. The Parts follow the usual construction process.

In general, each Chapter is made up of sections dealing with Design, Materials and Sitework. In some cases one or more of these aspects may not be included.

TECHNICAL REQUIREMENTS
Each Chapter (except former Practice Notes) contains the five mandatory Technical Requirements which MUST be met by the Builder.

The Technical Requirements are printed in red. Chapter 1.1 'Introduction to the Standards and Technical Requirements' contains full details.

PERFORMANCE STANDARDS
Most Chapters consist of detailed Performance Standards printed in dark blue, normally in the left-hand column of each Design, Materials or Sitework page, subdivided into Clauses designated D, M or S, respectively.

Alternative standards of performance will be acceptable ONLY if, in the opinion of NHBC, the Technical Requirements are met and the standard achieved is not lower than the stated Performance Standard.

GUIDANCE
Guidance on how the Performance Standard may be met is normally shown, printed in light blue, in the right-hand column opposite the relevant Performance Standard. Some Chapters contain pages which are all Guidance.

Guidance is based on normal procedures and recommended practices shown by experience to be satisfactory and acceptable. NHBC will consider alternative methods to meet specific requirements, subject to prior consultation and evaluation.

SCOPE

This Chapter gives the Technical Requirements and recommendations for drives, paths, fences and landscaping.

NHBC Standards do not cover aspects of health and safety relating to building operations and to the handling and use of certain building materials. Such matters are covered by statutory requirements.

FINDING INFORMATION

To find information on a particular subject, the following procedure is recommended:

1 Identify the **Part** most appropriate for the subject.

2 Identify the **Chapter** which deals with the particular element of construction.

3 Decide whether the information required relates to the Design, Materials or Sitework **Section** of the Chapter.

4 Decide from the Contents list the **heading** under which the required information is most likely to be found.

5 Review the **clauses** listed against the heading to see which has the relevant Performance Standard.

6 Review the **items** under the Performance Standards and decide which is relevant.

7 Review the guidance in the right-hand column opposite the item most relevant to the subject. If a clause number is known, use the above procedure to find the clause.

For example: **9.2 - S3(b)** means:

9	Part 9	External works
2	Chapter 2	Drives, paths, fences and landscaping
S	Section	SITEWORK
3	Clause 3	FOUNDATIONS FOR DRIVES AND PATHS
(b)	Item (b)	protection of drains or services.

CONTENTS   Clause

Technical Requirements	Performance Standards

R1 **Statutory requirements**
Work shall comply with all relevant Building Regulations and other statutory requirements

Chapter 1.1 gives the detailed Performance Standards which relate to these Technical Requirements.

R2 **Design requirement**
Design and specification shall provide satisfactory performance

R3 **Materials requirement**
All materials, products and building systems shall be suitable for their intended purpose

R4 **Workmanship requirement**
All work shall be carried out in a proper, neat and workmanlike manner

R5 **Structural design requirement**
Structural design shall be carried out by suitably qualified persons in accordance with British Standards and Codes of Practice

Drives, paths, fences and landscaping | 9.2

Performance Standards	Guidance

DESIGN STANDARD

9.2 - D1 **Design shall meet the Technical Requirements**

Design that follows the guidance below will be acceptable for drives, paths, fences and landscaping.

PROVISION OF ACCESS DRIVES AND PATHS

9.2 - D2 **Access shall be provided for vehicles and pedestrians to the home and any garage, car port or vehicular hardstanding around it**

Items to be taken into account include:

(a) drives

A garage, carport or vehicular hardstanding within the curtilage of a dwelling requires a drive to the highway. Drives should be designed to permit an average family motor car unimpeded access to and from any garage, carport or vehicular hardstanding.

(b) access paths

Every home should have a path or paths to provide pedestrian access from the highway to both the main entrance and, except for a mid-terrace home, the secondary entrance. The secondary entrance may be the kitchen door or that which is the most likely to serve the kitchen and/or utility areas and facilitate the removal and/or collection of refuse from the dwelling.

An external path to the secondary access door is not required where entry to the home can be gained from a garage, either directly or through a utility room.

If a garage, carport or vehicular hardstanding is provided within the curtilage, a path should be provided to it from the home.

Path widths should be as follows:

- between highway and refuse collection point (Scotland only)   900mm
- between highway and main entrance   900mm
- paths adjoining a dwelling   700mm
  - where it is 100mm or more from the wall   600mm
- all other cases   600mm

9.2 - D3 **Adequate provision shall be made to ensure safe access to, and around, the home**

At no place along an access path should the gradient be more than 1 : 6. On steeper slopes, steps may be introduced at intervals to ensure that the maximum gradient of the path is not exceeded. A separate access path should be provided where a drive has a gradient of more than 1 : 6.

9.2

Drives, paths, fences and landscaping

Performance Standards   **Guidance**

FOUNDATIONS AND CONSTRUCTION

9.2 - D4   **Drives and paths shall be adequate for their intended use**

Items to be taken into account include:

(a) foundations

Foundations for drives and paths should be provided as necessary and constructed of broken brick, stone, gravel or other suitable material compacted adequately.

Foundation thickness should be appropriate for the supporting ground and for the intended load and normally would be 150m for drives (on silt and clay) and 75mm for paths subject to pedestrian traffic only.

For further details, reference should be made to Sitework clause 9.2 - S3.

(b) surfaces

Drive surfaces, in conjunction with foundations, should be capable of supporting the weight of an average motor car.

Surfaces of the ground or paths adjacent to the home should:
- be at least 150mm below dpc (unless some alternative damp-proofing arrangement is provided)
- direct water away from the building
- not obstruct ventilators and air bricks.

For further details reference should be made to Sitework clause 9.2 - S4.

FENCING, HANDRAILS AND BALUSTRADES OUTSIDE THE DWELLING

9.2 - D5   **Where provided, fencing, handrails and balustrades shall be adequate in respect of:**
(a) stability
(b) resistance to wind forces
(c) durability

Fencing and gates designed to comply with the requirements of BS 1722 and BS 4092 will meet the Performance Standards. Other designs may also be suitable.

Boundary fences and other fences intended to provide security should be designed so that they cannot readily be climbed or damaged. Reference should be made to Chapter 1.3 'Improving security' and BS 6180 and BS 8220.

9.2 - D6   **Handrails or balustrades shall be provided, where necessary, to enable safe passage**

Handrails or balustrades should be provided where:
- the total rise of a flight of steps exceeds 600mm, or
- a path is adjacent to a vertical difference in level of more than 600mm.

Performance Standards   Guidance

FREESTANDING WALLS

9.2 - D7 **Where provided, freestanding walls shall be adequate in respect of:**

(a) stability

(b) foundations

(c) resistance to wind forces

(d) durability

Freestanding walls designed to comply with the following will be acceptable:
- BS 5390 and BS 5628, or
- NHBC recommendations on freestanding walls (when published).

VEHICULAR AREAS

9.2 - D8 **Appropriate measures shall be taken to prevent damage to fences, handrails and walls adjacent to vehicular areas**

Design may either:
- be in accordance with BS 6180, which includes impact resistance, or
- prevent contact by using bollards, curbs or other landscape features.

GARDEN AREAS

9.2 - D9 **The area immediately surrounding the home (up to 3m maximum) shall be left in a satisfactory condition**

Items to be taken into account include:

(a) ground levels

Finished ground levels should be established as part of the design. They should be consistent with:
- dpc levels
- cover levels of drainage access points
- depth of underground services (gas, electricity, water, drains)
- drive and path levels.

(b) waterlogging

Where waterlogging can reasonably be expected, precautions should be taken to prevent it. This could include the provision of land drains connected to a suitable outfall, such as a soakaway, surface water drains or a water course.

Performance Standards	Guidance

GARDEN AREAS (continued)

9.2 - D10 The garden area shall be stable

Items to be taken into account include:

(a) retaining walls

Retaining walls or terracing may be required to support land on uneven sites.

Retaining walls which give support to dwelling foundations should be designed by an Engineer in accordance with Technical Requirement R5. The use of gabion structures to retain ground supporting dwellings (including garages and drainage systems) is not acceptable to NHBC.

(b) grading of slopes

The ground around each dwelling should be laid out so that it is stable at all times. Where the undisturbed ground has a slope exceeding the natural angle of repose, it should be checked to ensure stability. Unless special precautions are taken, the maximum gradient of unsupported ground should be $5°$ less than the natural angle of repose.

9.2 - D11 Where provided, clothes drying facilities should be in a suitable location

Where provided, outside clothes drying should be conveniently located and be provided with hardstanding and safe access.

9.2 - D12 Access to useable garden areas shall be provided, where appropriate

Where the construction of retaining walls would otherwise result in any part of the useable garden area being rendered inaccessible, then steps or other suitable means shall be provided. In all cases, steps should have an appropriate and consistent rise and going.

TREES AND SHRUBS

9.2 - D13 Trees and shrubs shall not cause future damage to dwellings

Where trees or shrubs have been removed, or are to be retained (due to the presence of a preservation order or for any other reason), or are to be planted, precautions should be taken to prevent damage to dwellings. These include:
- allowing sufficient space to preserve the root system
- allowing for root spread and water uptake, especially on clay soils
- allowing for effects of water uptake where trees have been removed, especially on clay soils
- allowing for the future effects of tree and root growth
- providing foundation depth sufficient to allow for existing and new trees.

Guidance on these and other aspects is given in BS 5837 and in Chapters 4.2 and 4.3 'Building near trees' and its supplement.

Performance Standards

Guidance

PROVISION OF INFORMATION

9.2 - D14 Designs and specifications shall be produced in a clearly understandable format and include all relevant information

Drives and paths should be specified fully, including:

- removal of vegetable soil
- provision of foundation
- provision of edging
- provision of surfacing.

9.2 - D15 All relevant information shall be distributed to appropriate personnel

Ensure that design and specification information is issued to site supervisors and relevant specialist subcontractors and/or suppliers.

Performance Standards	Guidance

MATERIALS STANDARDS

9.2 - M1 All materials shall:
    (a) meet the Technical Requirements
    (b) take account of the design

Materials that comply with the design and the guidance below will be acceptable for drives, paths, fences and landscaping.

Materials for drives, paths, fences and landscaping should comply with all relevant standards, including those listed below. Where no standard exists, Technical Requirement R3 applies (see Chapter 1.1 'Introduction to the Standards and Technical Requirements').

References to British Standards and Codes of Practice include those made under the Construction Products Directive (89/106/EEC) and, in particular, appropriate European Technical Specifications approved by a European Committee for Standardisation (CEN).

CONCRETE

9.2 - M2 Concrete shall be of a mix design which will:
    (a) achieve sufficient strength for its purpose
    (b) be sufficiently durable to remain unaffected by chemical or frost action

For guidance on the specification and use of concrete, reference should be made to Chapter 2.1 'Concrete and its reinforcement' (Design).

ALL MATERIALS

9.2 - M3 All materials shall be suitable for their intended use

Items to be taken into account include:

(a) asphalt and macadam

Asphalt and macadam should comply with relevant standards, including:
BS 594   Hot rolled asphalt for roads and other paved areas
BS 4987 Coated macadam for roads and other paved areas.

(b) gravel

Gravel for surfacing should pass a 20mm mesh.

9.2 | Drives, paths, fences and landscaping

Performance Standards

Guidance

ALL MATERIALS (continued)

9.2 - M3   **(c) blocks, slabs and paviors**

Blocks, slabs, paviors, edgings, etc should comply with relevant standards, including:

BS 340   Precast concrete kerbs, channels, edgings and quadrants

BS 6073 Precast concrete masonry units

BS 6677 Part 1 : Clay and calcium silicate pavers for flexible pavements : Specification for pavers

BS 6717 Precast concrete paving blocks.

  (d) materials for freestanding walls

Materials in accordance with NHBC recommendations on freestanding walls (when published) will be acceptable.

  (e) fencing

BS 1722 Fences.

Performance Standards	Guidance

SITEWORK STANDARDS

9.2 - S1   All sitework shall:
   (a) meet the Technical Requirements
   (b) take account of the design
   (c) follow established good practice and workmanship

Sitework that complies with the design and the guidance below will be acceptable for drives, paths, fences and landscaping.

GROUND STABILITY

9.2 - S2   Precautions shall be taken on sloping sites to ensure stability of the ground

Where ground may become surcharged during construction, precautions should be taken to ensure stability.

Retaining walls which give support to the dwelling foundations should be completed before work starts on the construction of the dwelling foundations. The use of gabion structures to retain ground supporting dwellings (including garages and drainage systems) is not acceptable to NHBC.

FOUNDATIONS FOR DRIVES AND PATHS

9.2 - S3   Foundations for drives and paths shall adequately support the required loading

Items to be taken into account include:

(a) preparation

Vegetable soil should be removed before drives or paths are constructed.

(b) protection of drains or services

Where a drive or path is above underground drainage or services, the pipes should be protected against damage from traffic, as described in Chapter 5.3 'Drainage below ground' (Design and Sitework).

(c) foundation construction

Foundations for drives and paths should be provided as specified and constructed of broken brick, stone, gravel or other suitable material. Bottoming should be suitably compacted and blinded with clinker or gravel as a base course before the wearing surface is applied.

Foundations on silt or clay should be not less than 150mm thick. For paths subject to pedestrian traffic only, a foundation thickness of 75mm is normally acceptable.

Performance Standards	Guidance

SURFACING OF DRIVES

9.2 - S4 **Surfaces to drives shall be regular, stable, adequately drained and durable**

Surfaces other than gravel should be hard and reasonably even. Where required for safety reasons, for example on a gradient, a suitable non-slip surface finish should be provided. For concrete, a tamped finish is acceptable.

Drives abutting a dwelling should be at least 150mm below dpc and direct water away from the building.

Items to be taken into account include:

(a) asphalt and macadam

Asphalt and macadam surfacing should comply with one of the following:

Specification		Min thickness [mm]
Single course	rolled asphalt	40
	macadam	50
Two courses	base course of coated macadam	1.5 x nominal size of macadam
	wearing course of cold asphalt or coated macadam	20 (only if on a coated macadam base course)

(b) gravel

Gravel drives should be laid on a base of broken stone or gravel, blinded and consolidated to a thickness of not less than 50mm to provide a firm and compact surface.

Gravel material should pass a 20mm mesh.

(c) concrete

Concrete should be laid to a minimum thickness of 100mm. The concrete mix should be suitable to give a durable and frost resistant surface, as described in Chapter 2.1 'Concrete and its reinforcement' (Design).

For concrete, movement joints not less than 10mm wide, or expansion spaces, should be provided at intermediate centres not exceeding 4m, and at the abutment to walls where the opposite edge of the concrete is also restrained.

(d) paviors or precast concrete slabs

Precast concrete slabs not less than 50mm thick, may be used and should be laid on a foundation as specified above, or on lean-mix concrete, using a sand bed, or on dabs.

Paviors should be bedded into a uniform foundation.

Performance Standards	Guidance

(e) edgings

Edges to drives of materials other than concrete should be supported by concrete, treated timber or similar.

SURFACING OF PATHS

9.2 - S5   **Surfaces to paths should be regular, stable, adequately drained and durable**

Paths abutting the dwelling should be at least 150mm below dpc and direct water away from the building.

Any access path required in Chapter 1.2 'The home - its accommodation and services' should meet the specification for drives in Clause S4 above, subject to the modifications to the required thickness of materials given below. The specification for any other path is at the option of the Builder.

Items to be taken into account include:

(a) concrete

Concrete surfacing for paths should be not less than 75mm thick.

(b) paviors or precast concrete slabs

Precast concrete slabs, not less than 38mm thick, on a suitable foundation, may be used.

(c) gravel

Gravel paths on a blinded foundation will be acceptable. Gravel material should pass a 20mm mesh.

FENCING

9.2 - S6   **Fencing shall be plumb and adequately stable**

Items to be taken into account include:

(a) construction of foundations

Fence posts should be:
- erected at intervals appropriate for the fence construction and location
- secured in the ground by concrete foundations or rounded backfill at a depth appropriate for the height of the fence.

(b) protection of timber posts and panels in contact with the ground

Timber fencing elements, particularly those in contact with the ground, should be properly treated with preservative.

(c) fixing of fencings

Fence infill should be fixed to posts, wires and rails by a method appropriate for the material and construction.

Performance Standards

Guidance

FREESTANDING WALLS

9.2 - S7 **Freestanding walls shall be adequately stable**

Construction should be in accordance with the design or NHBC recommendations on freestanding walls (when published).

AREAS SURROUNDING THE DWELLING

9.2 - S8 **Upon handover, the area surrounding the dwelling shall be suitable for cultivation**

Garden areas should be left so that old foundations, concrete bases and similar obstructions occurring within 300mm of the finished ground surface are removed. Any ground disturbed during construction should be re-shaped to conform with the general shape of the adjacent ground.

Sub-soil should not be placed over vegetable soil and any vegetable soil disturbed should be re-instated or replaced. It is not necessary to provide further vegetable soil.

Rubbish and debris should be disposed of satisfactorily.

LANDSCAPING

9.2 - S9 **Landscaping work shall be completed in a manner appropriate for the site conditions and layout**

If landscaping is specified, the work should be carried out and completed in a neat manner. Landscaping should meet with the guidance given in the Design section of this Chapter.

The NHBC recommendations on the protection and planting of trees should also be followed (reference should be made to Chapter 4.2 'Building near trees').

Part 10 SNAGGING

Part 10 SNAGGING

10.1 Snagging

NHBC STANDARDS

Snagging

This Chapter gives the Technical Requirements and recommendations for snagging to ensure that a dwelling is prepared for handover.

LIST OF CHAPTERS

THE STANDARDS

The NHBC Standards give:
● Technical Requirements in red
● Performance Standards in dark blue
● Guidance   in light blue
for the design and construction of dwellings
acceptable to NHBC.

Diagrams may contain text in red. This is to highlight
points but has no mandatory significance.

The Standards come into effect for every NHBC
registered home whose foundations are concreted on
or after the publication date shown on the cover of
each Chapter and apply throughout the UK, unless
otherwise stated.

COMPOSITION OF THE STANDARDS
The Standards are divided into 10 Parts, each
containing one or more Chapters covering
a particular aspect. The Parts follow the usual
construction process.

In general, each Chapter is made up of sections
dealing with Design, Materials and Sitework.
In some cases one or more of these aspects
may not be included.

TECHNICAL REQUIREMENTS
Each Chapter (except former Practice Notes) contains
the five mandatory Technical Requirements which
MUST be met by the Builder.

The Technical Requirements are printed in red.
Chapter 1.1 'Introduction to the Standards and
Technical Requirements' contains full details.

PERFORMANCE STANDARDS
Most Chapters consist of detailed Performance
Standards printed in dark blue, normally in the left-
hand column of each Design, Materials or Sitework
page, subdivided into Clauses designated D, M or S,
respectively.

Alternative standards of performance will be
acceptable ONLY if, in the opinion of NHBC, the
Technical Requirements are met and the standard
achieved is not lower than the stated Performance
Standard.

GUIDANCE
Guidance on how the Performance Standard may be
met is normally shown, printed in light blue, in the
right-hand column opposite the relevant Performance
Standard. Some Chapters contain pages which are
all Guidance.

Guidance is based on normal procedures and
recommended practices shown by experience to be
satisfactory and acceptable. NHBC will consider
alternative methods to meet specific requirements,
subject to prior consultation and evaluation.

SCOPE

This Chapter gives the Technical Requirements and recommendations for snagging to ensure that a dwelling is prepared for handover.

NHBC Standards do not cover aspects of health and safety relating to building operations and to the handling and use of certain building materials. Such matters are covered by statutory requirements.

FINDING INFORMATION

To find information on a particular subject, the following procedure is recommended:

1 Identify the **Part** most appropriate for the subject.

2 Identify the **Chapter** which deals with the particular element of construction.

3 Decide whether the information required relates to the Design, Materials or Sitework **Section** of the Chapter.

4 Decide from the Contents list the **heading** under which the required information is most likely to be found.

5 Review the **clauses** listed against the heading to see which has the relevant Performance Standard.

6 Review the **items** under the Performance Standards and decide which is relevant.

7 Review the guidance in the right-hand column opposite the item most relevant to the subject. If a clause number is known, use the above procedure to find the clause.

For example: **10.1 - S2(a)** means:

10	Part 10	Snagging
1	Chapter 1	Snagging
S	Section	SITEWORK
2	Clause 2	IDENTIFICATION OF DEFECTS
(a)	Item (a)	checks for roofs.

CONTENTS   Clause

TECHNICAL REQUIREMENTS

SITEWORK

TECHNICAL REQUIREMENTS

Technical Requirements	Performance Standards

R1 Statutory requirements
Work shall comply with all relevant Building Regulations and other statutory requirements

Chapter 1.1 gives the detailed Performance Standards which relate to these Technical Requirements.

R2 Design requirement
Design and specification shall provide satisfactory performance

R3 Materials requirement
All materials, products and building systems shall be suitable for their intended purpose

R4 Workmanship requirement
All work shall be carried out in a proper, neat and workmanlike manner

R5 Structural design requirement
Structural design shall be carried out by suitably qualified persons in accordance with British Standards and Codes of Practice

There are no specific DESIGN implications for this Chapter

There are no specific MATERIALS implications for this Chapter

Performance Standards	Guidance

SITEWORK STANDARDS

10.1 - S1 All sitework shall:

    (a) meet the Technical Requirements

    (b) take account of the design

    (c) follow established good practice and workmanship

Work should be snagged in accordance with the guidance below.

This Chapter deals primarily with snagging at completion prior to the dwelling being offered for handover to the purchaser.

It is important that verification of work should be carried out regularly during the building process.

Builders are advised to include the following list of items if they compile their own snagging documents.

Performance Standards | **Guidance**

IDENTIFICATION OF DEFECTS

10.1 - S2 The Builder shall carry out checks to identify defects

Identification of defects should be carried out at all stages of construction.

GENERAL SNAGGING PROCEDURE
- snag each property before handover in a systematic sequence so as to identify any defects (see below)
- write down the defects
- pass a list of remedial work to the responsible trades foreman or subcontractor, with a suitable written deadline for completion of the work
- check that remedial work has been completed correctly
- check that all items listed in 'the Schedule' have been provided. Reference should be made to Chapter 1.2 'The home - its accommodation and services' for 'the Schedule'.

Snagging involves looking at all parts of the property in a systematic way. Establish a snagging system and use it consistently.

EXAMPLE
- check each external elevation in turn - like a book - from top to bottom and left to right
- check each room in a consistent way - either clockwise or anti-clockwise.

This document may be used as a checklist - all appropriate checks should be carried out, together with any others relevant to the specific dwelling.

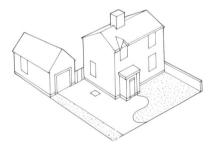

Snagging should be undertaken for the following:'
(a) roofs
(b) external walls
(c) garages
(d) around the dwelling
(e) loft spaces
(f) all interior spaces
(g) kitchens, bathrooms, etc
(h) common areas
(i) connection and testing of services
(j) remedial measures
(k) accuracy of information to be given to the purchasers.

Performance Standards

Guidance

ROOFS

10.1 - S2 (a) checks for ROOFS

Check that:

PITCHED ROOF COVERINGS
- roof tiles or slates are complete
- bedding mortar at verges, ridges, hips and valleys is complete and free from cracks
- proprietary venting tiles are present, where needed
- proprietary dry verge and ridge systems are complete
- there are no cracked or slipped tiles or slates
- the roof covering is free from mortar
- the line is even and the gauge is correct
- the covering is nailed/clipped/fixed, as appropriate.

DORMER ROOF AND CHEEKS
- tiling is complete and free from cracked or slipping tiles
- flashings and soakers are correctly installed
- flashings and edge details are complete.

CHIMNEY STACKS
- flashings are correctly installed, wedged and pointed up
- pointing and haunching is complete
- copings are bedded or sealed correctly
- throatings to cappings are formed correctly.

FLUES
- flashings are installed correctly
- cappings are sealed to flues correctly
- terminals are installed correctly.

ABUTMENTS WITH WALLS
- flashings are complete and fixed firmly
- flashings have sufficient lap
- flashings are wedged and pointed up
- weep holes to stepped trays are not blocked.

EAVES
- ventilation openings or proprietary ventilation units are adequate
- fly screens are fitted over large ventilation openings
- soffits, etc have been painted or stained.

RAINWATER DRAINAGE
- valley gutters are clean and free from debris
- gutters, brackets and stop ends are positioned properly, complete and undamaged
- falls to outlets are correct
- roof underlay laps into gutter
- joints in gutters are installed correctly and not leaking
- debris has been removed.

FLAT ROOF COVERINGS
- chippings are distributed evenly
- roof finish is free from blisters and cracks
- roof is free from ponding
- upstands and flashings are in correct locations and of sufficient height
- there are falls to outlets, eaves, gutters, etc.

Performance Standards

Guidance

EXTERNAL WALLS

10.1 - S2 (b) checks for EXTERNAL WALLS

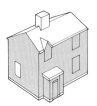

Check that:

BRICKWORK
- pointing is complete, include making good putlog holes
- brickwork is clean and free from mortar splashes
- mortar is of a consistent colour.

RENDERING
- junctions with half-timber mock-Tudor designs are correct
- details at openings are acceptable
- bell castings and stop beads are finished correctly
- texture and finish are even and consistent.

CLADDINGS
- details are correct and complete:
  - at openings
  - at external corners
  - abutting masonry
  - at terminations, eg top.

GUTTER DOWNPIPES
- fixings and joints are correct
- components are complete and undamaged
- downpipes are connected to outfall, where required.

WASTE PIPES
- making good has been completed neatly where waste pipes pass through the wall.

OVERFLOW PIPES
- overflows can be readily seen
- pipes are not too short (causing dampness)
- pipes are not too long at low level (possibly injuring people)
- making good is complete around pipes
- overflow from unvented hot water system has been installed correctly to provide safe discharge.

BALANCED FLUE TERMINALS
- guards have been installed correctly
- terminals are located away from fascia, soffit, windows and doors.

WINDOWS AND DOORS
- window frames are free from chips and splits
- sills and drip moulds are undamaged
- doors are undamaged
- mastic is present and applied properly, where specified
- glazing method is correct
- glass is not cracked or scratched
- glass is reasonably clean and free from paint splashes
- putty is complete
- beads are fixed securely.

PAINTWORK AND STAINING
- work is complete, especially at high level and underneath sills
- top coat has been applied to all painted surfaces.

Performance Standards

Guidance

GARAGES

10.1 - S2 (c) checks for GARAGES

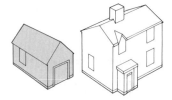

The items below are in addition to those in Clauses S2(a) and S2(b) where the garage is separate from the dwelling.

Check that:

GARAGE DOORS
● doors open and shut properly
● bolts engage and locks operate properly.

WATER SERVICES (where provided)
● insulation is provided to any water services.

ROOF STRUCTURE
● bracing in trussed rafter roofs is complete
● holding down and restraint straps are in place and fixed correctly.

FIRE SPREAD PRECAUTIONS
For *integral* garages:
● fire-resisting ceiling is complete
● making good is satisfactory around services, etc in fire-resisting ceiling.

For *integral and attached* garages:
● half-hour fire door between garage and house is fitted with a self-closer and adequate door stops
● there is a minimum 100mm step up to threshold.

INTERIOR
● debris and Builders' rubbish has been removed.

10.1 | **Snagging**

AROUND THE DWELLING

10.1 - S2 (d) checks for PATHS, DRIVES and GARDEN AREAS

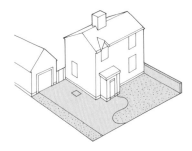

Check that:

DRIVES AND PATHS
- drives and paths are complete
- surfaces are even
- finishes are minimum 150mm below dpc levels
- falls are correct (should slope away from house)
- gradient and access allow unimpeded access
- surfacing material is satisfactory.

DRAINAGE AND OTHER SERVICES
- levels of gullies and manhole covers are consistent with surrounding surfaces
- manhole covers fit properly and are the correct grade
- gully gratings have been fitted
- stopcock boxes are at correct level (flush with adjacent surfaces)
- backfilling is completed properly to match surrounding ground levels.

GARDENS
- debris and Builders' rubbish has been removed
- the garden is graded to appropriate levels
- soil is at least 150mm below dpc levels
- soil, etc is not blocking air bricks
- landscaping has been carried out, where specified
- access is provided to all usable garden areas.

WALLS
- freestanding boundary and retaining walls are complete, including dpcs and copings as specified
- movement joints have been placed where required.

FENCES
- fences are complete.

GATES
- gates are in working order.

Performance Standards

Guidance

LOFT SPACES

10.1 - S2 (e) checks within LOFT SPACES

Check that:

MASONRY WALL/ROOF JUNCTIONS
- ends of purlins, binders, etc are properly supported and built into masonry
- making good is complete.

SEPARATING WALL/ROOF JUNCTION
- brickwork or blockwork is made good up to roof line
- mortar joints are fully filled with mortar
- firestopping to underside of underfelt/sarking is complete and imperforate.

UNDERFELT/SARKING
- underfelt is complete and undamaged
- underfelt is flashed properly around openings, soil stacks, ridge vent units, etc.

TRUSSED RAFTER ROOFS
- bracing and restraint strapping is complete and fixed adequately
- support is adequate to water tanks.

ROOF VENTILATION
- eaves ventilators are fitted where needed
- ventilation path is not blocked by insulation.

INSULATION
- insulation is complete.

TANK AND PIPE INSULATION
- insulation to tank is complete, including lid
- there is no insulation below tank
- water pipes and overflows above loft insulation are lagged fully.

ACCESS TO ROOF SPACE
- access hatch is insulated, is the correct size and fits the opening correctly
- gangway boarding is provided and fixed adequately (from hatch to tank and around tank).

FLUE PIPES
- flue pipe connections are correct (should be socket uppermost)
- flue pipe supports are directly below each socket
- combustible materials are a suitable distance from flue pipes
- flue pipes are connected correctly to ridge terminal.

VENT PIPES
- vent pipes are supported adequately through roof space and connected to a terminal
- insulation to extract ducting is fitted and ducting is terminated properly to the outside air.

ROOF SPACES
- debris and Builders' rubbish has been removed.

10.1 | Snagging

Performance Standards	Guidance

ALL INTERIOR SPACES

10.1 - S2 (f) checks inside ALL ROOMS, STAIRCASES and CIRCULATION AREAS

The items in this Clause apply to all rooms and staircases.

In addition, the extra items in Clause S2(g) apply to kitchens, bathrooms, utility rooms, shower rooms, etc and the extra items in Clause S2(h) apply to common areas serving flats.

Check that:

CEILINGS (and WALLS which are dry lined)
● cornices and corners are even, true and made neatly
● paintwork or decorative finish is complete and free from blemishes
● there are no damaged areas
● joints do not show through
● there is no surface cracking.

WALLS - PLASTERWORK
● the surface of the plasterwork is even, true and free from rough patches
● making good plaster has been completed neatly around pipes, light switches, socket outlets, etc
● paintwork is complete and free from blemishes
● junctions, corners, reveals and margins are all even and true.

WINDOWS
● paintwork or stain is complete, including exposed underside of window board
● frame and window board are undamaged
● glazing is free from paint splashes, not cracked or scratched
● windows open and shut properly
● trickle ventilators are in working order
● window opening lights are not warped or twisted badly.

DOORS AND FRAMES
● doors open and shut properly
● paintwork is complete, including hidden surfaces
● paintwork is free from blemishes
● doors are not warped or twisted badly
● there is an even gap between doors and frames.

IRONMONGERY
● ironmongery is complete and in working order
● ironmongery is free from paint splashes
● lockable devices are fitted to all ground floor windows and any others which can easily be reached from the outside
● security lock is fitted to front door
● there is a wide angle of view of the area immediately outside the front door, or a through-door viewer fitted
● there is an opening limitation device fixed securely to the front door
● secondary access doors have 5-lever locks
● front and secondary access doors have bolts fixed securely at both the top and bottom of the door.

SKIRTINGS, ARCHITRAVES, etc
● woodwork is undamaged and free from defects
● paintwork is complete and free from blemishes.

Performance Standards	Guidance

Check that:

FLOOR DECKING
- floor/skirting junction is finished neatly
- boarding or decking is fixed adequately
- boarding or decking is fitted neatly around pipes/services.

FLOOR FINISHES
- all floor tiling is complete, especially around cupboards, fittings, doorways
- tiling or sheet floor finishes are flat (ie no curling edges or bubbles)
- there are no paint splashes
- screeds are free from rough patches, cracks or hollow areas.

SERVICES
- sufficient clips or brackets support pipework
- sufficient clearance prevents pipes squeaking, etc
- radiators are fixed properly, painted and not leaking
- light switches and socket outlets are fixed adequately and free from paint splashes
- the correct number of lighting outlets, switches and socket outlets have been provided
- radiators are fixed and finished properly and left undamaged and not leaking
- TV aerial connection is provided near a double socket outlet in the main living room.

Note
For kitchens, bathrooms, utility rooms, shower rooms, etc apply extra checks as detailed in Clause S2(g).

FIREPLACES
- fire surround is clean and undamaged
- debris and Builders' rubbish has been removed
- the throating is clear
- where necessary, there is a sufficient source of air for combustion.

CUPBOARDS
All items in Clause S2(f) above have been checked and in addition:
- shelving is complete, including in airing cupboards (where provided)
- debris and Builders' rubbish has been removed
- where a hanging rail is provided, the fixings are adequate.

STAIRCASES
- balustrading, newels, handrails are all complete and fixed securely
- finish to staircase joinery, etc is clean and undamaged
- staircase steps have even rise and going.

GENERAL
- debris and Builders' rubbish has been removed
- floors are clean.

Performance Standards	Guidance

KITCHENS, BATHROOMS, etc

10.1 - S2 (g) checks inside KITCHENS, BATHROOMS, SHOWER ROOMS, WCs and UTILITY ROOMS

The items below are in addition to those in Clause S2(f).

They cover any room that contains a sanitary fitting, sink unit or plumbed-in appliance.

Check that:

SANITARY FITTINGS
- sanitaryware is undamaged
- labels are removed (except for instructions to purchaser)
- bath panel is fitted
- taps and showers are in working order
- fittings are clean
- WC flushes properly
- junctions with walls are watertight.

KITCHEN UNITS
- units are not damaged, chipped or stained
- units are fixed adequately, especially wall units
- units are free from paint splashes
- taps are in working order
- units are clear of debris and Builders' rubbish
- worktops are not scratched or damaged
- doors and drawers open and close properly
- doors are hung square to units.

PLUMBING
- there are no leaks, especially at traps and wastes
- pipes are clipped adequately.

DRAINAGE
- where long pipe runs have been used, there is adequate provision for rodding.

ELECTRICAL
- the cooker control is working
- ventilation units are fitted correctly and in working order.

GAS
- gas points are installed correctly.

APPLIANCES
- appliances are undamaged
- appliances are in working order
- operating instructions have been provided.

WALL TILING
- tiling is complete and undamaged
- grouting is finished neatly and tiles cleaned
- seal between tiling and fittings is complete
- making good around pipes is complete
- patterns are made correctly
- edging details are complete
- no discoloured tiles have been used.

OTHER FINISHES
- grilles are fitted over air bricks.

Performance Standards

Guidance

COMMON AREAS

10.1 - S2 (h) checks for COMMON AREAS of FLATS and MAISONETTES

The items below are in addition to those in Clause S2(f).

At least the following items should be checked when flats are completed individually, ie when one top flat is to be handed over before completion of the other flats.

Check that:

FRONT DOORS TO FLATS
● door and frame have correct fire resistance, especially doorstops
● intumescent strips are undamaged and free from paint
● ironmongery is in working order, especially any self-closing mechanism.

WINDOWS
● the means of ventilation (opening lights, trickle vents) is provided and in working order.

IRONMONGERY
● ironmongery is complete and in working order
● ironmongery is free from paint splashes
● lockable devices are fitted to all ground floor windows and any others which can be reached easily from the outside
● security lock is fitted to front doors (appropriate for flats and maisonettes)
● there is a wide angle of view of the area immediately outside the front door
● there is an opening limitation device fixed securely to the front door
● secondary access doors have 5-lever locks
● front and secondary access doors have bolts fixed securely at both the top and bottom of the door.

STAIRCASES
● finishes to treads and nosings are clean and undamaged
● handrails and balustrading are fixed securely
● scaffolding has been removed
● debris and Builders' rubbish has been removed
● staircases have been swept clean.

LIGHTING
● lighting is in working order
● lighting operates as intended.

LIFT
● the lift, where specified, is installed, tested and in working order.

SERVICE AREAS AND CUPBOARDS
● debris and Builders' rubbish has been removed
● service areas and cupboards are clean.

REFUSE CHUTES AND BIN STORES
● debris and Builders' rubbish has been removed
● refuse chutes, bin stores, etc are clean.

10.1 | ## Snagging

Performance Standards	Guidance

CONNECTION AND TESTING OF SERVICES

10.1 - S2 (i) checks on the SERVICES INSTALLATION

Check that:

MAINS CONNECTION
- mains are properly connected:
  - drainage
  - water
  - electricity
  - gas.

DRAINAGE
- drainage tests have been carried out
- drains are free of obstructions
- drains are connected to the proper outfall.

HEATING SYSTEMS
- systems are in proper working order
- the heating installer has carried out a performance test and made any necessary adjustments, for example on:
  - operation of thermostats and programmers
  - balancing of radiators
  - pump settings
- combustion ventilation supply is provided, where required.

REMEDIAL MEASURES

10.1 - S2 (j) carrying out REMEDIAL MEASURES

Remedial measures are best undertaken before handover.

Where this is not possible, arrangements should be made with the purchasers which are mutually acceptable.

ACCURACY OF INFORMATION TO BE GIVEN TO THE PURCHASERS

10.1 - S2 (k) checking information to the purchasers

The guidance given in Chapter 1.2 'The home - its accommodation and services' should be folllowed to ensure that the information given by Builders to purchasers is accurate in respect of each dwelling.

NHBC, Buildmark House, Chiltern Avenue, Amersham Bucks HP6 5AP

NHBC, 5 Manor Place, Edinburgh, Scotland EH3 7DH

NHBC, Holyrood Court, 59 Malone Road, Belfast BT9 6SA